PHYSICAL GAS DYNAMICS

PUBLISHER'S NOTICE TO REVIEWERS AND READERS

CONCERNING THE QUALITY OF PRODUCTION AND PUBLISHED PRICE OF THIS WORK

We much regret that in the interest of speedily making available the information contained in this publication, it has been necessary to produce the text by non-letterpress setting and photo lithography, with the result that the quality of production is not as high as the public have come to associate with and expect from the Pergamon Press.

To have re-set this manuscript by letterpress would have delayed its appearance by many months and the price would have had to be increased further.

The cost of translating scientific and technical works from the Russian in time, money, and publishing effort is very considerable. In the interest of getting the Soviet Authorities eventually to pay the usual authors' royalties to Western authors, the Pergamon Press is voluntarily paying to Russian authors the usual authors' royalties on this publication, in addition to the translators' and editors' fees. This and the somewhat limited market and the lack of any kind of subsidy accounts for what may appear to be a higher than usual published price.

I. R. MAXWELL
Publisher at Pergamon Press

Institute of Power Engineering,U.S.S.R. Academy of Sciences

PHYSICAL GAS DYNAMICS

Editor-in-chief

A. S. PREDVODITELEV

Translated from the Russian by

R. C. MURRAY, Ph.D., B.Sc.

and

D. R. H. PHILLIPS, B.A.

PERGAMON PRESS

OXFORD · LONDON · NEW YORK · PARIS

1961

PERGAMON PRESS LTD.,
Headington Hill Hall, Oxford.
4 and 5 Fitzroy Square, London W.1.

PERGAMON PRESS INC.,
122 East 55th Street, New York 22, N.Y.
P.O. Box 47715, Los Angeles, California.

PERGAMON PRESS S.A.R.L.
24 Rue des Ecoles, Paris Ve.

PERGAMON PRESS G.m.b.H.
Kaiserstrasse 75, Frankfurt-am-Main.

Library of Congress Card Number 60-13827

Printed in Great Britain by
PERGAMON PRINTING & ART SERVICES LTD.,
LONDON

Table of Contents

E.V. Stupochenko, I.P. Stakhanov, E.V. Samuilov,
A.S. Pleshanov, I.B. Rozhdestvenskii

Thermodynamic Properties of Air between 1000° and 12,000°K and 0.001 and 1000 Atmospheres

Introduction

Contemporary jet propulsion technology is concerned with the high temperatures arising in the motion of bodies in the atmosphere at supersonic speeds. This necessitates study of the properties of air under such conditions. At present experimental methods for directly studying the properties of gases have not been worked out in sufficient detail. Hence a theoretical calculation becomes extremely important. The methods of statistical physics in its quantum mechanical form, along with the data provided by spectroscopy, serve as a reliable foundation for the theoretical calculation of the thermodynamic properties of gases, and particularly of mixtures of gases capable of reacting chemically with one another. At high temperatures air is an example of such a mixture: for apart from the dissociation of O_2 and N_2 and the formation of NO, there is ionization of its molecular and atomic components.

The thermodynamic functions of air are determined by the thermodynamic parameters of its components and by its state, which varies with temperature and pressure. Hence the problem resolves itself into two stages: 1) calculating the thermodynamic parameters of the pure" components, and 2) calculating the composition of air and its thermodynamic functions.

Calculating the thermodynamic parameters of the "pure" components reduces to calculating statistical sums. For example, the free energy of one mole of a one-component ideal gas is expressed by the statistical sum Q of the internal degrees of freedom of the gas as follows:

$$F = -NkT \ln \left\{ \frac{eV}{N} \left(\frac{2\pi mkT}{h^2} \right)^{3/2} Q \right\},$$

where

$$Q = \sum_i g_i e^{-\frac{\varepsilon_i}{kT}};$$

ε_i = energy levels of gas particles;
g_i = statistical weights of the levels;
N = number of molecules in one gram mole;
k = Boltzmann constant;
h = Planck constant;
m = mass of particle;
T = absolute temperature;
V = volume of gas;
e = base of natural logarithms.

To determine the state of air, a system of non-linear algebraic equations must be solved, including the mass action equations for each of the possible reactions in air and the ionization processes, the Dalton equation, the mass balance equations and the equation of conservation of charge.

To calculate the thermodynamic functions of a mixture of reacting gases, two systems of linear equations must be solved.

1. Methods of Calculating Statistical Sums for Atoms, Molecules and their Ions

The statistical sums for atoms have the simplest form. Below we shall in all cases understand by "statistical sums" the statistical sums for the internal degrees of freedom.

In the calculation of statistical sums the energy of the unexcited (ground) states of the atom will be taken as zero, i.e., statistical sums of the form

$$Q = g_{nuc}(g_0 + g_1 e^{-\frac{\varepsilon_1}{kT}} + g_2 e^{-\frac{\varepsilon_2}{kT}} + \ldots).$$

are calculated.

For most atomic systems a few of the first excited levels are 20,000 cm^{-1} over the ground state and most of the excited levels are 100,000 cm^{-1} from the ground state, above this small group. At temperatures up to 6000-8000°K we can neglect the effect of the large number of levels 100,000 cm^{-1} above the ground state without introducing an appreciable error into the statistical sums. At higher temperatures (10,000°K and above), however, neglect of this would introduce appreciable errors into the values of the statistical sums and their first and second temperature differentials. Thus for nitrogen at 12,000°K, for example, neglect of the effect of all levels above 30,000 cm^{-1} would cause an error of 0.6 per cent in the values of the statistical sums, an error of 1.2 per cent in the first temperature differential, and one of 18 per cent in the second temperature differential.

In calculating the statistical sums of atoms and their ions we take all known levels into account, but instead of using the accurate values of ε_i for the excited levels, we use values rounded off to three significant figures. The error introduced into Q by this approximation can be estimated as follows. Let us put ε_i as

$$\varepsilon_i = \varepsilon_p + \Delta\varepsilon_i^{(p)},$$

where

$$\Delta\varepsilon_i^{(p)} \ll 1000 \text{ см}^{-1}.$$

The statistical sum has the form

$$Q = \sum_p e^{-\frac{\varepsilon_p}{kT}} \sum_i^{(p)} g_i e^{-\frac{\Delta\varepsilon_i^{(p)}}{kT}}.$$

By series expansion of $e^{-\frac{\Delta\varepsilon_i^{(p)}}{kT}}$ and taking the first two terms of the expansion, we obtain

$$Q = \sum_p e^{-\frac{\varepsilon_p}{kT}} \sum_i^{(p)} g_i \left(1 - \frac{\Delta\varepsilon_i^{(p)}}{kT}\right),$$

$$\Delta Q = -\sum_p e^{-\frac{\varepsilon_p}{kT}} \sum_i^{(p)} g_i \frac{\Delta\varepsilon_i^{(p)}}{kT}.$$

In calculating thermodynamic functions, it is convenient to use the quantities

$$Q; \quad Q' \equiv T\frac{dQ}{dT}; \quad Q'' = T^2\frac{d^2Q}{dT^2}.$$

The equations for calculating Q, Q', Q'' have the form:

$$Q = g_{nuc}\sum_p g_p e^{-\frac{\varepsilon_p}{kT}}, \tag{1}$$

$$Q' = g_{nuc}\sum_p g_p \frac{\varepsilon_p}{kT} e^{-\frac{\varepsilon_p}{kT}}, \tag{2}$$

$$Q'' = g_{nuc}\sum_p g_p \frac{\varepsilon_p}{kT}\left(\frac{\varepsilon_p}{kT} - 2\right) e^{-\frac{\varepsilon_p}{kT}},$$

$$g_p = \sum_i^{(p)} g_i. \tag{3}$$

The statistical sums for diatomic molecules have the form

$$Q = g_{nuc}\sum_l g_l e^{-\frac{\varepsilon_l}{kT}} \sum_{v=0}^{v=v\,\max} e^{-\frac{\varepsilon_v(l,v)}{kT}} \sum_{J=J\,\min}^{J=J\,\max} (2J+1) e^{-\frac{\varepsilon_r(l,v,J)}{kT}}, \tag{4}$$

where $\varepsilon_r, \varepsilon_v, \varepsilon_l$ are the rotational, vibrational and electronic energies of the molecules. In the simplest case, in which the total electron spin and the projection of the orbital moment of the electrons on the nuclear axis are zero, the rotational energy is expressed as follows:

$$\varepsilon_r = B_v J(J+1) - D_v J^2(J+1)^2 + F_v J^3(J+1)^3 + H_v J^4(J+1)^4 + \ldots \tag{5}$$

where

$$B_v = B_e - \alpha_e\left(v + \frac{1}{2}\right); \quad F_v = F_e + \gamma_e\left(v + \frac{1}{2}\right); \tag{6}$$

$$D_v = D_e + \beta_e\left(v + \frac{1}{2}\right); \quad H_v = H_e + \delta_e\left(v + \frac{1}{2}\right)$$

J = rotational quantum number, assuming all permitted values up to $J_{\max}$ (v, l), the maximum rotational quantum number at which the molecule is stable.

B_e, D_e, F_e, H_e, α_e, β_e, γ_e, and δ_e are constants, determined from analysis of spectra. The vibrational energy is given by the following series

$$\varepsilon_v = \omega_0 v - \omega_0 x_0 v^2 + \omega_0 y_0 v^3 + \omega_0 z_0 v^4 + \dots, \tag{7}$$

where v is the vibrational quantum number and ω_0, $\omega_0 x_0$, $\omega_0 y_0$, and $\omega_0 z_0$ are spectroscopic constants.

In calculating the rotational component of the statistical sum

$$Q_r = \sum_{J=J\,\min}^{J=J\,\max} (2J+1) e^{-\frac{\varepsilon_r}{kT}} \tag{8}$$

summation over the rotational quantum number is replaced by integration. This yields an expression for Q_r in the form of a series in powers of T with decreasing coefficients. Neglect of the sixth and all subsequent terms introduces errors not exceeding 0.001 per cent in Q_r, 0.008 per cent in $\frac{Q_r'}{T}$ or 0.3 per cent in $\frac{Q_r'}{T^2}$.

Calculations show that at temperatures from 8000°K upwards the energy levels above the dissociation limit for the ground electronic state of the molecules make a considerable contribution to the statistical sums for the diatomic molecules: O_2; N_2; NO: O_2^+; N_2^+; NO^+. Hence a finite number of rotational levels is allowed for in Q_r. The rotational part of the statistical sum is integrated between J_{min} and J_{max}. Up to 6000-8000°K, the integration can be made between J_{min} and infinity. For molecules with identical nuclei (O_2, N_2, O_2^+, N_2^+) the coefficient $\frac{1}{2}$ must be placed before the rotational part of the statistical sum. The lower electronic states of the molecules O_2, NO, N_2^+, O_2^+ have electronic terms differing from $^1\Sigma$. Hence, because of spin interaction with K or the axis there is a split of the rotational levels. Calculation shows that between 1000 and 12,000°K this split can be allowed for by a statistical weight in Q_r, calculated on the assumption of an absence of split, as was done in calculating Q_r for all electronic states. The final calculation equations for Q_r, Q_r', and Q_r'' are:

$$Q_r = b_v T + d_v T^2 + f_v T^3 + h_v T^4 + m_v T^5 -$$
$$- e^{-\frac{hc}{kT}\psi} \{l_v T + p_v T^2 + n_v T^3 + t_v T^4 + \pi_v T^5\}.$$
$$Q_r' = b_v T + 2d_v T^2 + 3f_v T^3 + 4h_v T^4 + 5m_v T^5 -$$
$$- e^{-\frac{hc}{kT}\psi} \{(\rho_v + 1) l_v T + (\rho_v + 2) p_v T^2 +$$
$$+ (\rho_v + 3) n_v T^3 + (\rho_v + 4) t_v T^4 + (p_v + 5) \pi_v T^5\}$$
$$Q_r^{\bullet} = 2d_v T^2 + 6fv_v T^3 + 12h_v T^4 + 20m_v T^5 -$$
$$- e^{-\frac{hc}{kT}\psi} \{\rho_v^2 l_v T + (\rho_v^2 + 2\rho_v + 2) p_v T^2 +$$
$$+ (\rho_v^2 + 4\rho_v + 6) n_v T^3 + (\rho_v^2 + 6\rho_v + 12) t_v T^4 + (\rho_v^2 + 8\rho_v + 20) \pi_v T^5\},$$

where

$$b_v = \frac{1}{B_v}\frac{k}{hc}; \quad d_v = 2\frac{D_v}{B_v^3}\left(\frac{k}{hc}\right)^2;$$

$$f_v = 12\frac{D_v^2}{B_v^5}\left(\frac{k}{hc}\right)^3; \quad h_v = 120\frac{D_v^3}{B_v^7}\left(\frac{k}{hc}\right)^4;$$

$$m_v = 1680\frac{D_v^4}{B_v^9}\left(\frac{k}{hc}\right)^5$$

$$l_v = \left\{\frac{1}{B_v} + 2\frac{D_v}{B_v^3}\psi + 12\frac{D_v^2}{B_v^5}\frac{\psi^2}{2} + 120\frac{D_v^3}{B_v^7}\frac{\psi^3}{6} + 1680\frac{D_v^4}{B_v^9}\frac{\psi^4}{24}\right\}\frac{k}{hc}$$

$$p_v = \left\{2\frac{D_v}{B_v^3} + 12\frac{D_v^2}{B_v^5}\psi + 120\frac{D_v^3}{B_v^7}\frac{\psi^2}{2} + 1680\frac{D_v^4}{B_v^9}\frac{\psi^3}{6}\right\}\left(\frac{k}{hc}\right)^2$$

$$h_v = \left\{12\frac{D_v^2}{B_v^5} + 120\frac{D_v^3}{B_v^7}\psi + 1680\frac{D_v^4}{B_v^9}\frac{\psi^2}{2}\right\}\left(\frac{k}{hc}\right)^3$$

$$t_v = \left\{120\frac{D_v^3}{B_v^7} + 1680\frac{D_v^4}{B_v^9}\psi\right\}\left(\frac{k}{hc}\right)^4; \quad \pi_v = 1680\frac{D_v^4}{B_v^9}\left(\frac{k}{hc}\right)^5$$

$$\psi = B_v J_{\max}(J_{\max}+1); \quad \rho_v = \frac{hc}{k}\psi.$$

The vibrational part of the statistical sum

$$Q_v = \sum_{v=0}^{v=v_{\max}} e^{-\frac{\varepsilon_v}{kT}} Q_r(v) \tag{9}$$

and its differentials are calculated by direct summation over the whole temperature range from 1000° to 12,000°K for all possible vs from 0 to $v_{\max}$. For calculating the vibrational parts of the statistical sums and their differentials, the following equations have been used:

$$Q_v = \sum_{v=0}^{v=v_{\max}} e^{-\frac{\varepsilon_v}{kT}} Q_r,$$

$$Q_v' = \sum_{v=0}^{v=v_{\max}} e^{-\frac{\varepsilon_v}{kT}}\left\{\frac{\varepsilon_v}{kT}Q_r + Q_r'\right\},$$

$$Q_v'' = \sum_{v=0}^{v=v_{\max}} e^{-\frac{\varepsilon_v}{kT}}\left\{\frac{\varepsilon_v}{kT}\left[\left(\frac{\varepsilon_v}{kT}-2\right)Q_r + 2Q_r'\right] + Q_r''\right\}.$$

In calculating the electronic part of the statistical sum

$$Q_l = g_{nuc}\sum_l e^{-\frac{\varepsilon_l}{kT}} Q_v(l) \tag{10}$$

allowance is made for all known levels 100,000 cm^{-1} above the ground level of the molecule. The equations for calculating the electronic part of the statistical sum are:

$$Q_l = g_{nuc}\sum_l g_l e^{-\frac{\varepsilon_l}{kT}}$$

$$Q_l' = g_{nuc}\sum_l g_l e^{-\frac{\varepsilon_l}{kT}}\left\{\frac{\varepsilon_l}{kT}Q_v + Q_v'\right\}$$

$$Q_l'' = g_{nuc}\sum_l g_l e^{-\frac{\varepsilon_l}{kT}}\left\{\frac{\varepsilon_l}{kT}\left[\left(\frac{\varepsilon_l}{kT}-2\right)Q_v + 2Q_v'\right] + Q_v''\right\}.$$

2. Spectroscopic Constants Used in Calculating Statistical Sums

The spectroscopic constants used in calculating statistical sums of atoms and molecules are shown in Tables 1-7. The sources for the figures in these tables are mostly references [1-3]. Results from later investigations not covered in these references have also been used. In each case the source for the constants is indicated. All the values in brackets were calculated from formulae obtained either by solving the wave equation for the particular case or from empirical or semi-empirical equations. The tables contain all the electronic levels of atoms and molecules considered in calculating the corresponding statistical sums.

For spectroscopically determined electronic states of molecules it is usual to give four, three or two terms of series (7). The possibility of determining the terms of this series depends on the number of bands which can be observed in spectra of the corresponding system. When the spectroscopic data were insufficient for determining $\omega_0 z_0$ or $\omega_0 y_0$, we did not calculate them theoretically. For the NO^+ ions the values of $\omega_e x_e$ were calculated for all four electronic states and ω_e was determined for the ${}^3\Pi$ state. The constant $\omega_e x_e$ for a known dissociation energy of a particular electronic state was calculated on the theory that the potential energy of an electronic state is described by a Morse function by the equation

$$\omega_e x_e = \frac{\omega_e^2}{4D_e} \quad . \tag{11}$$

ω_e for ${}^3\Pi$ was determined from empirical equations. For certain electronic states it is impossible in general, because of interaction with neighbours, to select an appropriate series (7) with a small number of terms, suitable for all vibrational levels. In such cases we selected two series, one of which corresponded to vibrational levels between $v=0$ and a certain v_k, the second to those between v_{k+1} and v_{max}. This is equivalent to introducing a fictitious electronic state. Such fictitious states are bracketed in Tables 1-7. The number of spectroscopically observed vibrational levels differs for different electronic states and varies between one and ten. For most low electronic states it is usual to examine many bands, so that calculations based on spectroscopic data can be regarded as reliable. However v_{max} has not been determined spectroscopically for most of the electronic states of interest to us, for O_2; N_2; NO; O_2^+; N_2^+ and NO^+. If we assume that the location of the vibrational levels above the levels examined follows the same pattern as for those observed, then v_m can be calculated from

$$\varepsilon_v (v_m) = D_0. \tag{12}$$

Almost all v_ms in Tables 2-7 were obtained by this method. However, for certain electronic states equation (12) does not have real positive roots. In such cases v_m was determined from the following considerations. The dissociation energy of any electronic state should be equal to the sum of all vibrational quanta $\Delta G(v)$ of the given electronic state

$$D_0 = \sum_{v=0}^{v=v_m} \Delta G(v).$$

In other words, if ΔG is plotted against v, the area enclosed by the curve and the abscissa and ordinate axes should be equal to the energy of dissociation of the given electronic state. In

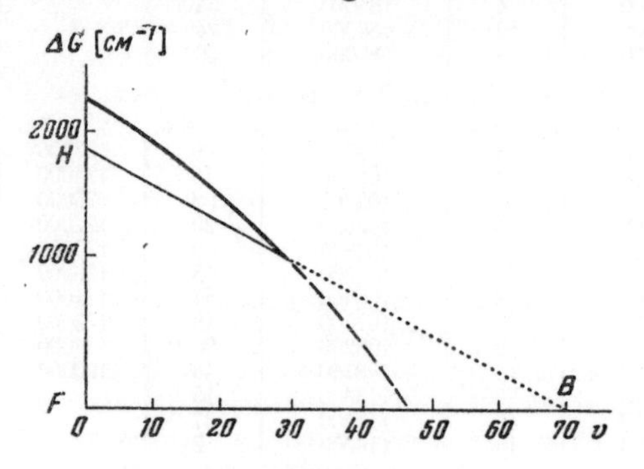

Fig. 1
Graph of ΔG against the vibrational quantum number v for the $X^2\Sigma$ state of the N_2^+ ion

Fig. 1, the continuous curve shows the examined values of ΔG for the $X^2\Sigma_g^+$ state of the N_2^+ ion. If this curve is continued to intersection with the abscissa (broken line) the area under the curve is less than 70358 cm^{-1} (dissociation energy of the $X^2\Sigma_g^+$ state of the N_2^+ ion). This corresponds to the fact that equation (12)

TABLE 1

ε_p, cm^{-1}	g_p	ε_p, cm^{-1}	g_p	ε_p, cm^{-1}	g_p
		Ar			
0	1	108700	1	119000	33
93144	5	111700	1	120000	71
93751	3	111800	3	121000	51
94550	1	112100	5	122000	73
95400	3	113500	10	123000	103
104100	2	113000	16	124000	176
105500	7	113700	10	125000	293
105600	5	114100	3	126000	362
106000	8	115000	24	127000	45
107000	1	116700	3	128000	24
107100	3	117000	15		
107300	5	117200	5		
107500	3	118000	12		
		Ar^+			
0	4	150000	15	190000	16
1432	2	155000	12	192000	8
108723	2	158000	20	193000	10
132000	14	160000	24	195000	50
133000	12	167000	2	196000	26
135000	6	170000	14	199000	30
139000	6	173000	26	200000	35
142200	10	175000	6	205000	14

Continuation of TABLE 1

ε_p, см$^{-1}$	g_p	ε_p, см$^{-1}$	g_p	ε_p, см$^{-1}$	g_p
143000	18	180000	12	209000	4
144700	2	183000	10	213000	10
145700	4	184000	34		
147500	12	186000	24		
149000	18	187000	30		
		O			
0	5	99760	9	123000	14
158,5	3	101150	15	124000	52
226.5	1	102000	8	126000	24
15868	5	102800	29	127000	18
13792	1	103870	9	129000	10
33768	5	105300	48	129800	61
76795	3	106700	57	131000	1
86630	15	107500	48	132000	51
88630	9	108200	96	134000	13
95480	5	108700	48	190000	3
96930	3	113300	15		
97420	45	114000	37		
99090	15	116000	8		
		O^+			
0	4	212700	2	254000	14
26808	6	214200	6	255000	56
26829	4	226800	2	156000	138
40467	6	228700	14	258000	14
120000	12	231200	38	259000	14
166000	10	233000	56	268000	38
185000	12	234000	12	266000	150
189000	6	238700	12	268000	18
195700	2	240400	6	276000	122
203900	2	245900	26	292000	36
207000	30	248200	16		
208400	12	251000	20		
212000	18	253000	28		
		N			
0	4	96800	12	107400	4
19223	6	97800	6	110000	14
19231	4	99660	10	110200	30
28840	6	103700	12	110300	48
83350	12	104200	6	110500	26
86130	2	104600	6	112300	6
86223	4	104700	28	113000	102
88110	6	104900	26	114000	100
88153	4	105000	20	115000	92
88173	2	105100	10	116000	340
93582	2	106500	2		
94800	20	106800	20		
95500	12	107000	12		
		N^+			
0	2	245700	6	334500	10
174,5	4	267200	10	336300	12
57192	2	287600	12	339800	14
57252	4	297000	6	342000	10
57333	6	301090	2	343000	32
101030	10	310000	26	355000	32
131000	2	311700	6	368600	12
145880	2	314200	4	374000	16
146000	4	317600	22	378000	56
186800	4	320800	18	387000	202
203080	10	327000	2		
221300	2	330300	28		
230400	7	332800	22		

TABLE 2

Molecular nitrogen N_2

$D(N_2) = 78715\ cm^{-1} = 224984$ g.cal (15°C)/g.mole (chem) - [2] [6]
$I(N_2) = 125702\ cm^{-1} = 359283$ g.cal (15°C)/g.mole (chem). From $I(N)$, $D(N_2)$, $I(N_2^+)$

Name of constant	Electronic state						
	$X^1\Sigma_g^+$	$A^3\Sigma_u^+$	$B^3\Pi_g$	$a'^1\Sigma_u^-$	$a^1\Pi_g$	N	$C^3\Pi_u$
ε_e	0	49756.5	59313.5	60000	68956.6	63959	88984
ω_0	2345.16	1446.46	1719.64	1515.5	1678.959	(1515.5)	2020.00
$\omega_0 x_0$	14.445	13.929	14.47	11.5	13.3181	(11.5)	26.40
$\omega_0 y_0$	0.64958	—0.0261	—	—	—0.95353	(—)	1.158
$\omega_0 z_0$	—0.000509	—0.000614	—	—	—0.002298	(—)	0.5542
B_e	2.010	1.440	1.6380	1.48	1.637	(1.49)	1.8259
α_e	0.01869	0.013	0.0184	0.015	0.0224	(0.015)	0.0197
D_e	$5.8 \cdot 10^{-6}$	$(5.61 \cdot 10^{-6})$	$(-5.86 \cdot 10^{-6})$	$(5.56 \cdot 10^{-6})$	$(6.14 \cdot 10^{-6})$	$(5.56 \cdot 10^{-6})$	$6.0 \cdot 10^{-6}$
β_e	$-0.001 \cdot 10^{-6}$	$(-0.154 \cdot 10^{-6})$	$(-0.0281 \cdot 10^{-6})$	$(-0.029 \cdot 10^{6})$	$(0.0645 \cdot 10^{6})$	$(-0.029 \cdot 10^{-6})$	$(-0.013 \cdot 10^{-6})$
v_m	50	26	30	30	25	30	4
Source	[2]	[3]	[2]	[3]	[3]	[3]	[3]

TABLE 3

Molecular Oxygen O_2

$D(O_2) = 41260\ cm^{-1} = 117930$ g.cal (15°C)/g.mole (chem) [7]

$I(O_2) = 38813.7\ cm^{-1} = 282430$ g.cal (15°C)/g.mole (chem). From $I(O)$, $D(O_2)$, $D(O_2^+)$

Name of constant	Electronic state						
	$^3\Sigma^-_g$	$\Delta^1\Delta_g$	$b\,^1\Sigma^+_g$	$^1\Sigma^-_g$	$^3\Delta_u$	$A^3\Sigma^+_u$	$B^3\Sigma^-_u$
ε_e	0	7892.39	13120.908	36212.74	—	35780.12	49363.1
ω_0	1568.33	1496.4	1418.7292	633.371	—	758.89	692.08
$\omega_0 x_0$	11.993	12.9	13.9662	17.2056	—	14.635	8.5653
$\omega_0 y_0$	0.0517	—	—0.01075	—0.1205	—	—0.55	—0.37535
$\omega_0 z_0$	—0.00143	—	—	—0.00744	—	—	—
B_e	1.445666	1.4264	1.400416	0.826	—	(0.902)	0.819
α_e	0.015791	0.0171	0.01817	0.02055	—	(0.0245)	0.011
D_e	$4.957 \cdot 10^{-6}$	4.8652	$5.356 \cdot 10^{-6}$	$(10.731 \cdot 10^{-6})$	—	$(3.32 \cdot 10^{-6})$	$(4.38 \cdot 10^{-6})$
β_e	$-0.088 \cdot 10^{-6}$	$-0.0104 \cdot 10^{-6}$	$-0.077 \cdot 10^{-6}$	$(0.262 \cdot 10^{-6})$	—	$(0.96 \cdot 10^{-6})$	$-0.0784 \cdot 10^{-6}$
v_m	36	30	27	13	—	11	21
Source	[12]	[13]	[12]	[14]	[14]	[15]	[7]

TABLE 4

Nitric oxide

D(NO) = 52477 cm^{-1} = 149990 g.cal(15°C)/g.mole (chem) [7]
I(NO) = 76626.8 cm^{-1} = 219015 g.cal (15°C)/g.mole (chem) [2]

Name of constant	Electronic state					
	$X^2\Pi_{1/2,\,3/2}$	$A^2\Sigma^+$	$B^2\Pi$	$D^2\Sigma^+$	$C^2\Sigma^+$	$E^2\Sigma^+$
ε_e	60.6	44199.2	45440	52817	—	60862.8
ω_0	1889.88	2356.82	1030.15	2304	—	2357.79
$\omega_0 x_0$	13.972	14.48	7.458	23	—	15.87
$\omega_0 y_0$	—0.012	—	0.0967	—	—	—
$\omega_0 z_0$	—	—	—	—	—	—
B_e	1.7046	1.9948	1.126	1.9912	—	1.9863
α_e	0.0178	0.0184	0.0152	(0.0243)	—	0.0182
D_e	$5\cdot10^{-6}$	$5.6\cdot10^{-6}$	$2.65\cdot10^{-6}$	$5.8\cdot10^{-6}$	—	$5.6\cdot10^{-6}$
β_e	$0.02\cdot10^{-6}$	$0.02\cdot10^{-6}$	$(0.0405\cdot10^{-6})$	$(-0.063\cdot10^{-6})$	—	$0.02\cdot10^{-6}$
v_m	38	3	29	25	25	20
Source		[8]	[2]	[3]	[3]	[8]

TABLE 5

Ionized molecular nitrogen N_2^+

$D(N_2^+) = 70358\ cm^{-1} = 201098\ g.cal\ (15°C)/g.mole\ (chem)$ [9]

Name of constant	Electronic State					
	$X^2\Sigma^+_g$	$(X^2\Sigma^+_g)$	$A^2\Pi$	$B^2\Sigma^+_u$	$(B^2\Sigma^+_u)$	$B^2\Sigma^+$
ε_e	0	(50470)	9057	25566	(51618)	64547
ω_0	2191.02	(1023.5)	1887.93	2396.22	(1007.5)	2162.8
$\omega_0 x_0$	13.19	(13.24)	14.91	24070	—	—
$\omega_0 y_0$	—0.0303	—	—	—0.6365	—	—
$\omega_0 z^0$	—0.00092	—	—	—0.04949	—	—
B_e	—1.932	(1.315)	1.722	2.083	(1.433)	1.65
α_e	0.02	(0.0192)	0.018	0.0195	(0.0294)	0.05
D_e	$5.75\cdot10^{-6}$	$(7.427\cdot10^{-6})$	$4\cdot10^{-6}$	$(6.15\cdot10^{-6})$	$(13.903\cdot10^{-6})$	$(3.8\cdot10^{-6})$
β_e	$0.29\cdot10^{-6}$	$(-0.0202\cdot10^{-6})$	$(-0.216\cdot10^{-6})$	$(0.216\cdot10^{-6})$	$(0.116\cdot10^{-6})$	$(0.6\cdot10^{-6})$
v_m	30	37	63	14	37	10
Source	[9]	[9]	[10]	[9]	[9]	[3]

TABLE 6

Molecular ionized oxygen O_2^+

$D(O_2^+) = 52283\ cm^{-1} = 149.436$ g.cal (15°C) g.mole (chem) [2]

Name of constant	Electronic state			
	$X^2\Pi_u$	$a^4\Pi_u$	$A^2\Pi_u$	$b^4\Sigma^-$
ε_e	97.5	31900	383.9	48567
ω_0	1859.87	1025.30	886.6	1179.68
$\omega_0 x_0$	16.53	1039	13.4	17.08
$\omega_0 y_0$	—	—	—	—
$\omega_0 z_0$	—	—	—	—
B_e	1.6722	1.10466	1.0617	1.28729
α_e	0.01984	0.01575	0.01906	0.02206
D_e	$(6.84 \cdot 10^{-6})$	$4.88 \cdot 10^{-6}$	$(5.33 \cdot 10^{-6})$	$5.81 \cdot 10^{-6}$
β_e	$(-0.0356 \cdot 10^{-6})$	$-0.095 \cdot 10^{-6}$	$(-0.0955 \cdot 10^{-6})$	$-0.0185 \cdot 10^{-6}$
v_m	53	27	25	27
Source	[2]	[2]	[2]	[2]

TABLE 7

Ionized nitric oxide NO^+

$D(NO^+) = 85686.9\ cm^{-1} = 244911$ g.cal (15°C)/g.mole (chem)
(from I(O), D(NO), I(NO))

Name of constant	Electronic state			
	$(^1\Sigma+)$	$(^3\Pi)$	$(^3\Sigma+)$	$(^1\Pi)$
ε_e	0	37000	57000	71000
ω_0	(2334)	(1636)	(1322.4)	(1265)
$\omega_0 x_0$	(16.1)	(14)	(15.6)	(12)
$\omega_0 y_0$	—	—	—	—
$\omega_0 z_0$	—	—	—	—
B_e	(1.96)	(1.54)	(1.35)	(1.31)
α_e	(0.0181)	(0.174)	(0.0196)	(0.0163)
D_e	$(5.4 \cdot 10^{-6})$	$(5.3 \cdot 10^{-6})$	$(5.5 \cdot 10^{-6})$	$(5.5 \cdot 10^{-6})$
β_e	—	—	—	—
v_m	(73)	(59)	(42)	(25)

does not have a solution satisfactory to us. To get an area of 70358 cm^{-1} under the curve, an extremely simple assumption was made about the course of the curve $\Delta G(v)$ above $v = 30$, namely that $\Delta G(v)$ is a linear function of v, as is shown on the diagram in dots.

TABLE 8

No.	Quantity	Numerical value
1	Speed of light	$c = 299792 \pm 0.8$ km/sec
2	No. of molecules per g.mole, physical	$N_{ph} = (6.02472 \pm 0.00036) \times 10^{23}$ 1/g.mole
	chemical	$N_{ch} = (6.02308 \pm 0.00033) \times 10^{23}$ 1/g.mole
3	Planck constant	$h = (6.6252 \pm 0.0005) \times 10^{-27}$ erg.sec
4	Boltzmann constant	$k = (1.38042 \pm 0.00010) \times 10^{-16}$ erg/°K
5	Electron mass	$m = (9.1085 \pm 0.0006) \times 10^{-28}$ g
6	$^1/_{16}$ th of mass of oxygen atom	$16g/(16\ N_x) = 1.66028 \times 10^{-24}$ g
7	Gas constant	$R_{ph} = (8.31662 \pm 0.00038) \times 10^{7}$ erg/g.mole °K
		$R_{ch} = (8.31436 \pm 0.00034) \times 10^{7}$ erg/g.mole °K
		$R_{ch} = 1.98647 \pm 0.000008$ g.cal (15°C)/g.mole °C
8	Gram calorie at 15°C	1 g.cal (15°C) = 4.1855 abs.joule
9	Atmosphere (physical)	1 atm = 1.01325×10^{6} dynes/cm²

Relation between energy units

	erg	ev	cm^{-1}
erg	1	0.624192×10^{12}	5.0347×10^{15}
ev	1.60207×10^{-12}	1	8.06598
cm^{-1}	1.98620×10^{-16}		1

$$\frac{hc}{k} = 1.43883 \text{ cm/°}$$

The constants $\omega_0 x_0$ and ω_0 for the fictitious electronic state were determined from the equations:

$$\Delta G = \omega_0 - \omega_0 x_0$$

$$D_0 = \frac{\omega_0^2}{4\omega_0 x_0},$$

where ΔG is the height of the first vibrational level above the zero (ground state) (HF on the graph), and D_0 is the area of the triangle FBH.

From rotational constants not more than four constants, B_e, α_e, D_e, β_e are usually determined spectroscopically. When there was no information about these constants, we calculated them from the equations:

$$B_e = \frac{h}{8\pi^2 c\mu r_e^2} \tag{13}$$

$$D_e = \frac{4B_e^3}{\omega_e^2} \tag{14}$$

$$\alpha_e = \frac{6\sqrt{\omega_e x_e B_e^3}}{\omega_e} - \frac{6B_e^2}{\omega_e} \tag{15}$$

$$\beta_e = -D_e\left(\frac{8\omega_e x_e}{\omega_e} - \frac{5\alpha_e}{B_e} - \frac{\alpha_e^2 \omega_e}{24B_e^3}\right). \tag{16}$$

These equations, in most cases, give the correct order of magnitude of the constants. The rotational constants B_v and D_v cannot always be properly represented in the form of equation (6). Since the deviations from the usual variations of B_v and D_v with v are those for vibrational constants, introduction of fictitious electronic states simultaneously involves a choice of convenient methods for calculating the rotational and the vibrational parts of the statistical sums.

As already mentioned, the rotational parts of the statistical sums of molecules in this study were calculated for a finite number of values of J. The maximum value of J at which the molecule is still stable was estimated as follows:

The potential energy function for a rotating molecule can be written:

$$U(r) = D_e(1 - e^{-2\beta\xi})^2 + \frac{h}{8\pi^2 c\mu r^2} J(J+1),$$

where $\xi = \frac{r - r_e}{r_e}$; r_e is the equilibrium distance between nuclei:

$$\beta = \frac{\omega_e}{4(B_e D_e)^{1/2}};$$

$$D_e = D_0 + \frac{\omega_e}{2} - \frac{\omega_e x_e}{2} + \ldots$$

$U(r)$ has a maximum above the dissociation limit, forming a potential barrier, beyond which there are stable states of the molecule with an energy greater than the dissociation energy. The position of the maximum for each value $J(J+1)$ can be found from the condition

$$\frac{\partial U(r)}{\partial r} = 0,$$

which after transformation reduces to the form

$$J(J+1) = \frac{8\pi^2 c}{h} \mu D_e \frac{2\beta}{r_l} r^3 (1 - e^{-2\beta\xi}) e^{-2\beta\xi}. \tag{17}$$

From the value of r_{max} found here for the given $J(J+1)$ we can calculate

$$U_m = D_e (1 - e^{-2\beta \frac{r_m - r_e}{r_e}} + \frac{1}{8\pi^2 c \mu r_m^2} J (J + 1)$$

and from

$$U_m = \omega_e \left(v + \frac{1}{2}\right) - \omega_e x_e \left(v + \frac{1}{2}\right)^2 + \ldots + B_v J(J+1) - D_v J^2 (J+1)^2 + \ldots \quad (18)$$

we can find J(J + 1), which corresponds to the given v. Equations (17) and (18) were solved graphically.

The scantiest data about spectroscopic constants are the data on NO^+. Not one of the electronic states of this ion has as yet been studied spectroscopically. There is information only about the position of the first four electronic states, obtained from a spectroscopic study of the Rydberg series for NO. For three electronic levels of the four, about whose existence we are convinced from similarity with the Rydberg series for NO, the values of ω_e are known, also obtained from the NC spectrum. For the lower electronic state the equilibrium distance $r_e = 1{,}073$ Å is also known. The energy of ionization of NO, equal to 9.5eV, was determined by electron impact, whence with the equation

$$I(\mathrm{NO}) + D(\mathrm{NO}^+) = D(\mathrm{NO}) + I(0),$$

we obtain:

$$D(\mathrm{NO}^+) = D(\mathrm{NO}) + I(\mathrm{O}) - I(\mathrm{NO}) = 10{,}5\,\mathrm{eV}.$$

All this fragmentary information is to be found in Rosen [3]. It is possible in calculating the statistical sums for NO^+ from such information to make errors through ignorance of the types of electronic terms, in two, three, or all of the calculations. Hence an attempt was made to determine the types of electronic terms for the four known electronic states. One of the methods of determining the possible types of electronic term is by building up electronic configurations by successive addition of electrons. This building-up of electronic configurations can be carried out for molecules in two limiting cases: firstly, when the distance between the nuclei is small compared with the distance of the electrons from the nucleus, and secondly, when it is large compared with the distance of the electrons from the nucleus.

For atoms of N and O "connected" together $(r_e \to 0)$ we would obtain the following order of completion of electrcnic shells:

$$(1s\sigma)^2 (2s\sigma)^2 (2p\sigma)^2 (2p\pi)^4 (3s\sigma)^2 (3p\sigma)^2.$$

For atoms of N and O separated by a large distance, we would obtain an order of filling up of the electron shells as follows:

$$(\sigma 1s_O)^2 (\sigma 1s_N)^2 (\sigma 2s_O)^2 (\sigma 2s_N)^2 (\sigma 2p_O)^2 (\pi 2p_O)^4.$$

The order of the electrons in a real NO^+ ion will be intermediate between a system in which the internuclear distance approaches zero and a system in which this distance approaches infinity. The

NO^+ system is electronically the same as the molecules of N, and CO, having fourteen electrons. The value of r_e for the lower electronic state of CO($^1\Sigma^+$) is 1.12819 Å, and for $N_2(^1\Sigma^+)$ it is 1.094 Å. For the lower electronic state of NO^+, as already mentioned, r_e is 1.073 Å. This justifies us in assuming that the lower electronic configuration of NO^+ will coincide with that for CO and N_2

$$KK\,(\sigma 2s_O)^2\,(\sigma 2s_N)^2\,(\pi 2p_O)^4(\sigma 2p_N)^2.$$

An important argument in favour of this configuration is that it corresponds to the removal of one upper electron $\pi 2p_N$ from the NO molecule, having a lower electronic configuration

$$KK\,(\sigma 2s_O)^2\,(\sigma 2s_N)^2\,(\pi 2p_O)^4\,(\sigma 2p_N)^2\,(\pi 2p_N).$$

Such a method of determining the electronic configurations (removing the electron from the ground state of the unionized molecule) proves reliable for other molecules (e.g., for finding the electronic states of N_2^+).

The first excited electronic configuration of NO^+ can, evidently, be

$$KK\,(\sigma 2s_O)^2\,(\sigma 2s_N)^2(\pi 2p_O)^4(\sigma 2p_O)\,(\pi 2p_N)$$

or

$$KK\,(\sigma 2s_O)^2\,(\sigma 2s_N)^2\,(\pi 2p_O)^4\,(\sigma 2p_O)\,(\sigma 2p_N)$$

Removal of one of the $\sigma 2p_O$ electrons of NO forms the electronic configuration:

$$KK\,(\sigma 2s_O)^2\,(\sigma 2s_N)^2\,(\pi 2p_O)^4\,(\sigma 2p_O)\,(\pi 2p_N),$$

which coincides with the first of the possible excited electronic configurations of NO^+. The electronic configuration

$$KK\,(\sigma 2s_O)^2\,(\sigma 2s_N)^2\,(\pi 2p_O)^4\,(\sigma 2p)\,(\pi 2p_N)$$

can therefore be reckoned the first excited electronic configuration of NO^+.

The next excited electronic configuration of NO^+ may be

$$KK\,(\sigma 2s_O)^2\,(\sigma 2s_N)^2\,(\pi 2p_O)^4\,(\sigma 2p_O)\,(\sigma 2p_N) \qquad \text{I}$$

or

$$KK\,(\sigma 2s_O)^2\,(\sigma 2s_O)^2\,(\pi 2p_O)^3\,(\sigma 2p_O)^2\,(\pi 2p_N) \qquad \text{II}$$

or

$$KK\,(\sigma 2s_O)^2\,(\sigma 2s_N)^2\,(\pi 2p_O)^3\,(\sigma 2p_O)^2\,(\sigma 2p_N) \qquad \text{III}$$

Removal of a $(\pi 2p_O)$ electron of the NO molecule leads to the electronic configuration

$$KK\,(\sigma 2s_O)^2\,(\sigma 2s_N)^2\,(\pi 2p_O)^3\,(\sigma 2p_O)^2\,(\pi 2p_N),$$

which coincides with the second of the possible configurations of

NO^+ of the series (I, II, III). We thus conclude that the possible electronic configurations of NO^+ will be:

Normal state

$$KK(\sigma 2s_O)^2(\sigma 2s_N)^2(\pi 2p_O)^4(\sigma 2p_O)^2$$

First excited state

$$KK(\sigma 2s_O)^2(\sigma 2s_N)^2(\pi 2p_O)^4(\sigma 2p_O)(\pi 2p_N)$$

Second excited state:

$$KK(\sigma 2s_O)^2(\sigma 2s_N)^2(\pi 2p_O)^3(\sigma 2p_O)^2(\pi 2p_N).$$

Their corresponding terms are:

Normal state $^1\Sigma^+$

First excited state: $^1\Pi$; $^3\Pi$

Second excited state: $^1\Sigma^+$; $^1\Sigma^-$; $^1\Delta$; $^3\Sigma^+$; $^3\Sigma^-$; $^3\Delta$

The possible electronic terms can also be obtained by using the Wigner-Witmer rules for adding moments from the dissociation products of NO^+. Table 9 sets out the possible dissociation products of NO^+, the corresponding possible electronic terms and the relative positions of the dissociation limits.

TABLE 9

Dissociation Products	Possible electronic terms	Dissociation limit for different products above the limit of the lowest electronic state, cm^{-1}
$N(^4S) + O^+(^4S)$	$^{1;\,3;\,5;\,7}\Sigma^+$	0
$N^+(^3P) + O(^3P)$	$^{1;\,3;\,5}\Sigma^+(2)$; $^{1;\,3;\,5}\Sigma^-$; $^{1;\,3;\,5}\Pi(2)$; $^{1;\,3;\,5}\Delta$	7508,3
$N(^2P) + O^+(^4S)$	$^{3;\,5}\Sigma^+$; $^{3;\,5}\Pi$; $^{3;\,5}\Delta$	19223
$N^+(^3P) + O(^1D)$	$^3\Sigma^-(2)$; $^3\Sigma^+$; $^3\Pi(3)$; $^3\Delta(2)$; $^3\Phi$	23376

A comparison of Table 9 with the possible terms obtained from the electronic configurations shows that the term for the normal state of NO^+ is $^1\Sigma^+$. Of the remaining terms for the first dissociation limit, $^7\Sigma^+$; $^5\Sigma^+$ and $^3\Sigma^+$; only the last is evidently stable, having only one pair of uncompensated spins. The other two terms, as for the N_2 molecule, are unstable, since in them the number of uncompensated spins is greater than the number of compensated. We arrive at the same result from the fact that among the terms obtained by compounding electronic configurations, the $^5\Sigma^+$ and the $^7\Sigma^+$ terms are not found. The $^3\Sigma^+$ term is found in Table 9 in all four cases. However, to satisfy the rule of non-intersection of electron terms it must be assumed that the $^3\Sigma^+$ term has as dissociation products $N(^4S)$ and $O^+(^4S)$. The term for the first excited state $^3\Pi$ is met with in Table 9 for the dissociation products:

$$N^+(^3P) + O(^3P);\ N(^2D) + O^+(^4S);$$
$$N^+(^3P) + O(^1E).$$

Using the non-intersection rule, we can show that $^3\Pi$ has as dissociation products $N^+(^3P)$ and $O(^3P)$. The term $^1\Pi$ has the same dissociation products, since in Table 9 it is encountered in none of the lines (except the second).

We can thus evidently say that at a considerable height from the ground state of the $^1\Sigma^+$ NO^+ ion the terms $^1\Pi$, $^3\Pi$ and $^3\Sigma^+$ are relatively close to one another. This is because the orbital ($\pi 2P_N$) is at a considerable height from the closed electron configuration for NO. The $\sigma 2P_O$ and $\pi 2P_O$ orbitals from which the $^1\Pi$, $^3\Pi$, and $^3\Sigma^+$ terms are obtained are close to one another. Using the Hund rule, according to which the state with the greatest multiplicity lies lower than the others, we can say that $^3\Pi$ lies below $^1\Pi$. The $^3\Sigma^+$ state is evidently above $^3\Pi$. It cannot be below it, since it is obtained by a transition of a lower-lying electron from the $\pi 2P_O$ orbital to the $\pi 2P_N$ orbital while $^3\Pi$ is obtained by a a transition of the electron from the $\sigma 2P_O$ orbital to the $\pi 2P_N$ one. This is further confirmed by the fact that r_e for NO^+ is less than r_e for CO for the lowest electron state, i.e., the NO^+ ion is closer than CO to the limiting case of $r_e \to 0$, and the $\sigma 2P_O$ orbital is still further removed from $\pi 2P_O$. The $^1\Pi$ term is evidently above the $^3\Sigma^+$. The only argument in favour of such a mutual position of the $^3\Sigma^+$ and $^1\Pi$ states is the similar position of the same states in the electronically similar molecules CO and N_2. Also, these states are high (respectively 57,000 and 71,000 cm^{-1}), and the error in selecting the term is that we have before the statistical sum of the electron state with T = 57,000 cm^{-1} either the coefficient 3 or the coefficient 2.

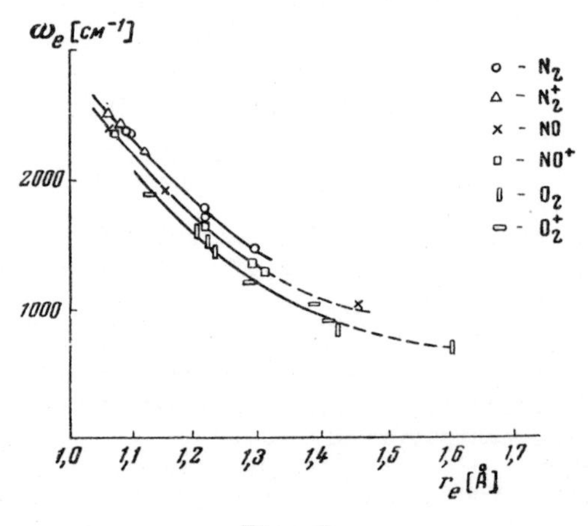

Fig. 2
Dependence of r_e on ω_e for N_2, N_2^+, NO, NO^+, O_2, O_2^+.

For calculating the rotational part of the statistical sum, we must have at least the value of r_e, from which the quantity B_e is to be calculated. For NO^+, r_e is known only for the $^1\Sigma^+$ state. An estimate of r_e for the three other states was obtained from empirical equations. For N_2, N_2^+, O_2, O_2^+ and NO it was observed that the dependence of r_e on ω_e for electron states not above 70,000 cm above the ground state is a relatively smoothly descending curve. For N_2 and N_2^+ all values of r_e lie on one curve, while for O_2 and O_2^+ they lie on another, parallel to the curve for N_2 and N_2^+. The curve for NO is between the curves for nitrogen and oxygen. The one known value of r_e for NO^+ lies satisfactorily on the NO curve. All the other values of r_e for NO^+ were obtained from the curve for NO. Fig. 2 shows all the curves and points from which r_e for NO^+ was taken.

3. Estimate of the Effect of Ionization, Coulomb Interactions and Degeneracy of the Electron Gas on the Magnitude of Thermodynamic Functions

To estimate the degree of ionization, as will be shown below, we can neglect the coulomb interaction of charged particles. Let us denote by $N_0, N_1, N_2, \ldots, N_n \ldots N_m$ the number of neutral, singly, doubly, $n$thly and $m$thly charged atoms in a gram mole of gas, and by N the total number of atoms per gram mole of gas:

$$N = N_0 + N_1 + N_2 + \ldots + N_n + \ldots + N_m;$$

N_e will denote the number of electrons in a gram mole of gas; $\alpha_1; \alpha_2; \alpha_n \ldots$ are defined by:

$$\alpha_0 = \frac{N_0}{N}; \quad \alpha_1 = \frac{N_1}{N} \ldots \alpha_n = \frac{N_n}{N} \ldots \alpha_m = \frac{N_m}{N}.$$

The process of ionization can be regarded as a system of chemical reactions

$$A^+ + e \rightleftarrows A + I(A) \tag{1}$$

$$A^{++} + e \rightleftarrows A^+ + I(A^+) \tag{2}$$

$$\ldots\ldots\ldots\ldots\ldots\ldots$$

$$A^{n(+)} + e \rightleftarrows A^{(n-1)(+)} + I(A^{(n-1)(+)}) \tag{n}$$

$$\ldots\ldots\ldots\ldots\ldots\ldots$$

$$A^{m(+)} + e \rightleftarrows A^{(m-1)(+)} + I(A^{(m-1)(+)}) \tag{m}$$

The condition of thermodynamic equilibrium for such a system of reactions is expressed as a system of algrbraic equations

$$\frac{C_n C}{C_{n-1}} = \frac{K_p^{(n)}}{p} \qquad (n = 1, 2 \ldots m),$$

where $C_0, C_1, \ldots C_n \ldots C_m$ are the concentrations of neutral, singly-charged, doubly-charged, $m$thly charged atoms in a gram mole of gas; C is the concentration of electrons,

$$C = \frac{N_e}{N + N_e}; \quad C_0 = \frac{N_0}{N + N_e}; \ldots C_n = \frac{N_n}{N + N_e}; \ldots C_m = \frac{N_m}{N + N_e}$$

$K_p^{(n)}$ are the equilibrium constants for the corresponding reactions dependent on the ionization potentials and temperature; p is the pressure.

To the m equations with $m+2$ unknowns, we must add the condition

$$1 = C_0 + C_1 + \ldots + C_4 + \ldots + C_m + C$$

and the law of conservation of charge

$$N_e = N_1 + 2N_2 + \ldots + nN_n + \ldots + mN_m,$$

which on conversion to concentrations takes the form:

$$C = C_1 + 2C_2 + \ldots + nC_n + \ldots + mC_m.$$

Transforming from concentrations to degrees of ionization $\alpha_0; \alpha_1 \ldots \alpha_m$ we obtain the following system of $m+1$ equations for the $m+1$ unknowns:

$$\frac{\alpha_n(\alpha_1 + 2\alpha_2 + \ldots + n\alpha_n \ldots + m\alpha_m)}{(1 + \alpha_1 + 2\alpha_2 + \ldots + n\alpha_n + \ldots + m\alpha_m)\alpha_{n-1}} = \frac{K_p^{(n)}}{p}; \quad n = 1, 2 \ldots m$$

$$\alpha_0 + \alpha_1 + \ldots + \alpha_n + \ldots + \alpha_m = 1.$$

Calculation of the equilibrium constants shows that, generally,

$$K_p^{(n)} \gg K_p^{(n+1)},$$

so that ionization is stepwise at high temperatures. Initially the gas is almost completely singly ionized, later completely doubly ionized and so on. With this pattern of ionization, as direct calculations show, the system of $(m+1)$ equations for $\alpha_0, \alpha_1 \ldots \alpha_n \ldots \alpha_m$ is considerably simplified. When the $n-1$th degree of ionization is complete and the nth degree starts, we get these relationships:

$$\alpha_n + \alpha_{n-1} = 1$$

$$\alpha_{n+1} = \alpha_{n+2} = \alpha_{n+3} = \ldots = \alpha_m = 0$$

$$\alpha_{n-2} = \alpha_{n-3} = \ldots = \alpha_0 = 0.$$

The $m+1$ th equation for α transforms into a system of two equations for α_{n-1} and α_n

$$\frac{\alpha_n[(n-1)\alpha_{n-1} + n\alpha_n]}{[1 + (n-1)\alpha_{n-1} + n\alpha_n](1-\alpha_n)} = \frac{K_p^{(n)}}{p}$$

$$\alpha_{n-1} + \alpha_n = 1$$

After transformation we obtain

$$\alpha_n = -\frac{n-1}{2} + \sqrt{\left(\frac{n-1}{2}\right)^2 + \frac{nK_p^{(n)}}{p + K_p^{(n)}}}$$

$$\alpha_{n-1} = 1 - \alpha_n.$$

With $n = 1$ the expression obtained transforms into the known Saha equation

$$\alpha_1 = \frac{1}{\sqrt{1 + \frac{p}{K_p^{(1)}}}}.$$

Table 10 shows the results of calculations for $\alpha_0, \alpha_1, \alpha_2$. The determinations were made for N. The ionization potentials for N, O, Ar and those for N^+, O^+ and Ar^+ are approximately equal. Hence Table 10 is useful for estimating the ionization of O and Ar.

TABLE 10

atm	0,001		0,01		0,1		1		10		100		300		1000	
α % / T °K	α_1	α_2	α_1	α_2	α_1	α_2	α_1	α_2	α_1	α_2	α_0	α_1	α_0	α_1	α_0	α_1
6000	0.16	0														
7000	1.4	0														
12000	97	0	78	0	36	0	12		4							
14000	100	0	97	0	78	0	37		12							
15000	99	1	100	0	95	0										
18000	86	14	98	2	100	0										
20000	45	55	88	12	99	1	95.6	0			65	35	86	14	99	1
22000	13	87	57	43	92	8	99	1	100	0						
24000	3	97	16	84	67	33	96	4	99.5	0.5	38	62	66.5	33.5	75.6	24.4

Deviation of the gas from an ideal gas because of coulomb interactions is represented, in the Debye-Huckel approximation, by a correcting term to the equation of state for the ionized gas:

$$p = \frac{kT}{V} \sum_n N_n - \frac{e^3}{3V^{3/2}} \sqrt{\frac{\pi}{kT}} \left(\sum_n N_n z_n^2 \right)^{3/2},$$

where z_n is a positive or negative number, characterizing the charge on the corresponding ion; N_n is the number of particles of the nth sort in a gram mole of gas. The subscript n is not connected with the number of charges on the atom. The results of calculation are in Table 11.

TABLE 11

T	p	Δp	$\frac{\Delta p}{p}$
12 000	0.001	$0.7 \cdot 10^{-6}$	0.07%
14 000	0.01	$13.6 \cdot 10^{-6}$	0.14%

From this table it can be seen that up to 12,000-14,000°K the coulomb interactions between 0.001 and 1000 atm can be neglected. The degree of degeneracy of the electron gas is described by the parameter

$$D = \frac{h^3 n_0}{2 (2\pi m k T)^{3/2}},$$

where n_0 is the electron density.

At $T = 25{,}000$°K and $p = 1000$ atm, $D = 0.003 \ll 1$, i.e., electron gas degeneracy can be neglected.

4. Computational Equations for Enthalpy, Heat Capacity and Equilibrium Constants Between 1000 and 12,000°K

In Section 3 it has been shown that in the ranges indicated the gas can be considered ideal so that the computational equations for enthalpy and heat capacity have the form:

$$H = RT\left(\frac{5}{2} + \frac{Q'}{Q}\right) + C$$

$$C_p = R\left[\frac{5}{2} + 2\frac{Q'}{Q} + \frac{Q''}{Q} - \left(\frac{Q'}{Q}\right)^2\right],$$

where R is the gas constant, and C has the following values in g.cal (15°C)/g.mole (chem.).

Table 12

	C		C		C
N_2	0	Ar	0	N_2^+	359 283
O_2	0	N^+	447 889	O_2^+	282 430
NO	21 467	O^+	372 901	NO^+	219 015
N	112 492	Ar^+	363 307		
O	58 965	e	0		

The computational equations for the equilibrium constants are, for the reaction $2N \rightleftarrows N_2 + D(N_2)$

$$K_p = 0{,}474542\, T^{\frac{5}{2}} \frac{Q_N^2}{Q_{N_2}} e^{-\frac{113257}{T}} \text{ atm},$$

for $2O \rightleftarrows O_2 + D(O_2)$

$$K_p = 0{,}579281\, T^{\frac{5}{2}} \frac{Q_O^2}{Q_{O_2}} e^{-\frac{59366}{T}} \text{ atm},$$

for $N + O \rightleftarrows NO + D(NO)$

$$K_p = 0{,}522569\, T^{\frac{5}{2}} \frac{Q_N Q_O}{Q_{NO}} e^{-\frac{75505}{T}} \text{ atm},$$

for $A^+ + e \rightleftarrows A + I(A)$

$$K_p = 6{,}57936 \cdot 10^{-7}\, T^{\frac{5}{2}} \frac{Q_{A^+}}{Q_A} e^{-\frac{I(A)}{T}} \text{ atm},$$

where

$$I(N) = 168\,840^\circ$$

$$I(O) = 157\,036^\circ$$

$$I(Ar) = 182\,890^\circ$$

$$I(N_2) = 180\,864^\circ$$

$$I(O_2) = 142\,176^\circ$$

$$I(NO) = 110\,253^\circ$$

5. Computational Equations for Chemical Equilibrium in Ideal Gas Systems

For the thermodynamic analysis of reacting gas systems, the composition of these systems must first of all be calculated. The solution of this problem is known in principle. However, a direct solution of the corresponding equations, when there are a large number of reactions and components, involves an enormous amount of calculation.

In this section we shall briefly expound the method of symmetrizing the chemical equilibrium equations without and with allowance for ionization.

It is known that a closed system of chemical equilibrium equations (CEE) for an ideal gas system of k different non-ionized components (the case of ionized components will be considered below) containing a different forms of atoms consists of one Dalton equation (DE) and $a-1$ mass balance equations (MBE) and $r=k-a$ mass action equations (MAE). Here r is the number of reactions in the system.

Let us introduce the notation

K_i = component $i\,(i=1,\ldots,k)$;
A_m = atom $m\,(m=1,\ldots,a)$;
n_{im} = number of A_ms in the K_i molecule;
ν_{si} = stoichiometric coefficient to K_i in the reaction $s\,(s=1,\ldots,r)$.

The molecule K_i has the form $\sum_{m=1}^{a} n_{im} A_m$, and the reactions s — $\sum_{i=1}^{k} \nu_{si} K_i = 0$ for chemical equilibrium have the form

$$\sum_{i=1}^{k} x_i = 1\,, \qquad \text{(DE) (19a)}$$

$$\sum_{i=1}^{k} n_{im} x_i \Big/ \sum_{i=1}^{k} n_{i1} x_i = p_{m1}\,, \qquad \text{(MBE) (19b)}$$

$$K_{p,\,a+s}\, p^{-\nu_s} = \prod_{i=1}^{k} x_i^{\nu_{si}}\,, \qquad \text{(MAE) (19c)}$$

where p_{m1} = const and $p_{11} = 1$.

The physically obvious singularity of the solution for CEE is shown in [15].

The solution of equations (19) is made difficult by the non-linearity of equation (19c) and the assymmetry of (19a), (19b).

The main numerical methods of solving CEE are the iteration method and the Newton-Raphson method. Numerical methods have to be used because equation (19c) is non-linear. The iterated components are the a components the content of which predominates (the x_i quantities) in the region of the $p-T$ diagram, in which the solution of (19) lies. The different regions of the $p-T$ diagram have different collections of such components.

Let us separate out the association of such predominant components, whose number is equal to the number of different kinds of atoms, i.e., a. This association it is proposed to arrange so that the mth component has a greater content of the mth atoms than all the other components. With this definition, there can be components in this association even with a small absolute content. It will be assumed that the predominating components will be the first a components of the total number k. The asymmetry of (19a) and (19b) is eliminated by solving them for the predominating component, i.e., by obtaining symmetrical equations for the concentration of the predominating component (EPC). Let us introduce as the concentration of the predominating component x_m^0 in the absence of other components. This concentration is determined by (19a) and (19b):

$$\sum_{m=1}^{a} x_m^0 = 1; \quad \frac{n_{mm} x_m^0}{n_{11} x_1^0} = p_{m1} \quad (p_{11} = 1).$$

whence, obviously:

$$x_m^0 = \frac{p_{m1}}{n_{mm}} \Bigg/ \sum_{m=1}^{a} \frac{p_{m1}}{n_{mm}}. \tag{20}$$

Let us also introduce the notation

$$\Phi_0 = \sum_{l=a+1}^{k} x_l, \tag{21a}$$

$$n_{mm}\Phi_m = \sum_{i=1}^{k} n_{im} x_i - n_{mm} x_m. \tag{21b}$$

In view of the above definition of the predominating components, $n_{mm} \neq 0$, and (19a) and (19b) take the form:

$$\sum_{m=1}^{a} x_m = 1 - \Phi_0,$$

$$\frac{x_m + \Phi_m}{x_1 + \Phi_1} = \frac{x_m^0}{x_1^0}.$$

Hence it is easy to obtain EPC, equivalent to the DE and MBE:

$$x_m = x_m^0 \Phi - \Phi_m, \tag{22a}$$

where

$$\Phi = 1 + \sum_{m=1}^{a} \Phi_m - \Phi_0 = 1 + \sum_{i=1}^{k} x_i \left(\sum_{m=1}^{a} \frac{n_{im}}{n_{mm}} - 1 \right). \tag{22b}$$

A simple form of the EPC is obtained, when each K_m only contains A_m. Then $n_{lm} = 0$ $(l \neq m;\ l, m = 1, \ldots, a)$ and equations (21b) and (22b) assume the forms

$$n_{mm}\Phi_m = \sum_{l=a+1}^{k} n_{lm} x_l, \tag{21b'}$$

$$\Phi = 1 + \sum_{m=1}^{a} \Phi_m - \Phi_0 = 1 + \sum_{l=a+1}^{k} x_i \left(\sum_{m=1}^{a} \frac{n_{lm}}{n_{mm}} - 1 \right). \tag{22b'}$$

In this case the EPC express the concentrations of the predominating components in terms of the concentrations of the other components. Since in the case of most of the MAE applied, the concentrations of the other components can be expressed in the concentration of the predominating ones, systems (22a) and (19c) are suitable for generalized iteration. Note that one can always reduce the MAE to the most symmetrical form by combining with equation (19c), and this enables one to express the other components simply in terms of the predominating ones.

Iteration, which of course is purely algebraic, is simple, but since iterations converge only in the middles of regions of predominance of the components in the $p-T$ diagram their application is limited. The Newton-Raphson method is considerably more promising.

The main advantage of this method is that the region of its application extends far beyond the boundaries of the regions on the $p-T$ diagram, where the components relative to which the EPC are solved predominate. This is because of the differential character of the method. The amount of calculation by this method, thanks to the symmetry of the EPC and with reduced MAEs with proper numbering of the components and itemization of the calculation scheme, is considerably less than the amount of direct calculation from the DE, MBE, and unreduced MAE. Finally the method gives the information needed for the calculation of heat capacities, sonic speeds and other thermodynamic functions of reacting gas systems in the equilibrium state.

Let us give the scheme of calculation of the ionization of arbitrary orders of all k components. Since the composition does not depend on the particular choice of the complete system of independent reactions, the equations of ionizational equilibrium for the n th ionization can be written:

$$\frac{x_{k+1}x_e}{x_1} = \frac{1}{p}K_{p,\,k+1} \ldots \frac{x_{nk+1}x_e^n}{x_1} = \frac{1}{p^n}K_{p,\,nk+1}$$
$$\cdots\cdots\cdots\cdots\cdots\cdots \tag{23a}$$
$$\frac{x_{2k}x_e}{x_k} = \frac{1}{p}K_{p,\,2k} \ldots \frac{x_{(n+1)k}x_e^n}{x_k} = \frac{1}{p^n}K_{p,\,(n+1)k},$$

where x_e is the concentration of electrons

$$x_e = \sum_{t=1}^{n} t \sum_{i=1}^{k} x_{tk+i} \ . \tag{23b}$$

Equation (23b) expresses the conservation of charge.

Multiplying (23b) by x_e and using equation (23a), we obtain:

$$x_e^2 = \sum_{t=1}^{n} \frac{1}{x_e^{t-1}} \frac{t}{p^t} \sum_{i=1}^{k} K_{ti}, \tag{24a}$$

where

$$K_{ti} = K_{p,\,tk+i}\, x_i. \tag{24b}$$

If $x_1, \ldots, x_k$ are known, then with given $K_{p,\,tk+i}$ equation (24a) is an algebraic equation of the $n+1$ **th** degree relative to x_e. In the general case it is solved numerically. For first-order ionization

$$x_e = \sqrt{\frac{1}{p}\sum_{i=1}^{k} K_{1i}}$$

After determining x_e, the ionized components are found from the equation

$$x_{t,\,k+i} = \frac{1}{p^t}\frac{K_{ti}}{x_e^t} \ .$$

The scheme of calculation for the general case of CEE is as follows: we specify the predominating components $x_1, \ldots, x_a$; from the transformed equations (19c) we find $x_{a+1}, \ldots, x_k$, from equation (24a) x_e and from equation (23a) $x_{k+1}, \ldots, x_{(n+1)k}$. Then to equation (22a) we apply the Newton-Raphson method and obtain new equations $x_1, \ldots$ x_a, etc., until the needed accuracy is achieved.

6. Thermodynamic Analysis of Reacting Ideal Gas Systems in the Equilibrium State

Let us first of all consider the calculation of the molar and specific heat capacities C_p and C_v for the reacting ideal gas systems in an equilibrium state. (Molar quantities will be denoted by large, and specific by the corresponding small, letters).

Calculation of these quantities is dealt with in [16]. Below it will be shown that these calculations are not accurate.

The equations for calculating c_p and c_v are:

$$c_p = \left(\frac{\partial h}{\partial T}\right)_p \quad c_v = \left(\frac{\partial u}{\partial T}\right) \tag{25a}$$

where h and u are the specific enthalpy and internal energy of the system. Multiplying and dividing equation (25a) by the constant mass of the system $M = \mu N$ $\left(\mu = \sum_{i=1}^{K} \mu_i x_i\right.$ = molecular weight of the system, $N = \sum_{i=1}^{K} N_i$ = total number of moles in the system $\Big)$, we obtain:

$$\frac{C_p}{\mu} = \left(\frac{\partial \frac{H}{\mu}}{\partial T}\right)_p; \quad \frac{C_v}{\mu} = \left(\frac{\partial \frac{u}{\mu}}{\partial T}\right)_v \tag{25b}$$

or

$$C_p = \frac{1}{N}\left(\frac{\partial \sum_{i=1}^{K} H_i N_i}{\partial T}\right)_p; \quad C_v = \frac{1}{N}\left(\frac{\partial \sum_{i=1}^{K} U_i N_i}{\partial T}\right)_v, \tag{26}$$

where K is the number of components, among which the first k are unionized components;

μ_i is the molecular weight of component i;

N_i is the number of moles of component i;

$x_i = \frac{N_i}{N}$ = concentration of component i.

H_i, U are the molar enthalpies and internal energies of the same components.

The symmetrical CEEs consist of symmetrical equations of the predominating components and the reduced MAEs (cf. section 5);

$$x_m = x_m^0 \Phi - \Phi_m \ (m = 1, \ldots, a), \qquad \text{(EPC)} \quad (27a)$$

$$K_{p,\, a+s}\, p^{-\nu_s} = \prod_{i=1}^{K} x_i^{\nu_{si}} \ (s = 1, \ldots, R), \qquad \text{(MAE)} \quad (27b)$$

where a is the number of different atoms in the system; and R is the number of independent reactions, among which the first r are ordinary reactions and the others ionization reactions.

If we go over from x_i to N_i and use the equation of state $pV = NRT$, equation (27) becomes

$$N_m + \Psi_m = \text{const}, \tag{28a}$$

$$K_{p,\,a+s}\left(\frac{V}{RT}\right)^{\nu_s} = \prod_{i=1}^{K} N_i^{\nu_{si}}. \tag{28b}$$

Here Ψ_m is Φ_m with x_i replaced by N_i.

From equations (25)-(28) we find:

$$C_p = \sum_{i=1}^{K} C_{pi}\, x_i + \left\{\sum_{i=1}^{K} H_i\, y_i + H\Sigma_p\right\},$$

where

$$\Sigma_p = \frac{1}{N}\left(\frac{\partial N}{\partial T}\right)_p = -\frac{1}{\mu}\sum_{i=1}^{K} \mu_i\, y_i,$$

$$y_i = \left(\frac{\partial x_i}{\partial T}\right)_p.$$

$$C_v = \sum_{i=1}^{K} C_{pi}\, x_i - R + \left\{\sum_{i=1}^{K} H_i\, v_i - RT\Sigma_v\right\}$$

where

$$\Sigma_v = \frac{1}{N}\left(\frac{\partial N}{\partial T}\right)_v = \sum_{i=1}^{K} v_i,$$

$$v_i = \frac{1}{N}\left(\frac{\partial N_i}{\partial T}\right)_v.$$

Thus calculation of C_p and C_v reduces to finding y_i and v_i respectively. By taking logarithms and differentiating equation (27b) with respect to T at p = const, we obtain

$$y_m = x_m^0\,\overline{\Phi} - \overline{\Phi}_m, \tag{29a}$$

$$\frac{Q_{a+s}}{RT^2} = \sum_{i=1}^{K} \nu_{si}\,\frac{y_i}{x_i}. \tag{29b}$$

The lines over the Φ s denote replacement of x_i by y_i. In equation (29b) the known relation

$$\frac{d\ln K_{p,\,a+s}}{dT} = \frac{Q_{a+s}}{RT^2},$$

is used, where $Q_{a+s} = \sum_{i=1}^{K} \nu_{si} H_i$ is the heat of the reaction s.

Similarly, from equation (28) with V = const, we obtain

$$v_m + \overline{\Psi}_m = 0, \tag{30a}$$

$$\frac{\Delta U_{a+s}}{RT^2} = \sum_{i=1}^{K} \nu_{si}\,\frac{v_i}{x_i}, \tag{30b}$$

where

$$\Delta U_{a+s} = \sum_{i=1}^{K} \nu_{si}\, U_i = Q_{a+s} - \nu_s RT.$$

Here the line over the symbol indicates replacement of x_i by v_i A direct solution of equations (29) and (30) is inadvisable. It is simpler to find first of all y_m from equation (29a) and v_m from equation (30a), and from them to find $y_{a+1}, \ldots, y_K$ from equation (29b) and $v_{a+1}, \ldots, v_K$ from equation (30b). This sequence of operations (from EPC to MAE), natural for the forms of equations (29) and (30), is rational for $a < R$. For $a > R$ the procedure should be the reverse (from MAE to EPC). Of course, with $a > R$ the procedure can be restricted simply to solving the MAEs, appropriately transformed. The $a > R$ case will be examined below.

Returning to equations (29) and (30), we note a fairly obvious fact: the determination matrix from equation (29a) coincides with the matrix for the next cycle of determining δx_m by the Newton-Raphson method from equation (27a).

For calculating C_p with $a > R'$, we start from the system:

$$N_m + \overline{\Psi}_m = \text{const}, \qquad (31a)$$

$$K_{p,s}\, p^{-\nu_s} = \sum_{i=1}^{K} N_i^{\nu_{si}} N^{-\nu_s}, \qquad (31b)$$

differing from equation (30) by the obvious substitution and the replacement of the subscript in K_p. Note that for each reaction the number of atoms of each type must be conserved (section 5), i.e.

$$\sum_{i=1}^{K} \nu_{si}\, n_{im} = 0. \qquad (32)$$

For calculating C_p from (26) it is necessary to determine $u_i = \frac{1}{N}\left(\frac{\partial N_i}{\partial T}\right)_p$. After taking logarithms in equation (31b), we obtain by differentiating equation (31) with respect to T at p = const a system of linear equations for u_i:

$$\sum_{i=1}^{K} n_{im}\, u_i = 0 \qquad (33a)$$

$$\frac{Q_s}{RT^2} = \sum_{i=1}^{K} \nu_{si} \frac{u_i}{x_i} - \nu_s \sum_{i=1}^{K} u_i \qquad (33b)$$

If we put u_i in the form:

$$u_i = \sum_{s=1}^{R} \nu_{si}\, \Gamma_s, \qquad (34)$$

equation (33a) is automatically satisfied, in view of equation (32).

For determining Γ_s we obtain the system of equations:

$$\frac{Q_s}{RT^2} = \sum_{t=1}^{R} \frac{\Gamma_t}{F_{st}}, \qquad (35)$$

where

$$\frac{1}{F_{st}} = \sum_{i=1}^{K} \frac{\nu_{si}\nu_{ti}}{x_i} - \nu_s \nu_t. \tag{35a}$$

For C_p we obtain from (25) the equation

$$C_p = \sum_{i=1}^{K} C_{pi} x_i + \sum_{s=1}^{R} Q_s \Gamma_s \tag{36}$$

For calculating C_v with $a > R$, first of all let us start from equation (28), which means from equation (30), which, transformed, can be written like equation (33)

$$\sum_{i=1}^{K} n_{im} v_i = 0 \tag{37a}$$

$$\frac{\Delta U_s}{RT^2} = \sum_{i=1}^{K} \nu_{si} \frac{v_i}{x_i}. \tag{37b}$$

Here the subscript in ΔU is also replaced.

Further operations are similar to those in calculating C_p and for

$$v_i = \sum_{s=1}^{R} \nu_{si} \gamma_s \tag{38}$$

we obtain an equation for determining γ_s

$$\frac{\Delta U_s}{RT^2} = \sum_{t=1}^{R} \frac{\gamma_s}{f_{st}}, \tag{39}$$

where

$$\frac{1}{f_{st}} = \sum_{i=1}^{k} \frac{\nu_{si}\nu_{ti}}{x_i} = \frac{1}{F_{st}} + \nu_s \nu_t. \tag{39a}$$

For C_v we obtain from (25) the equation:

$$C_v = \sum_{i=1}^{K} C_{vi} x_i + \sum_{s=1}^{R} \Delta U_s \gamma_s.$$

Epstein [16], proposing to calculate C_p and C_v by a method similar to that given for $a > R$, did not obtain systems (35) and (39), and implicitly assumed a material independence, which in the general case is untrue.

The term "materially independent reactions" means reactions for which the corresponding sets of components do not overlap. (For each reaction there is a specific set of components participating in the reaction).

Epstein determined Γ_s and γ_s from the equations:

$$\Gamma_s = \frac{Q_s}{RT^2} F_{ss}, \quad \gamma_s = \frac{\Delta U_s}{RT^2} f_{ss},$$

thus not solving systems (35) and (39). With weakly interacting reactions, Epstein's calculation is fairly accurate. This is true when the regions of maximum intensities of all reactions do not overlap on the $p-T$ diagram. For a single reaction in the system

Epstein's calculation is of course correct. Hence the good agreement between theory and experiment in McCollum's experiments [17] on the single reaction $2\ NO_2 - N_2O \rightleftarrows 0$* is unconvincing. For strongly interacting reactions Epstein's calculation is inapplicable. In calculations for concrete reaction systems a divergence has been found between the heat capacities calculated by the proposed scheme and by the Epstein scheme of up to 40 per cent over a fairly wide range of the $p-T$ diagram.

Note that equation (35a) shows that material independence of reactions does not prove the correctness of the Epstein scheme in calculating C_p. Actually, this condition only leads to $v_{si}v_{ti} = 0$ $(s \neq t)$. Obviously it is necessary to specify constancy of the number of particles in all reactions but one. The latter condition reduces to $v_s = 0$ where s has all values from 1 to R except one. The material independence of reactions is sufficient for the Epstein scheme to be correct only in calculating C_v, as is evident from equation (39a).

The equation for the speed of sound has the form [16]

$$a = \sqrt{\gamma \frac{RT}{\mu} \cdot \frac{1 + \frac{T}{N}\left(\frac{\partial N}{\partial T}\right)_v}{1 + \frac{T}{N}\left(\frac{\partial N}{\partial T}\right)_p}}. \qquad (40)$$

The speed of sound as calculated from this equation differs from that calculated by the Epstein scheme, though the difference is smaller than is obtained in calculating heat capacities.

Let us now turn our attention to other thermodynamic characteristics.

It can easily be seen that a solution of the systems of equations (29) and (30) enables us to find the partial differentials with respect to T with p or V const of arbitrary quantities characterizing the system studied. We will only give the equations:

$$\left(\frac{\partial H}{\partial T}\right)_p = C_p - H\Sigma_p,$$

$$\left(\frac{\partial H}{\partial T}\right)_v = c_v + \frac{R}{\mu}(1 + T\Sigma_v),$$

$$\left(\frac{\partial \rho}{\partial T}\right)_p = -\frac{\rho}{T}(1 + T\Sigma_p).$$

Similarly we can find $\left(\frac{\partial s}{\partial T}\right)_{p,v}$.

With differentials with respect to T of H_i of order higher than the first given we can find the partial differentials of all quantities with respect to T with p or V = const, and of higher orders, not exceeding however, the order of differentiation of H_i with respect to T. The corresponding systems can be obtained by differentiating the appropriate order of systems (29) and (30).

We can equally successfully find the partial differential of arbitrary quantities with respect to p or ρ with T const. For

*Sic.

example, to study the Joule-Thomson effect we must know the values of $\left(\frac{\partial u}{\partial \rho}\right)$, the equation for which has the form

$$\left(\frac{\partial u}{\partial \rho}\right)_T = \frac{1}{\mu}\sum_{i=1}^{K} U_i v_i = \frac{1}{\mu}\left[\sum_{i=1}^{K} H_i v_i - RT\Sigma_v\right],$$

where

$$v_i = \frac{1}{N}\left(\frac{\partial N_i}{\partial \rho}\right)_T \quad \Sigma_v = \sum_{i=1}^{K} v_i.$$

The corresponding system for v_i from the viewpoint of structure differs little from the systems of equations (30), namely: all $Q_{a+s} \equiv 0$ and T is replaced by ρ, i.e., for calculating $\left(\frac{du}{d\rho}\right)_T$ the finished system of solution of the equations (30) can be used.

Finally, using the property of Jacobians [18], we can calculate first-order partial differentials of arbitrary quantities (f) with respect to other arbitrary quantities (x) with a third kind of arbitrary quantity (y) constant.

Note that the partial differentials of any quantities with respect to arbitrary quantities at T = const can be found for as high an order as is desired.

7. Discussion of the Results

From the methods given above of calculating the thermodynamic properties of mixtures of gases free to react chemically and to be ionized, the authors have calculated the thermodynamic properties and composition of atmospheric air between 1000 and 12,000°K and between 0.001 and 1000 atm.

The volume composition of air for normal conditions was taken as 78.08 per cent nitrogen and 20.95 per cent oxygen, all the rest being assumed to be of argon. The error in such an approximation is less than the error in assuming the composition of air to be independent of height.

Preliminary estimates and later accurate calculations showed that:

1) up to 6000°K at pressures from 0.001 to 1000 atm the effect of ionization on the thermodynamic properties and composition of air can be neglected;

2) from 6000 to 12,000°K the effect of ionization higher than the first stage can be neglected.

Hence a two-stage calculation was made over the temperature range 1000 to 12,000°K:

1) from 1000 to 6000°K without ionization;

2) from 6000 to 12,000°K with single-stage ionization of all components.

Calculations were made for each 100K° interval (111 values of T altogether). Calculations for different pressures were made according to the following scheme.

from 1×10^k to $2 \times 10^{k'}$ for each 0.2×10^k
from 2×10^k to 5×10^k for each 0.5×10^k
from 5×10^k to 10×10^k for each 1×10^k

where $k = -3, -2, -1, 0, 1, 2$ (16 points for each power of ten of p, in all 97 values of p for each temperature, total 10,767 points).

Between 1000 and 6000°K, for each point calculations were made of the mole fractions of N_2, O_2, NO, N, O and Ar, and between 6000 and 12,000°K calculations were made for these and N_2^+, O_2^+, NO^+, N^+, Ar^+, e; between 1000 and 12,000°K in addition to the composition of air, for each point we calculated:

h = enthalpy (g.cal/g)
u = internal energy (g.cal/g)
s = entropy (g.cal/g.°K)
μ = molecular weight (g/g.mole)
c_p = specific heat at p = constant (g.cal/g.°K)
c_v = specific heat at v = constant (g.cal/g.°K)
a = speed of sound (m/second)
ρ = density (g/cm³).

From the calculations 44 graphs were plotted, of which we present here those for x_{N_2}, x_{O_2}, x_{NO}, x_N, x_O, x_{Ar}, x_e, h, c_p, a, μ, s (Figs. 3-10) as a function of temperature for pressures of 0.001, 1, and 1000 atm.

Analysis of the composition of air from the graphs shows that increase of temperature increases the content first of the atomic, and then of the ionized components; increase of pressure, on the other hand, lowers the content of atomic and ionized components and increases the content of molecules. At any pressure, increase of temperature first brings about a dissociation of oxygen. Nitrogen molecules start to dissociate somewhat later since they have about twice the dissociation energy of oxygen molecules. Dissociation of oxygen goes hand in hand with formation of NO. Usually the NO content of air becomes greatest in the temperature range in which dissociation of oxygen is most extensive; after this the NO content decreases with rise of temperature.

Ionization of the atomic and molecular components starts to become significant above 6000°K. With increase of temperature the percentage of ionized components increases and at 0.001 atm and 12,000°K air is almost completely ionized.

The curves for enthalpy and entropy increase continuously with increase of T and decrease continuously with increase of p. On the enthalpy curves portions can be found where this quantity rises

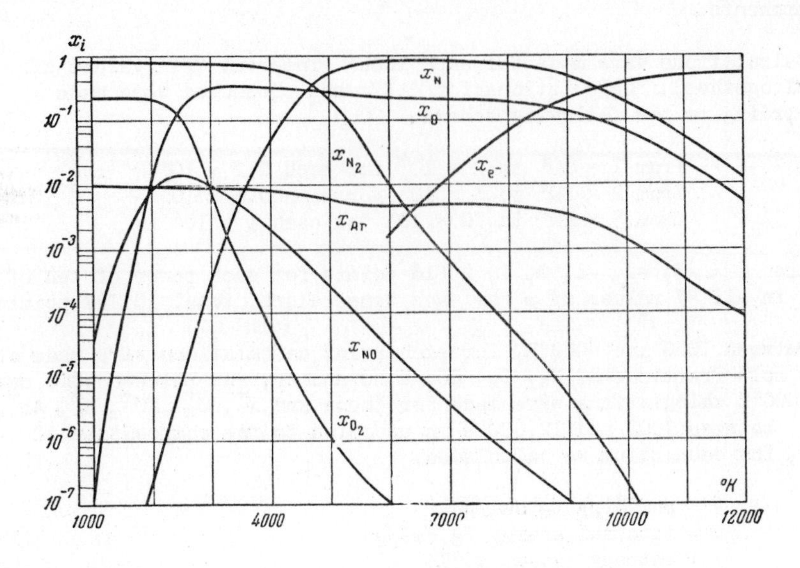

Fig. 3
Mole fractions of molecular and atomic components of air and of electrons as a function of temperature at 0.001 atm

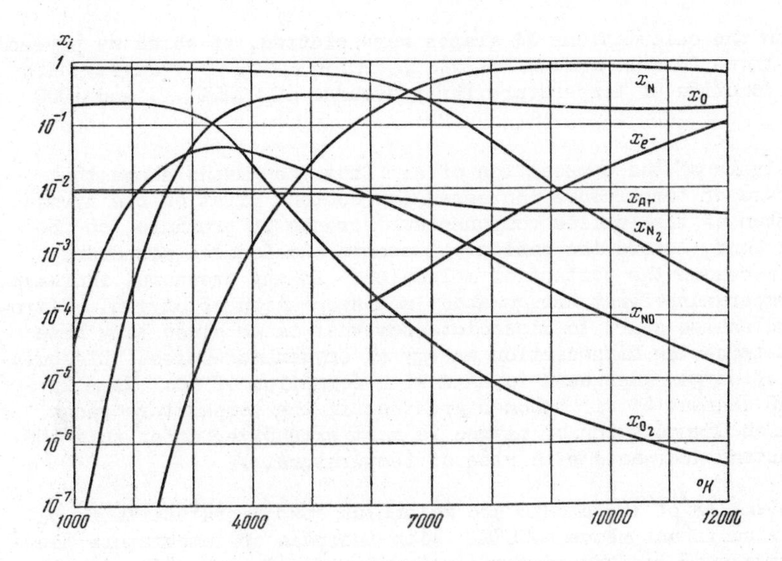

Fig. 4
Mole fractions of molecular and atomic components of air and of electrons as a function of temperature at 1 atm

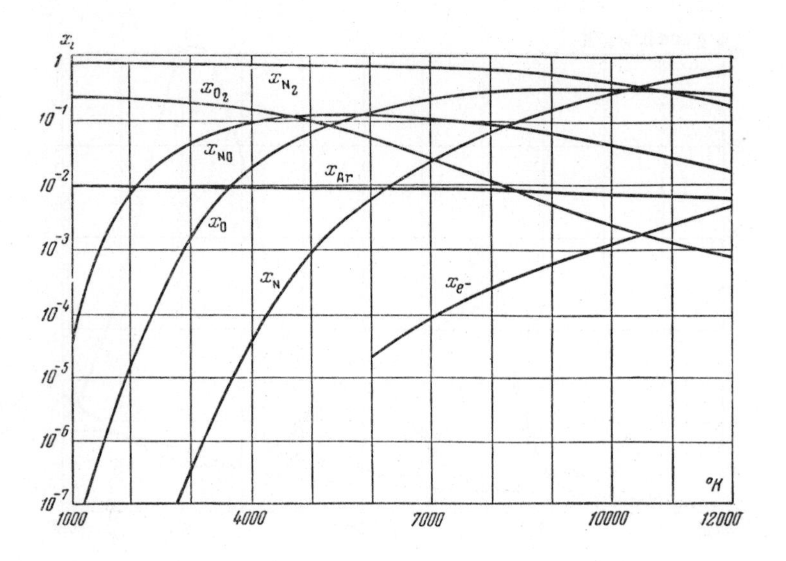

Fig. 5
Mole fractions of molecular and atomic components of air and of electrons as a function of temperature at 1000 atm

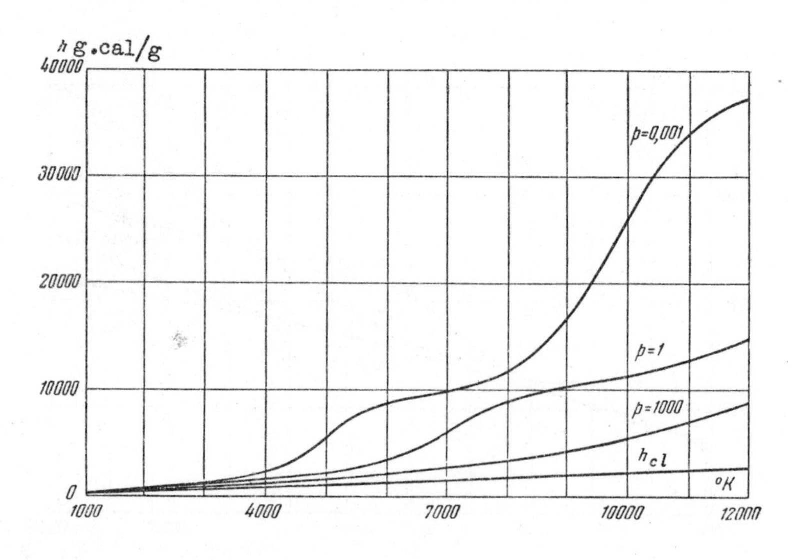

Fig. 6
Enthalpy of air in g.cal/g as a function of temperature at 0.001, 1 and 1000 atm. The bottom curve is that of h calculated from equation (41)

$h\,(T = 273.16°\,K) = 65.4$ (g.cal/g)
$h\,(T = 290.16°\,K) = 69.48$ (g.cal/g)

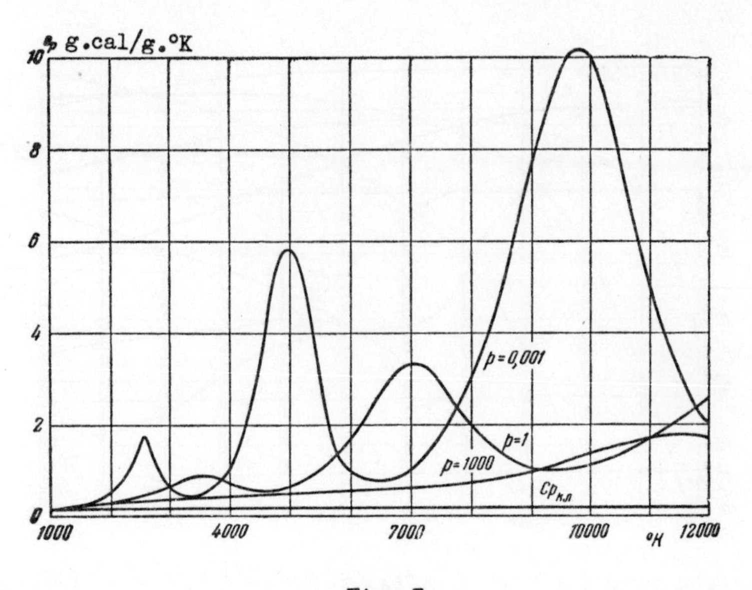

Fig. 7
Heat capacity of air at constant pressure in g.cal/g.°K as a function of temperature at 0.001, 1, and 1000 atm. The bottom curve is of c_p calculated from equation (41)

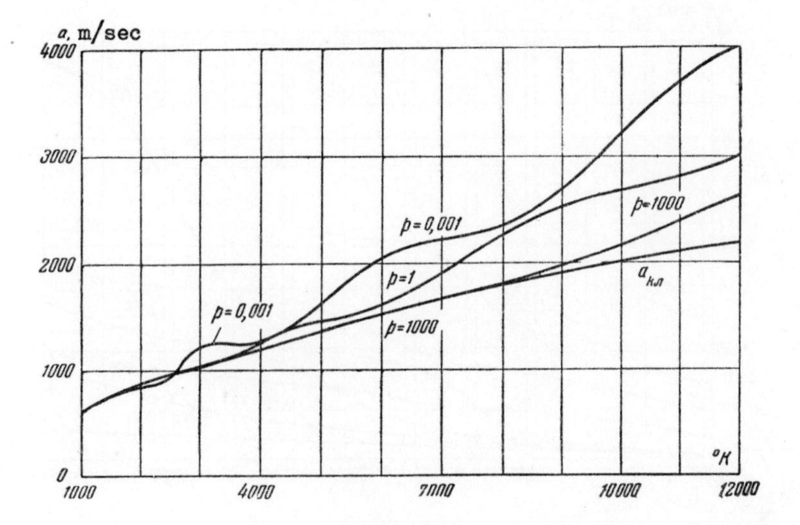

Fig. 8
Speed of sound in m/sec as a function of temperature at 0.001, 1 and 1000 atm. The bottom curve is the curve calculated from equation (41)

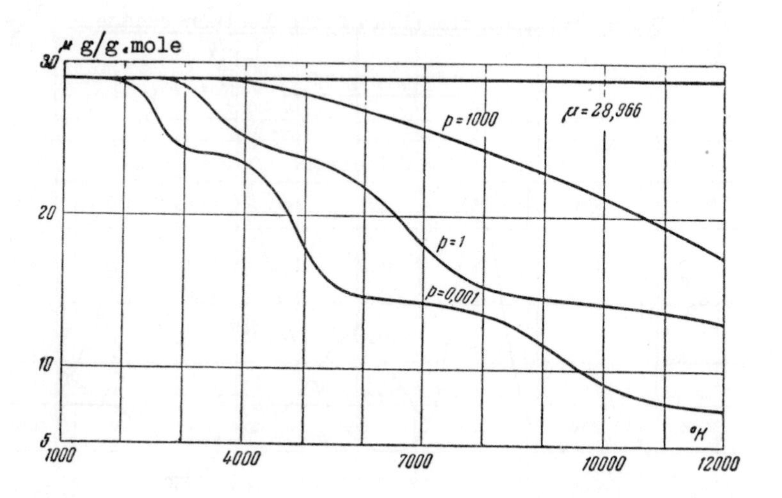

Fig. 9
Molecular weight of air as a function of temperature at 0.001, 1 and 1000 atm. The horizontal line at the top represents μ = 28.966.

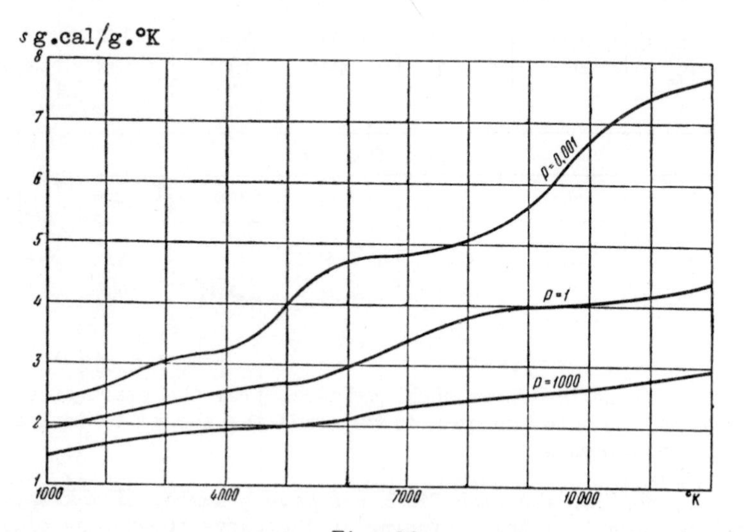

Fig. 10
Entropy of air in g.cal/g °K as a function of temperature at 0.001, 1 and 1000 atm.

$s(T = 273.16°\text{K}, p = 1 \text{ atm}) =$
$= 1.735$ (g.cal/g °K)
$s(T = 290.16°\text{K}, p = 1 \text{ atm}) =$
$= 1.750$ (g.cal/g °K)

TABLE 13

Degree of approximation of the Epstein scheme

$$\omega_f = \frac{f_{\text{Epstein}} - f}{f} \times 100\%$$

p = 0.001 atm

T °K	6000	7000	8000	9000	10000	11000	12000
ω_{c_p}	1,99	12,4	15,5	12,9	7,19	2,29	0,471
ω_{c_v}	2,46	14,0	16,8	15,5	10,9	4,30	1,01

p = 0.1 atm

T °K	6300	7300	8300	9300	10300	11300
ω_{c_p}	0,327	0,970	7,10	11,8	13,1	12,3
ω_{c_v}	0,474	1,40	8,34	13,0	14,6	14,6

p = 10 atm

T °K	6500	7500	8500	9500	10500	11500
ω_{c_p}	16,1	3,80	0,914	0,821	3,52	7,25
ω_{c_v}	16,8	4,29	1,45	1,61	4,68	8,56

p = 1000 atm

T °K	6700	7700	8700	9700	10700	11700
ω_{c_p}	24,5	29,2	35,8	17,0	8,84	4,56
ω_{c_v}	27,2	30,0	37,8	17,9	10,1	6,01

more rapidly. The first such increase, from the start of the curve, is due to dissociation of nitrogen, and the second to ionization of the air components.

The curves for the specific heats have a number of maxima. The first portion from the beginning of the curve covers the dissociation of oxygen, the second that of nitrogen, and the third the ionization of air components.

The molecular weight of air decreases as temperature increases, and in some places the slope of the curves is greater than in others. The first portion of the curves from the origin corresponds to oxygen dissociation, the second to nitrogen dissociation, and the third to ionization of the components of air.

The density curve is not reproduced, since density is almost a linear function of pressure.

On the graphs of enthalpy, specific heats at constant pressure, sound velocity and molecular weight we give for comparison the values of these quantities calculated from the equations:

$$h=\frac{7}{2}\frac{RT}{\mu};\quad c_p=\frac{7}{2}\frac{R}{\mu};\quad a=\sqrt{1{,}4\frac{RT}{\mu}};\quad \mu=28{,}966. \tag{41}$$

These values of the thermodynamic functions will be seen to differ considerably from the actual values.

The authors have calculated at 25 points values of c_p, c_v, γ and a according to the Epstein method. Table 13 gives a comparison of the results with those calculated by the authors' method, for c_p and c_v. The differences in γ and a calculated by the two methods can be pretty well neglected, but those for c_p and c_v cannot.

The mathematical error in the calculations of thermodynamic functions and of the composition of air is low, and is lower than the limits of physical error. The reason for the physical error is the inaccuracy in calculating the thermodynamic functions of the components of air, the approximation in the determination of the composition of air, already noted, and some inaccuracy in the Clapeyron equation because of Van-der-Waals-type corrections, for low temperatures and high pressures, and because of Debye-Huckel type corrections for Coulomb interactions between ionized particles and electrons, for high temperatures.

The calculations were made with a high-speed electronic computer constructed in the Institute of Fine Mechanisms and Computing Technology of the U.S.S.R. Academy of Sciences.

The results of the calculations are published in [19] in the form of tables of thermodynamic functions and composition of air between 1000 and 12,000°K and 0.001-1000 atm.

REFERENCES

1. E.C. MOORE, Atomic Energy Levels (1949).
2. G. HERZBERG, Spectra of Diatomic Molecules (1951).
3. B. ROSEN, Données spectroscopiques concernant les molecules diatomiques, Paris (1951).
4. M.P. VUKALOVICH, Thermodynamic Properties of Gases (Termodinamicheskiye svoistva gazov), Moscow (1953).
5. J.W.M. DUMOND and R.E. COHEN, Rev. Mod. Phys., 25, 691 (1953).
6. A.E. DOUGLAS, J. Chem. Phys. (1953).
7. P. BRIX and G. HERZBERG, Canad. J. Phys., 32, 112 (1954).
8. M.W. TEAST, ibid., 28, 488 (1950).
9. A.E. DOUGLAS, ibid., 30, 302 (1952).

10. A.E. DOUGLAS, Astrophys. J., 117, 380 (1953).
11. G. HERZBERG, ibid., 108, 163 (1948).
12. G. HERZBERG, ibid., 105, 353 (1947).
13. G. HERZBERG, Canad. J. Phys., 31, 657 (1953).
14. G. HERZBERG, ibid., 30, 185 (1952).
15. Ya.B. ZEL'DOVICH, Zh. fiz. khim., 11, 385 (1936).
16. P.S. EPSTEIN, Treatise on Thermodynamics (Reference to translation into Russian).
17. E.D. McCOLLUM, J. Am. Chem. Soc., 49, 28 (1927).
18. L. LANDAU and E. LIFSHITS, Statistical Physics (Statisticheskaya fizika), Gos. izd. tekh. teoret. lit. (1951).
19. A.S. PREDVODITELEV et al., Tables of Thermodynamic Functions of Air between 1000 and 12,000°K and 0.001 and 1000 atm (Tablitsy termodinamicheskikh funktsii vozdukha v intervale temperatur ot 1000 do 12000°K i intervale davlenii ot 0.001 do 1000 atm), Izd. Akad. Nauk SSSR (1957).

E.V. Stupochenko, B.B. Dotzenko, I.P. Stakhanov and E.V. Samuilov

Methods of Calculating the Kinetic Coefficients of Air at High Temperatures

INTRODUCTION

This paper presents a theoretical calculation of the kinetic coefficients of air - the viscosity and thermal conductivity - between 2000 and 8000°K and 0.001 to 1000 atm. As in the case of the thermodynamic quantities, experimental methods have still not been sufficiently worked out for the direct study of the kinetic properties of gases at such high temperatures. Also, in the solution of the more important problems of present-day technology, particularly in that of reaction propulsion, a knowledge of kinetic coefficients of air at high temperatures and over a wide range of pressures is necessary. Hence theoretical calculation acquires here, as in the case of thermodynamic properties, special importance. However, there is a great difference between the problems of statistical thermodynamics and kinetics. In the first (for ideal gases) the mechanism of intermolecular (or interatomic) attractions is of subsidiary importance - one needs to know only the energy levels of the particles (molecules, atoms, etc.) and their statistical weights. In kinetics the laws of particle interaction, the probabilities of transitions in impact, are quite important; they enter gas kinetic equations. This is the reason for the special difficulty in calculating kinetic properties.

It is known that the statistical methods of calculating kinetic coefficients, due to Enskog and Chapman, who developed and improved the Hilbert method, were worked out mainly for central forces, decaying fairly rapidly with increase in the distance between the molecules. In the case of Coulomb forces and of inelastic collisions, in particular those accompanied by chemical reactions and ionizations, complications arise. In a considerable part of the T and p region under examination in air there are extensive dissociations and ionizations, not to mention excitations of internal degrees of freedom. Hence in different ranges of T and p the problem of calculating the kinetic coefficients is solved in different ways.

The probability of collision of molecules with reaction is relatively small, and so is the probability of a conversion of translational energy into vibrational and vice versa. The conversion of translational energy into rotational and vice versa is more probable, but its effect on momentum transfer is small. Hence in calculating viscosities, equations can be used for gas mixtures, neglecting **inelastic** collisions even with dissociation. The main problem then becomes that of selecting the form of the interaction potential and the numerical values of the constants in its equation.

The principles in calculating the viscosity of air under the above conditions are expounded in section 1 of this paper. A number of expressions for the interaction potential of molecules is known, giving results that agree fairly well with experiment with appropriate choice of constants. However it would be wrong to use most of them for our calculations, since this would mean an extremely long extrapolation of the experimental data at very high temperatures. For example, the term proportional to r^{-12} in the Lennard-Jones potential (r = intermolecular distance), allowing for repulsive forces, is purely empirical. Also, at high temperatures the part played by repulsive forces is large. These considerations forced us to pay attention to the potential proposed by Buckingham, the form of which receives theoretical justification from a quantum mechanical examination of the interaction between two molecules.

There is very little information about the gas-kinetic cross-sections of atoms, either experimental or theoretical. The same atoms can interact according to very different laws depending on the mutual orientation of the spins of the outer electron envelopes of the colliding atoms. In particular, there can be purely repulsive interaction or interaction with a small potential trough. Since such interaction does not produce stable molecules, there are of course no spectroscopic data which could be used for calculating the interaction potential curve. Also, most collisions follow a repulsive pattern.

To obtain the necessary values of the cross-sections of N and O atoms, not measured experimentally, we interpolated in experimental data on the cross-sections of atoms of other elements on the basis of correlations derived from the periodic system.

A consideration of thermal conductivity is complicated by the need for allowing for internal degrees of freedom and for chemical transformations in the colliding molecules. In Part II of this paper transfer in a mixture of reacting gases is analysed. Recently various authors (Onsager, Hasse, Eckert, Meixner, De Groot, etc.) have worked out general methods of studying different microscopic processes, such as diffusion, thermal conduction, electrical conduction, etc. These methods are described in the literature as the "thermodynamics of irreversible processes". The most interesting and novel results are obtained where there is interaction of several processes, such as: thermal conductivity and diffusion, thermal conductivity and electrical conductivity, etc. In gases and liquids, where diffusion occurs freely, transfer of heat is always accompanied by diffusive mass transfer. However in the absence of reaction the amount of heat flow due to diffusion is small and persists only until the steady state is set up, in which diffusion and thermodiffusion cancel out. When there is reaction the amount of heat transferred with diffusing substance is considerably greater (by the amount of the "energy of chemical affinity") and moreover this component of the heat flow does not decrease to zero in time, since there is a non-zero mass transfer in local chemical equilibrium.

The problem consists in determining the concrete form of the equation of heat transfer under local chemical equilibrium and in finding the phenomenological coefficients in this equation. The first part of the problem is solved in this paper by the methods of the thermodynamics of irreversible processes. The equation of thermal conductivity is expressed in terms of the kinetic coefficients which are given by contemporary kinetic theory [5], thanks to which these coefficients can be calculated from certain molecular models. We also make no assumption about the absence of pressure gradients in the medium, as is done in, for instance, Hasse's work [4]. This is necessary because heat exchange in gas dynamics, as a rule, occurs under non-isobaric conditions.

I. Viscosity of Air with Molecular Dissociation

1. Preliminary Remarks

In this section we present the results of examination of the viscosity of air between 2000 and 8000°K and 0.001 and 1000 atm. The viscosity of a gas, if there is no chemical reaction in it, depends on temperature but scarcely at all on pressure. At temperatures of the order of several thousands of degrees Kelvin, the molecules of air start to dissociate into atoms, and chemical reactions occur in the air so that its viscosity becomes pressure-dependent.

The viscosity of air can only be measured up to 2000°K. We are interested in the viscosity between 2000 and 8000°K; hence we must study theoretical methods of determining it. Among the work on this problem is that of Enskog and Chapman, who give approximate expressions for the viscosity and thermal conductivity of a gas in terms of "collision integrals" depending on the equation of interaction between the gas particles.

The interaction equations between atoms and between molecules are known only approximately, and this causes additional inaccuracy in the expressions for kinetic properties.

There are a number of equations for the dependence of the viscosity on temperature, corresponding to different theories about the form of intermolecular interaction. Thus, the equation for the dependence of viscosity η on temperature T:

$$\eta \sim T^n, \quad n = \text{const} \tag{1}$$

corresponds to the power equation for the dependence of the interaction potential on distance. However, at $T \leqslant 1000°K$ the Sutherland equation fits the measurements much better:

$$\eta = \frac{aT^{1/2}}{1 + C/T}, \quad \left. \begin{matrix} a = \text{const} \\ C = \text{const} \end{matrix} \right\}, \tag{2}$$

allowing for weak forces of attraction between molecules. But at about 2000°K the C/T term can be neglected, since C is about 100°K. Then equation (2) becomes $\eta = aT^{1/2}$, with fits the experimental results worse even than the power equation. Other empirical equations are also known [5].

The above equations were obtained from extremely simple theories about intermolecular forces, not consistent with present-day ideas in this field. Hence to obtain a more accurate expression for viscosity we must turn to more recent information on the study of intermolecular forces.

At high temperatures the viscosity of air can only be determined extremely inaccurately, since at such temperatures free atoms appear, the equations of interaction between which are still unknown. But it can be taken as established that the gas-kinetic cross-sections of nitrogen and oxygen molecules, and of nitrogen and oxygen atoms, are similar, and hence in our approximate calculations of kinetic properties it can be assumed that air at such temperatures is a binary mixture of gas components, molecular (N_2, O_2, NO) and atomic (N, O, Ar).

2. Interaction between Molecules and Viscosity of the Molecular Components of a Mixture

From quantum mechanics we can establish that at large distances (compared with molecular radii) non-polar molecules attract one another with a force the potential of which can be represented as

$$U(r) = -\frac{C}{r^6} - \frac{C'}{r^8} \cdots \tag{3}$$

It is obvious that at large distances the first term is the more important. Without any theoretical basis, the repulsive forces have also been expressed by a power equation, with an appropriate exponent. The Lennard-Jones intermolecular action potential is extremely widely known:

$$U = 2\varepsilon\left(\frac{1}{2}\xi^{-12} - \xi^{-6}\right), \tag{4}$$

where ε is the depth of the potential trough, and $\xi = \frac{r}{r_m}$ (where r_m is the distance between the molecular centres).

For O_2 and N_2 the quantity ε/k, where k is the Boltzmann constant, is about 100°K, r_m is about 4Å, and ε and r_m can be determined from experimental data concerning kinetic coefficients, or, independently, concerning values of the virial coefficients. The values of r_m and ε thus determined by independent methods are practically the same.

TABLE 1 [6]

Gas	ε/k °K		r_m Å	
	viscosity	virial coefficients	viscosity	virial coefficients
Air,	97.0	99.2	3.617	3.692
O	91.46	95.9	3.681	3.72
N	113.2	117.5	3.433	3.58

The "collision integrals" for the Lennard-Jones potential were tabulated by Hirschfelder, Bird and Spots [6]. Viscosities computed from the results of these calculations are in good agreement with experimental values. However it is found that at high temperatures the dependence of the viscosities thus calculated on temperature is the power equation:

$$\eta \sim T^n, \tag{5}$$

where $n=0.666$.

The explanation is that at high temperatures repulsive forces predominate, and these are covered in the Lennard-Jones equation by the r^{-12} term, which does not describe their effect very accurately. Hence it is undesirable to use the Lennard-Jones potential for calculating viscosities at high temperatures. It can be taken as proved [7] that the repulsive forces vary with distance exponentially. One of the most useful expressions of the intermolecular action with allowance for the nature of the repulsive forces is the modified Buckingham potential

$$U = \frac{\varepsilon}{1 - 6/\alpha}\left\{\frac{6}{\alpha} e^{\alpha(1-\xi)} - \xi^{-6}\right\}. \tag{6}$$

Here α is a dimensionless parameter, which may be 12-17 or higher, depending on the kind of molecule. Values of α, r_m and ε can be obtained by comparing the results of theoretical calculation with experimental data on viscosity and the second virial coefficient and data on the interaction of molecules in crystals at around 300°K (Table 2 overleaf).

The differences between the values of the parameters obtained from different experiments on the same diatomic molecules arise because strictly speaking the potential (6) is applicable only to the spherically symmetrical molecules, and diatomic molecules can only approximately be considered to have this symmetry. Non-sphericity least of all affects the equilibrium properties, i.e., the second virial coefficient.

For the viscosity of the nitrogen molecule the error due to non-sphericity is of the order of 2 per cent above 600°K, i.e., quite within acceptable limits.

TABLE 2 [8]

Gas	α	r_m Å	ε, ergs	Gas	α	r_m Å	ς, ergs
Ne	14.5	3.147	38		(16.2	4.040	113.2
Ar	14	3.866	123.2	N	(17.0	4.011	101.2
Kr	12.3	4.056	158.3		(17	4.10	132
Xe	13.0	4.450	231.2	CO	(17	3.937	119.1
CH	14.0	4.206	152.1				

For the oxygen molecule we do not know of any similar information, but by using the similarity of the Lennard-Jones potential with the potential in equation (6), at not very small r ($r \geq 0.3\, r_m$) these parameters can be found. The viscosity η calculated by the Enskog-Chapman method with equation (6) has the form:

$$\eta = \frac{5}{16}\left(\frac{mkT}{\pi}\right)^{1/2} \frac{f_\eta}{r_m^2 \Omega^{(2,2)}(T^*)}, \qquad (7)$$

where m is the mass of the molecule, k is the Boltzmann constant, and T the absolute temperature,

$$T^* = \frac{kT}{\varepsilon},$$

where ε has the same meaning as in equation (4).

The functions $\Omega^{(2,2)}$ and f_η have no analytical expressions. They have been tabulated by Mason [7] and Mason and Rice [5]. From equation (7) it can be seen that the ratio

$$\frac{\eta(T^*)}{\eta(T_0^*)} = \Psi(T^*),$$

where T^*_0 is some fixed value of T^*, is the same function of the reduced temperature T^* for all gases. A calculation of the function $\Psi(T^*)$ for solid elastic balls shows that at high temperatures ($T \geq 4000$°K) its value is 33.3-50 per cent less than its value as calculated from the Buckingham potential.

3. Gas Kinetic Cross-sections of Atoms and Viscosity of the Atomic Components of Air

There are very few expressions for the interaction between atoms, from which kinetic coefficients can be calculated. They have been published only for inert gases, for which the forces of interaction between atoms and their gas-kinetic cross sections are known with fair accuracy. (The gas-kinetic diameter at temperature T is $\sigma_T = \sqrt{0.998 \frac{(mkT)^{1/2}}{\pi^{3/2} \eta(T)}}$ where $\eta(T)$ is the viscosity at T).

TABLE 3

Gas	T (°K)	σ_T (Å)	Gas	T (°K)	σ_T (Å)
He	273	2.19	Kr	273	4.18
Ne	293	2.59	Xe	273	4.93
Ar	273	3.66	Kn	288	5.2

The outer shell of the atoms of inert gases is closed, which greatly simplifies theoretical and experimental investigation. In particular, the attractive forces between them, to a first approximation, are inversely proportional to the sixth power of the distance.

The overall interaction between the atoms of inert gases agrees well with the Lennard-Jones potential, which makes it possible to define the parameters ε and r_m for them with satisfactory accuracy.

A completely different position is found for atoms with an unsaturated electron shell. The energy of interaction between such atoms either has a very marked minimum or corresponds to purely repulsive forces, depending on the mutual orientation of the spins of their outer electrons.

For interactions corresponding to a curve with a minimum, the variations of interaction energies with distance are known fairly well from spectroscopic data. From these data a number of empirical equations have been deduced, e.g., the Morse, Gilbert-Hirschfelder functions, etc.

Spectroscopic data, however, permit determination of the course of a curve only close to the minimum, and information about the form of the curve at distances large compared with r_m and also about its repulsive part can only be obtained by extrapolation. There is neither experimental nor any reliable theoretical information about the curves of the purely repulsive type, since in spectroscopy interactions corresponding to curves with minima are considered. The energy of interaction has been theoretically calculated for hydrogen, but for more complicated molecules the calculations encounter considerable difficulties, connected with the solution of multielectron problems.

Hence in calculating the kinetic coefficients for atoms, any sort of dependence of the interaction on distance must be avoided, and calculations must be based on the model of solid elastic spheres. But even then it appears that there is still no reliable experimental data for the solution of the problem.

The effective cross-sections for viscosity can be determined if the effective sections for scattering are known, since there is a definite relation between these two quantities. (See, for example, Mott and Massey, Theory of Atomic Collisions). If we denote by $I\vartheta d\omega$ the probability of scattering of particles inside the solid angle $d\omega$, at an angle ϑ to the original direction, then the total effective scattering cross-section Q is

$$Q = 2\pi \int_0^\pi I(\vartheta) \sin(\vartheta)\, d\vartheta, \tag{8}$$

and the effective cross-section for viscosity is:

$$Q_\eta = 2\pi \int_0^\pi I(\vartheta) \sin^3 \vartheta\, d\vartheta. \tag{9}$$

The angle ϑ depends on the equation of interaction between atoms. Since there is no accurate theoretical expression for this, we must make use of experimental determinations of the effective scattering cross-sections. However, there are not many such determinations at present, and it appears besides that the scattering diameters for the same atom in different gases differ greatly.

Another and apparently more reliable source of the information required is represented by data on viscosity and diffusion. From viscosity data the diameters (σ_T) of atomic hydrogen [9] are known: 2.52 Å at 273°K and 2.48 Å at 373°K. The diameter of deuterium is equal to the diameter of ordinary hydrogen. If the temperature dependence of the σ_T is represented as :

$$\sigma_T^2 = \sigma_\infty^2 (1 + C/T), \tag{10}$$

we obtain for different atoms the following values of σ_∞ and C

TABLE 4

Gas	σ_∞ (Å)	C (°K)	Gas	σ_∞ (Å)	C (°K)
He	1.82	173	Xe	3.55	252
Ne	2.52	128	H	2.39	31
Ar	2.99	142	D	2.39	31
Kr	3.22	188			

From diffusion experiments the gas-kinetic diameter for sodium has been found to be 3.7 Å at 291°K, in the calculation of which it is assumed that $\sigma_{12} = \frac{1}{2}(\sigma_1 + \sigma_2)$. There is also information about the diameters for zinc, cadmium and mercury atoms. Hence the information about the gas kinetic diameters of atoms is very scanty, and their values for O and N, in which we are interested, are still only approximate.

The sparse information presented above shows that the gas kinetic diameters of atoms depend directly on the atomic number of the element.

The fact is rather important that instead of a continuous increase of atomic diameter with atomic number there is a periodic variation. Within one period there is a decrease of diameter with increase of atomic number. The diameter for the hydrogen atom at 273°K is 2.52 Å , which is considerably greater than the diameter for He (2.19 Å), and about equal to the diameter for Ne (2.59Å at 293°K), although the latter contains 10 electrons against the single one in hydrogen. Also, for hydrogen σ_∞ is 2.39 Å , whereas for helium it is 1.82 Å and for neon 2.25 Å .

The diameter of the sodium atom, with which the third period of the periodic system starts, is 3.7 Å at 291°K - considerably greater than the diameter for Ne, which has an atomic number one less than sodium, and somewhat greater than that of Ar (3.66 Å), at the end of the third period. Finally for lithium, which is on the vertical between hydrogen and sodium, the cross-section should also be intermediate, i.e., about 3 Å, or considerably in excess of the diameter for neon (2.52 Å), which ends the second period.

This indicates that the gas-kinetic diameter of an atom, at least in the early periods, decreases from start to end of the period, and then sharply increases in passing from the inert gas, which ends the period, to the alkali metal, starting a new period.

There is another physical quantity which also depends on the atomic number - the ionization potential, with which the atomic radius (quantum mechanical) is directly connected. The values of the ionization potential have been adequately studied for almost all gases. It increases with atomic number within a period and drops sharply in going to another period. It is particularly important for us that the change of potential within a period is practically continuous, which indicates also a continuous change in gas kinetic diameter. It is of interest that the products of the ionization potential V_i and the gas-kinetic radius for the atoms of the inert gases are very similar (Table 5).

TABLE 5

gas	V_i(in volts)*	σ_T (Å)	$\sigma_T V_i$
He	24.46	2.19	53.6
Ne	21.47	2.59	55.6
Ar	15.68	3.66	57.4
Kr	13.93	4.18	58.3
Xe	12.08	4.93	59.5
Rn	10.7	5.2	55.7

*Handbook of Chemistry and Physics, Ch. D. Hodgeman, 1951.

It can therefore be surmised that for each group (more accurately subgroup) of the periodic table the products of gas-kinetic radii and ionization potentials are similar to one another, i.e. this product is a constant for each group or subgroup.

An indirect confirmation of this is provided by the fact that the ionization potential, which is the energy needed for tearing an electron out of an atom, is inversely proportional to the distance between this electron and the atomic nucleus, and this distance, or quantum mechanical radius, should be directly proportional to the gas-kinetic radius. It can also be assumed that this product changes along a period with the number of external-shell electrons or as a function of the total spin of the electrons of the external shell.

However, since changes of kinetic diameter along a period are not very great, we shall not commit any great error if we assume that they are linear within a period. The diameter for lithium can be found by taking the arithmetic average for the diameters of hydrogen and sodium, between which Li lies:

$$\sigma_{Li} = \frac{2{,}39 + 3{,}7}{2} \text{Å} = 3.05\,\text{Å}.$$

Let us now determine the diameter of the Ne atom at very high temperatures. The value of σ_∞ from Table 4 cannot be used, because equation (10) cannot be used at such high temperatures. Nor is there any experimental information for 3000-10,000°K. However, since the electron shell of Ne is full, the Buckingham molecular potential can be applied to it. Hence the gas-kinetic diameter of Ne at the necessary temperatures can be calculated from the collision integrals and the kinetic coefficients for Ne for these temperatures. The gas-kinetic diameter thus found is 1.8 Å.

If we assume that the gas kinetic diameter (GKD) changes linearly along a period, we obtain for the oxygen atom 2.16 Å , and for the nitrogen atom 2.3 Å . Obviously, within the present acceptable limits of accuracy we can use a general gas-kinetic diameter for atomic components:

$$\sigma_1 = 2{,}2\,\text{Å} \ (\text{or} \ \ 2{,}3\,\text{Å}). \tag{11}$$

Knowing the GKD, we can also calculate the viscosity by the Chapman equation

$$\eta = 0{,}998\frac{(m_1 kT)^{1/2}}{\pi^{3/2}\sigma_1^2}, \tag{12}$$

where m_1 is the mass of an atom.

4. Viscosity of Air

For calculating the viscosity of air, a mixture of atoms and molecules, we must know the law of interaction between atoms and molecules. Information about this is practically non-existent, so that the elastic sphere model must again be used. Collisions between molecules and atoms are regarded as collisions between elastic spheres of the effective diameter

$$\sigma_{12} = \frac{1}{2}(\sigma_1 + \sigma_2), \tag{13}$$

where σ_1 is the diameter of the atoms, determined above; and σ_2 is the diameter of the molecules, calculated from:

$$\sigma_2(T) = \sqrt{0{,}998\frac{(m_2 kT)^{1/2}}{\pi^{3/2}\eta_2(T)}}, \tag{14}$$

$\eta_2(T)$ is the viscosity of the molecular component at temperature T .

Obviously molecular diameters depend on temperature.

Expressions for the viscosity of a binary mixture of gases are to be found in the papers by Enskog and Chapman, but since the calculated viscosity of the atomic component is still rather inaccurate, it is worth while to use an older equation, obtained by Enskog from an examination of transfer processes in a gas consisting of molecules with an interaction which rapidly decreases with distance [10]:

$$\eta = \frac{\dfrac{\eta_1}{1+\alpha_{12}(x_2/x_1)} + \dfrac{\eta_2}{1+\alpha_{21}(x_1/x_2)} + \dfrac{2d(\eta_1\eta_2)^{1/2}}{[1+\alpha_{12}(x_2/x_1)][1+\alpha_{21}(x_1/x_2)]}}{1 - \dfrac{d^2}{[1+\alpha_{12}(x_2/x_1)][1+\alpha_{21}(x_1/x_2)]}}, \tag{15}$$

where η_1 is the viscosity of the atomic components;
η_2 that of the molecular component;
x_1 and x_2 are the mole fractions of the first and second components;

$$\alpha_{12} = \frac{1}{3}\left(\frac{\sigma_{12}}{\sigma_1}\right)^2 \left[\frac{2m_2}{m_1+m_2}\right]^{1/2} \frac{5m_1+3m_2}{m_1+m_2}$$

$$\alpha_{21} = \frac{1}{3}\left(\frac{\sigma_{12}}{\sigma_2}\right)^2 \left[\frac{2m_1}{m_1+m_2}\right]^{1/2} \frac{3m_1+5m_2}{m_1+m_2}$$

$$d = \left(\frac{8}{9}\right)^{1/2} \frac{(m_1 m_2)^{3/4}}{(m_1+m_2)^{3/2}}$$

σ_1 is the effective diameter (ED) of the atoms;
σ_2 that of the molecules;
σ_{12} the ED for collision of atoms with molecules, and
m_1, m_2 are the masses of atoms and molecules.

We note that the viscosity of air calculated from the accurate Enskog-Chapman equation deviates from that calculated by the approximate equation (15) by 2-3 per cent, which is obviously within the error of calculation of the viscosity of the atomic component.

Information about the composition of air at high temperatures, needed for calculating x_1 and x_2, will be found in [5], which contains information about the composition and thermodynamic properties of air between 2000° and 8000°K and 0.001 and 1000 atm. From this information it is evident that molecules of air dissociate completely only at pressures below atmospheric. At higher pressures and 8000°K there is still a certain proportion of undissociated molecules; at several hundreds of atmospheres about 50 per cent of the molecules are undissociated.

Another point is that at 8000-10,000°K, and at very low pressures even somewhat below these temperatures, the degree of ionization becomes so large that it is impossible to calculate kinetic parameters without allowance for ionization.

The results of calculating the viscosity of air in the appropriate temperature and pressure ranges will be found in [5] and [11], which are concerned with calculations of kinetic coefficients (Fig. 1).

II. Thermal Conductivity in a Binary Mixture of Chemically Reacting Gases

1. Heat Flow in a Binary Gas Mixture

Unlike the viscous stress tensor, which always depends only on the velocity gradient tensor, the flow of heat in liquids and gases, in which diffusion can occur, is closely connected with the diffusion of substance and hence depends not only on the temperature gradient, but also on the chemical potential gradient. In conditions of chemical reaction, heat flow due to diffusion of molecules is much increased.

To study thermal conductivity in the presence of reaction we must first dwell on how to define the concept "heat flow". We shall write the energy equation as follows:

$$\rho\frac{\partial E}{\partial t}+\rho u_k\frac{\partial E}{\partial x_k}-\pi_{ik}\frac{\partial u_i}{\partial x_k}+\frac{\partial I_k^{(q)}}{\partial x_k}=0, \qquad (1)$$

where E is the internal energy of unit mass of mixture;
π_{ik} is the stress tensor;
u_k is the hydrodynamic velocity;
ρ is the density of the mixture;
$\vec{I}^{(q)}$ is the vector of heat flow.

Writing a subscript twice means summating with respect to it. In a binary mixture of A_1 and A_2

$$E=\eta_1E_1+\eta_2E_2, \qquad (2)$$

where

$$\eta_i=\frac{\rho_i}{\rho_1+\rho_2}=\frac{\rho_i}{\rho}$$

η_1 and η_2 are the mass fractions of components A_1 and A_2;
ρ_1 and ρ_2 are the densities of A_1 and A_2. E_1 and E_2 are the internal energies of unit masses of A_1 and A_2.
The diffusional flow $\vec{I}^{(1)}$ of component A_1 is defined as follows:

$$\vec{I}^{(1)}=\rho_1(\vec{u}^{(1)}-\vec{u})=\frac{\rho_1\rho_2}{\rho}(\vec{u}^{(1)}-\vec{u}^{(2)})=-\vec{I}^{(2)}, \qquad (3)$$

where $\vec{u}$ is the hydrodynamic velocity, defined by:

$$\vec{u}=\eta_1\vec{u}^{(1)}+\eta_2\vec{u}^{(2)}, \qquad (4)$$

$\vec{u}^{(1)}$ and $\vec{u}^{(2)}$ are the velocity components of A_1 and A_2;
$\vec{I}^{(2}$ is the diffusional flow of A_2.

The thermodynamics of irreversible processes gives [1,2]:

$$\vec{I}^{(q)}=-L_{q1}\frac{1}{T}\nabla\left(\frac{\varphi^{(1)}-\varphi^{(2)}}{T}\right)-L_{qq}\frac{1}{T}\nabla T \qquad (5)$$

$$\vec{I}^{(1)}=-\vec{I}^{(2)}=-L_{11}\frac{1}{T}\nabla\left(\frac{\varphi^1-\varphi^2}{T}\right)-L_{q1}\frac{1}{T}\nabla T, \qquad (6)$$

where L_{q1}, L_{11}, L_{qq} are phenomenological coefficients;
$\varphi^{(1)}$ and $\varphi^{(2)}$ are the partial specific thermodynamic potentials of A_1 and A_2;
T is the absolute temperature,

$$\nabla=\text{grad}=\frac{\partial}{\partial x_1}+\frac{\partial}{\partial x_2}+\frac{\partial}{\partial x_3}.$$

Equations (5) and (6) are derived on the assumption of no mass forces, and with application of the Onsager principle of symmetry of kinetic coefficients.

The coefficients L_{qq}, L_{11}, L_{q1} completely define the heat and diffusion flows, and thus any other coefficients introduced to describe the diffusion and thermal conductivity should be expressed only in terms of these coefficients.

Let us introduce a new phenomenological coefficient of heat transfer (for details see [1] and [2]):

$$L_{q1}=L_{11}Q^{*}. \qquad (7)$$

so that instead of equations (5) and (6) we obtain:

$$\vec{I}^{(1)} = L_{11}\left\{-\frac{1}{T}\nabla\left(\frac{\varphi^{(1)}-\varphi^{(2)}}{T}\right) - Q^{\bullet}\frac{1}{T}\nabla T\right\} \tag{8}$$

$$\vec{I}^{(q)} = Q^{\bullet}\vec{J}^{(1)} - \{L_{qq} - L_{q1}Q^{\bullet}\}\frac{1}{T}\nabla T \tag{9}$$

or, putting

$$\frac{L_{pp} - L_{q1}Q^{\bullet}}{T} = \lambda, \tag{10}$$

we obtain the following expression for the heat flow:

$$\vec{I}^{(q)} = Q^{\bullet}\vec{I}^{(1)} - \lambda\nabla T. \tag{11}$$

The steady state, in the absence of chemical reaction, will be given by:

$$\vec{I}^{(1)} = 0. \tag{12}$$

So that in the steady state:

$$\vec{I}^{(q)} = -\lambda\nabla T \tag{13}$$

and, consequently, λ is the coefficient of thermal conductivity in the steady state.

Furthermore, bearing in mind that $\varphi = \varphi(T, p, \eta_1)$ and using the Gibbs-Duhem equation:

$$\eta_1\frac{\partial\varphi^{(1)}}{\partial\eta_1} + \eta_2\frac{\partial\varphi^{(2)}}{\partial\eta_2} = 0, \tag{14}$$

we get from equation (8) the following equations for $\vec{I}^{(1)}$:

$$\vec{I}^{(1)} = L_{11}\left\{-(v_1 - v_2)\nabla p - \frac{1}{\eta_2}\left(\frac{\partial\varphi^{(1)}}{\partial\eta_1}\right)_{p,T}\nabla\eta_1 - (Q^{\bullet} - h_1 + h_2)\frac{\nabla T}{T}\right\}, \tag{15}$$

where p is the hydrostatic pressure;
h_1 and h_2 are the specific enthalpies of A_1 and A_2,
v_1 and v_2 are the specific volumes of A_1 and A_2.

By comparing equations (11) and (15) we find that even in the absence of a temperature gradient the heat flow is not zero, if the concentration or pressure gradients are not zero. Substituting (15) into (11), we find that the coefficient for ∇T is

$$\varkappa = \lambda + L_{11}Q^{\bullet}(Q^{\bullet} - h_1 + h_2)\frac{1}{T}; \tag{16}$$

where $\varkappa$ is the coefficient of thermal conductivity, determining the heat flow in the state of uniform movement, i.e., when $\nabla p = 0$ and $\nabla\eta_1 = 0$; obviously $\varkappa \neq \lambda$. In the absence of reaction the calculation for the initial energy levels of the molecules A_1 and A_2 can be obtained, independently of one another. In particular, in this case the energy of each molecule can be calculated from the lower energy level of the corresponding molecule. Then $h_1 - h_2$ is small, and as is shown by theoretical calculations based on kinetic theory and by experiment the second term in equation (16) is small compared with the first and in equation (11) for the heat flow only the second term $-\lambda \operatorname{grad} T$ may be retained. For this case calculations of the heat flow have been made on the basis of the kinetic theory of gases [3] which yield the expression

$$\vec{I}^{(q)} = pk_T(\overline{\vec{C}_2} - \overline{\vec{C}_2}) - \lambda\nabla T, \tag{17}$$

where k_T is the thermodiffusional ratio and $\overline{\vec{C}_1}$ and $\overline{\vec{C}_2}$ are the average thermal speeds of A_1 and A_2.

Since $\overline{\vec{C}_1} - \overline{\vec{C}_2} = \vec{u}^{(1)} - \vec{u}^{(2)}$, with equation (3) we can rewrite equation (11) in the form

$$\vec{I}^{(q)} = Q^{*} \frac{\rho_1\rho_2}{\rho}(\overline{\vec{C}_1} - \overline{\vec{C}_2}) - \lambda\nabla T. \tag{18}$$

and by comparing (18) with (17) we find that the coefficient of thermal conductivity calculated on the basis of the Enskog-Chapman theory for a binary gas mixture coincides with the coefficient of thermal conductivity for the stationary state [equation (10)].

2. Heat Flow in a Reacting Gas Mixture in Equilibrium

Let us consider the case of chemical reaction. From a molecular-kinetic viewpoint the heat flow in a reacting mixture contains more terms than when there is no reaction. The heat flow is expressed as follows:

$$n_1\overline{E_1\vec{C}^{(1)}} + n_2\overline{E_2\vec{C}^{(2)}},$$

where

$$E_1 = \frac{1}{2}m_1C^{(1)2} + U^{(1)};$$
$$E_2 = \frac{1}{2}m_2C^{(2)2} + U^{(2)} + \varepsilon$$

are the energies of A_1 and A_2 respectively;
U^1 U^2 are the energies of the internal degrees of freedom of A_1 and A_2;
ε is the difference in the lower energy levels of A_1 and A_2.

Below we shall assume equilibrium between the translational and internal degrees of freedom of the molecule.

In the absence of reaction the calculation of the initial energy level can be obtained independently, so that it can be assumed that $\varepsilon = 0$. This cannot be done when there is reaction, which produces in the heat flow an additional term:

$$\varepsilon\overline{\vec{C}^{(2)}},$$

which can also be written in a more symmetrical form

$$\varepsilon_1\overline{\vec{C}^{(1)}} + \varepsilon_2\overline{\vec{C}^{(2)}}.$$

The physical meaning of these terms is obvious: in the presence of reaction heat flow includes transfer of energy of chemical affinity because of movement of molecules. This energy, like internal energy, is transferred by diffusion.

Suppose that at time $t<0$ there is no reaction, and that reaction starts at $t=0$. If τ is the time of relaxation of the reaction, then at $t \ll \tau$ the reaction will not affect heat flow and other macroscopic processes. Let us see what happens when $t \gg \tau$. The occurrence of reaction does not affect the form of the two thermodynamic equations for heat flow, (5) and (11), because the reaction is defined by scalar quantities - reaction rate and chemical activity - whereas heat flow is a vector. There can be a linear relation between the vector and the scalar only if the coefficient of proportionality is a vector. Hence the phenomenological coefficient, describing the relation between heat flow and chemical reaction, should be a vector. But this coefficient should be isotropic, since it relates to an isotropic medium. The only isotropic vector is the zero vector, and this explains the absence of a direct connexion between heat flow and chemical reaction.

However the occurrence of reaction means that the steady state is changed. While in the absence of reaction the steady state is defined by:

$$\vec{I}^{(1)} = 0,$$

in the presence of reaction, if $t \gg \tau$, the steady state is a state of local chemical equilibrium, which is defined by the condition

$$\nu_1\bar{\varphi}^{(1)} - \nu_2\bar{\varphi}^{(2)} = \nu_1^0\varphi^{(1)} - \nu_2^0\varphi^{(2)} = 0, \tag{19}$$

where:

$\bar{\varphi}^{(1)}$ and $\bar{\varphi}^{(2)}$ are the partial molar thermodynamic potentials of A_1 and A_2;

ν_1 and ν_2 are the stoichiometric reaction coefficients in the binary gas mixture:

$$\nu_1 A_1 - \nu_2 A_2 = 0. \tag{20}$$

Finally:

$$\nu_1^0 = \nu_1\mu_1 \quad \nu_2^0 = \nu_2\mu_2, \tag{21}$$

where μ_1 and μ_2 are the molecular weights of A_1 and A_2. Since equation (19) is satisfied at each point, then

$$\nabla\left(\nu_1^0\varphi^{(1)} - \nu_2^0\varphi^{(2)}\right) = 0. \tag{22}$$

Thus in the case of chemical reaction the diffusion flow cannot become zero in the steady state.

For calculating the heat flow with local chemical equilibrium, we use equations (11) and (15). Substituting $\vec{I}^{(1)}$ from (15) into (11) we find:

$$\begin{aligned}\vec{I}^{(q)} = &-L_{11}Q^*(v_1 - v_2)\nabla p - L_{11}Q^*\frac{1}{\eta_2}\left(\frac{\partial\varphi^{(1)}}{\partial\eta_1}\right)_{p,T}\nabla\eta_1 - \\ &-\left\{L_{11}Q^*\frac{Q^* - h_1 + h_2}{T} + \lambda\right\}\nabla T.\end{aligned} \tag{23}$$

The condition of local equilibrium (22) we can write as follows with the aid of (19):

$$v_R\nabla p - h_R\frac{\nabla T}{T} + \frac{\nu_1^0\eta_2 + \nu_2^0\eta_1}{\eta_2}\left(\frac{\partial\varphi^{(1)}}{d\eta_1}\right)_{p,T}\nabla\eta_1 = 0, \tag{24}$$

where

$$v_R = \nu_1^0 v_1 - \nu_2^0 v_2; \tag{25}$$

$$h_R = \nu_1^0 h_1 - \nu_2^0 h_2. \tag{26}$$

By solving (24) for $\nabla\eta_1$, and inserting the result into (23), we obtain:

$$\vec{I}^{(q)} = -L_{11}Q^{*}v\,\frac{\nu_2^0-\nu_1^0}{\nu_1^0\eta_2+\nu_2^0\eta_1}\,\nabla p -$$
$$-\left\{L_{11}Q^{*}\,\frac{Q^{*}-h_1+h_2}{T} + L_{11}Q^{*}\,\frac{h_R}{\nu_1^0\eta_2+\nu_2^0\eta_1}\,\frac{1}{T}+\lambda\right\}\nabla T,$$

where $v=\eta_1 v_1+\eta_2 v_2$ is the specific volume. Hence, in consequence of conservation of mass

$$\nu_1\mu_1=\nu_2\mu_2$$

or

$$\nu_1^0=\nu_2^0=\nu^0, \tag{27}$$

it follows that

$$h_R=\nu^0(h_1-h_2), \tag{28}$$

$$\nu_1^0\eta_1+\nu_2^0\eta_2=\nu^0, \tag{29}$$

i.e.,

$$\vec{I}^{(q)} = -\left\{\frac{L_{11}Q^{*2}}{T}+\lambda\right\}\nabla T. \tag{30}$$

Hence, if the steady state in chemical reaction in a binary mixture is a state of local chemical equilibrium, the term proportional to $\mathrm{grad}\,p$ disappears from the expression for heat flow (just as in the steady state in the absence of reaction). Equation (30) is a simpler expression for heat flow in chemical equilibrium, but the coefficients L_{11} and Q^* are still not in general use. It is therefore expedient to obtain an expression for heat flow in terms of the better-known diffusion and thermodiffusion coefficients. Let us introduce the coefficient of ordinary diffusion D_{12} by the equation

$$\vec{I}^{(1)} = -\rho D_{12}\nabla\eta_1 \tag{31}$$

with $\nabla T=0$ and $\nabla p=0$, and the coefficient of thermodiffusion D_{12}^T:

$$\vec{I}^{(1)} = -\rho D_{12}^T\eta_1\eta_2\nabla T \tag{32}$$

with $\nabla p=0$, $\nabla\eta_1=0$.

Then the coefficients L_{11} and Q^* are expressed in terms of D_{12} and D_{12}^T as follows:

$$L_{11}=\frac{\rho\eta_2 D_{12}}{\left(\frac{\partial\varphi^{(1)}}{\partial\eta_1}\right)_{p,T}}, \tag{33}$$

$$Q^{*}=\frac{D_{12}^T}{D_{12}}\,\eta_1 T\left(\frac{\partial\varphi^{(1)}}{\partial\eta_1}\right)_{p,T}+h_1-h_2. \tag{34}$$

From equations (30), (33) and (34) we find

$$\vec{I}^{(q)} = -\left\{\lambda+\rho\,\frac{(D_{12}^T)^2}{D_{21}}\,\eta_2\eta_1^2 T\left(\frac{\partial\varphi^{(1)}}{\partial\eta_1}\right)_{p,T}+\right.$$
$$\left.+\frac{\rho\eta_2 D_{12}(h_1-h_2)^2}{\left(\frac{\partial\varphi^{(1)}}{\partial\eta_1}\right)_{p,T} T}+2\rho\eta_1\eta_2 D_{12}^T(h_1-h_2)\right\}\nabla T = -\lambda_0\nabla T. \tag{35}$$

This expression for heat flow is just as useful for a reacting binary mixture of liquids as for one of gases. Let us consider the case in which the reacting mixture can be regarded as a mixture of ideal gases:

$$\varphi^{(1)} = \varphi_0^{(1)}(T) + \frac{RT}{\mu_1} \ln \frac{p \frac{\eta_1}{\mu_1}}{\frac{\eta_1}{\mu_1} + \frac{\eta_2}{\mu_2}}, \quad (36)$$

$$\left(\frac{\partial \varphi^{(1)}}{\partial \eta_1}\right)_{p,T} = \frac{RT}{\eta_1} \frac{1}{\eta_1\mu_2 + \eta_2\eta_1}. \quad (37)$$

and we obtain the following expression for the thermal conductivity of the mixture:

$$\lambda_0 = \lambda + \frac{\left(D_{12}^T\right)^2}{D_{12}} \eta_2\eta_1 \frac{\rho RT}{\eta_1\mu_2 + \eta_2\mu_1} + \\ + D_{12}\eta_1\eta_2(\eta_1\mu_2 + \eta_2\mu_1) \frac{\rho(h_1 - h_2)^2}{RT^2} + 2\rho\eta_1\eta_2 D_{12}^T (h_1 - h_2) \quad (38)$$

or with

$$k_T = \frac{D_{12}^T T}{D_{12}} \quad (39)$$

the thermodiffusional ratio, and:

$$\bar{\mu} = \frac{\mu_1\mu_2}{\mu_2\eta_1 + \mu_1\eta_2} \quad (39a)$$

the mean molecular weight, we finally obtain

$$\lambda_0 = \lambda + k_T^2 \frac{\eta_1\eta_2\bar{\mu}^2}{\mu_1\mu_2} D_{12} \frac{p}{T} + \\ + \eta_1\eta_2\mu_1\mu_2 \frac{p}{T} D_{12} \left\{ \left(\frac{h_1 - h_2}{RT}\right)^2 + 2k_T \frac{\bar{\mu}}{\mu_1\mu_2} \left(\frac{h_1 - h_2}{RT}\right) \right\}. \quad (40)$$

This expression defines the coefficient of thermal conductivity of the reacting binary mixture of gases in local equilibrium. The heat flow is then given by:

$$\vec{I}^{(q)} = -\lambda_0 \nabla T. \quad (41)$$

The coefficient λ_0 is expressed by the following transfer coefficients:

λ, coefficient of thermal conductivity for the steady state of non-reacting gases;

D_{12} the coefficient of ordinary diffusion, defined by equation (31);

k_T the thermodiffusional ratio, equation (39). It is defined in terms of D_{12}^T which is defined by equation (32).

If the number of inelastic collisions accompanying reaction is small compared with the total number of collisions, all these coefficients can be calculated by the ordinary means of kinetic theory of gases (Chapman-Enskog method). A correction is applied to λ for the thermal conductivity of the internal degrees of freedom (i.e., a correction of the same type as that introduced by Eucken).

Since $\frac{h_1-h_2}{RT}\bar{\mu}$ is large, and k_T is small, the second term in expression (40) is small compared with the others. The third term is therefore larger than the fourth, but not so much that the latter can be neglected in calculating thermal conductivities. The third and fourth terms are comparable with λ, and in some cases considerably greater than it.

The problem of the thermal conductivity of a binary mixture of reacting gases was considered at the beginning of this century by Nernst (see [4]). He considered a mixture of ideal gases and did not allow for thermodiffusion, so he only obtained one of the three additional terms to the ordinary thermal conductivity (λ), that is the one proportional to $\left(\frac{h_1-h_2}{RT}\right)^2$ In 1953 the matter was studied with contemporary thermodynamic methods by Haase [4]. He obtained an expression similar to that we have obtained, but without the first correcting term (proportional to k_T^2). This was due, apparently, to a difference in the definitions of "heat flow". Also, Haase considered reaction in a mixture in which there is no pressure gradient, which is of little interest in hydrodynamics.

Note that the coefficients of transfer for a binary mixture, calculated in [3], are related to coefficients in (40) as follows:

$$\lambda^1 = \lambda, \tag{42}$$

$$D_{12}^1 = D_{12}, \tag{43}$$

$$D_{12}^{T1} = D_{12}^T T \xi_1 \xi_2, \tag{44}$$

$$k_T^1 = k_T \xi_1 \xi_2, \tag{45}$$

where λ^1 is the coefficient of thermal conductivity for a binary mixture of gases, according to Chapman;

D_{12}^1 and D_{12}^{T1} are the Chapman coefficients of diffusion and thermodiffusion respectively;

k_T^1 is the Chapman thermodiffusion ratio,

ξ_1 and ξ_2 are the mole fractions of A_1 and A_2.

The relation between the molar (ξ) and the mass (η) fractions is:

$$\xi_i = \frac{\frac{\eta_i}{\mu_i}}{\frac{\eta_1}{\mu_1} + \frac{\eta_2}{\mu_2}} = \frac{\eta_i}{\eta_1 + \eta_2 \nu}, \tag{46}$$

$$\eta_i = \frac{\mu_i \xi_i}{\mu_1 \xi_1 + \mu_2 \xi_2} = \frac{\xi_i}{\xi_1 + \frac{\xi_2}{\nu}}, \tag{47}$$

where $\nu = \frac{\nu_1}{\nu_2}$ is the ratio of the stoichiometric reaction coefficients.

For solving any hydrodynamic problem we need, apart from the energy equation, to write also the continuity and momentum equations. These two equations do not change if there is a reaction. In local equilibrium, for this system of equations to be closed, it is enough to add to it a system of chemical equilibrium equations, which in the case of a reaction in a binary mixture of gases reduces to one mass action equation. We thereby obtain a system of equations which includes the following kinetic parameters: L_{q1}, L_{qq}, ν' and ν'', where the latter two terms are respectively the shear and bulk viscosities in the stress tensor. In the general case heat flow depends on L_{q1} and L_{qq}, but on the basis of what has been expounded above, for local equilibrium it can be expressed in terms of one coefficient λ_0 in equation (40).

In a boundary layer the stress tensor, proportional to the bulk viscosity, disappears, and the system of phenomenological equations depends only on the shear viscosity ν' and the thermal conductivity of the equilibrium reacting mixture λ_0.

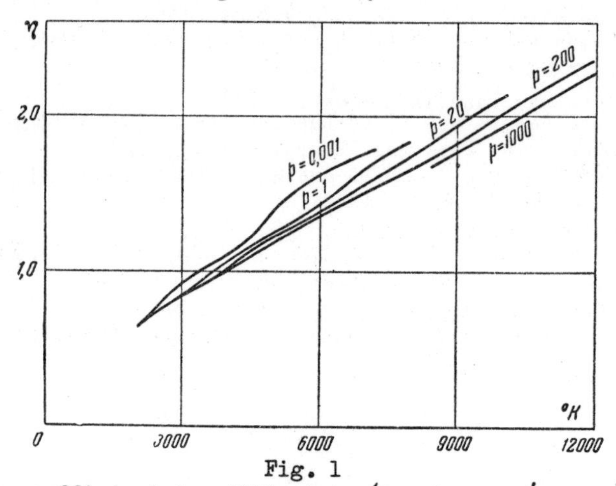

Fig. 1
Viscosity coefficient in millipoises (1 poise = g/cm.sec) as a function of the temperature for different pressures p in atm

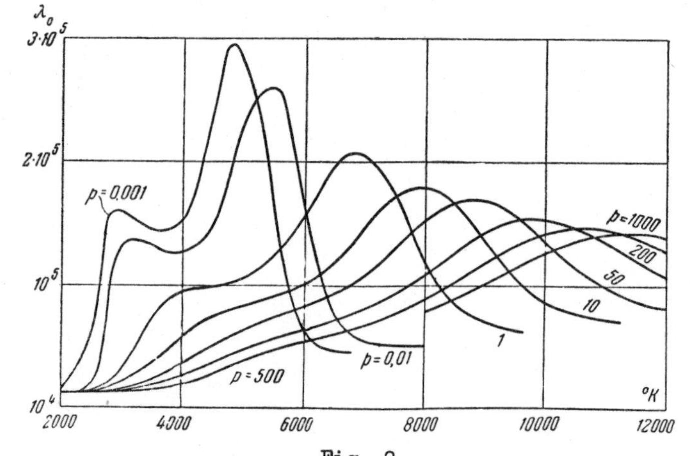

Fig. 2
Thermal conductivity in erg/cm. sec °K for different pressures in atmospheres, as a function of temperature

Calculations of the thermal conductivities in reacting binary gas mixture (λ_0) in equilibrium, made on the basis of (40), are to be found in [11] (Fig. 2).

REFERENCES

1. De GROOT, Thermodynamics of Irreversible Processes.
2. K. DENBIGH, Thermodynamics of Steady Irreversible Processes (Termodinamika statsionarnykh neobratimykh protsessov) (Translation into Russian), Moscow (1954).
3. S. CHAPMAN and T.G. COWLING, The Mathematical Theory of Non-uniform Gases, Cambridge (1953).
4. R. HAASE, Z. f. Naturforsch., 1953.
5. Report of Laboratory of Combustion Physics of Energy Institute (Otchet. lab. fiz. gor. Energ. Inst.), 1955.
6. J.O.HIRSCHFELDER, R.B.BIRD and E.L.SPOTZ, J.Chem.Phys., 16, 968 (1948); 17, 1343 (1949).
7. E.A. MASON, J. Chem. Phys., 22, 2 (1954).
8. J.O. HIRSCHFELDER, C.F. CURTISS and R.B. BIRD, Molecular Theory of Gases and Liquids, New York (1954).
9. I. AMDUR, J. Chem. Phys., 4, 339 (1936).
10. Report of Laboratory of Combustion Physics of Energy Institute, 1954.
11. Ibid., 1955.

E.V. Samuilov

Effect of Internal Degrees of Freedom of Particles on the Transfer Coefficients in Multicomponent Gas Mixtures

The thermal conductivities and shear and bulk viscosities of gases can be calculated by the methods of kinetic theory. For monatomic gases, the agreement between the predictions of kinetic theory and experiment is satisfactory. The results of theory with an appropriate selection of the interaction potential between molecules at ordinary temperatures can also be successfully used for calculating the shear viscosities of multiatomic gases. However, the thermal conductivity includes terms which cannot be obtained from the theory of monatomic gases, as Eucken first pointed out. The shear viscosity of monatomic gases is connected with the bulk viscosity by the Stokes equation. This equation does not fit the facts for multiatomic gases. An analysis of the effect of internal degrees of freedom of particles of a gas on the kinetic coefficients has been made by several authors. Leontovich [1] solved the Boltzmann equation for the propagation of small perturbations in a static gas in a general form for $\omega\tau \ll 1$ where ω is the frequency of the perturbations and τ is the time of relaxation of the exchange of energy between the translational and internal degrees of freedom of the particles. A solution was obtained by the Hilbert method for a continuous spectrum of internal energies. Wang-Chang and Uhlenbeck [2] obtained transfer coefficients with the Enskog apparatus from scattering cross-sections, in a general form for a discrete spectrum of internal energies. However, these authors did not make direct calculations of transfer coefficients.

Pidduck [3] calculated kinetic coefficients with the Braun "rough" spheres molecular model. Ishida [4] solved the Boltzmann equation for "hard ovaloids". Jeans [5] used "loaded spheres" as a molecular model. These attempts, however, have a common defect. The cross-sections of inelastic scattering, which strictly speaking can be calculated from the quantum-mechanical theory of collision, are replaced by various artificial mechanisms of energy transfer from the internal to the translational degrees of freedom of the particles.

In this paper we use the probabilities of various kinds of molecular collision, obtained by a number of authors from quantum mechanical calculations. The system of generalized kinetic equations is solved by the Enskog method [6].

The system of integral-differential equations for the distribution function f_i of the gas components with allowance for internal degrees of freedom of the particles has the form:

$$\frac{\partial f_i}{\partial t} + \vec{c}_i \cdot \frac{\partial f_i}{\partial \vec{r}} = \sum_{j,\, \varepsilon_j,\, \varepsilon_i',\, \varepsilon_j'} \int (f_i' f_j' - f_i f_j) K(\varepsilon_i \varepsilon_j \rightarrow \varepsilon_i' \varepsilon_j') g_{ij} b\, db\, d\varphi\, d\vec{c}_j . \quad (1)$$

In equation (1) $f_i = f_i(\vec{r}, \vec{c}_i, \varepsilon_i, t)$, $f_i' = f_i'(\vec{r}, \vec{c}_i', \varepsilon_i', t)$; $\vec{c}_i$, ε_i are the speed and internal energies of the ith particle before collision; $\vec{c}_i'$, ε_i' represent the same after collision; $\vec{r}$ is the radius vector; t is time,

$$\vec{g}_{ij} = \vec{c}_i - \vec{c}_j; \quad g_{ij} = |\vec{g}_{ij}|;$$

b is the collision parameter; φ is the azimuthal angle, and $K(\varepsilon_i, \varepsilon_j \rightarrow \varepsilon_i', \varepsilon_j')$ is the probability of collision of two molecules with a change of the values from $\varepsilon_i, \varepsilon_j$ to $\varepsilon_i', \varepsilon_j'$. For given g_{ij}, ε_i and ε_j, K satisfies the standardizing condition:

$$\sum_{\varepsilon_i', \varepsilon_j'} K(\varepsilon_i, \varepsilon_j \rightarrow \varepsilon_i', \varepsilon_j') = 1.$$

The equilibrium distribution functions $f_i^{(0)}$ have the form:

$$f_i^{(0)} = n_i \left(\frac{m_i}{2\pi kT}\right)^{\frac{3}{2}} e^{-\frac{m_i C_i^2}{2kT} - \frac{\varepsilon_i}{kT}} \left(\sum_{\varepsilon_i} e^{-\frac{\varepsilon_i}{kT}}\right)^{-1}. \quad (2)$$

Here n_i is the number of particles of the ith type in unit volume; m_i is the mass of the ith particle, $\vec{C}_i$ is the speed of the ith type of molecule relative to the local mean mass speed of the gas $\vec{c}_0$.

$$\vec{C}_i = \vec{c}_i - \vec{c}_0.$$

The local mean mass velocity is defined as follows:

$$\vec{c}_0 = \frac{1}{\rho} \sum_i n_i m_i \bar{\vec{c}}_i,$$

where ρ is the gas density $\rho = \sum_i n_i m_i$;

$\bar{\vec{c}}_i$ is the mean velocity of the ith type of molecule relative to the laboratory coordinate system.

In accordance with the Enskog method we shall assume that the distribution functions f_i are not explicit functions of time, but are functions of the macroscopic parameters of the medium, which change with time. When there are small gradients of these parameters, the f_i s deviate only a little at each point from the local equilibrium functions $f_i^{(0)}$. To a first approximation.

$$f_i = f_i^{(0)} (1 + \Phi_i), \quad (3)$$

where Φ_i is a function of $\vec{C}_i$, ε_i and the macroscopic parameters of the medium. In equation (3) $f_i^{(0)}$ coincides with equation (2) when the following standardizing conditions are observed for mean number of particles of each type in unit volume, mean mass velocity and temperature:

$$n_i = \sum_{\varepsilon_i} \int f_i^{(0)}\, d\vec{c}_i, \tag{4}$$

$$\rho \vec{c}_0 = \sum_{j,\varepsilon_j} \int m_j \vec{c}_j f_j^{(0)}\, d\vec{c}_j, \tag{5}$$

$$\frac{3}{2} nkT + \sum_{j,\varepsilon_j} n_j \varepsilon_j e^{-\frac{\varepsilon_j}{kT}} \Big(\sum_{\varepsilon_j} e^{-\frac{\varepsilon_i}{kT}}\Big)^{-1} = \sum_{j,\varepsilon_j} \int E_j f_j^{(0)}\, d\vec{c}_j. \tag{6}$$

Here

$$\sum_{j\varepsilon_j} \int f_j^{(0)} \Phi_j\, d\vec{c}_j = 0, \tag{7}$$

$$\sum_{j,\varepsilon_j} \int m_j \vec{c}_j f_j^{(0)} \Phi_j\, d\vec{c}_j = 0, \tag{8}$$

$$\sum_{j,\varepsilon_j} \int E_j f_j^{(0)} \Phi_j\, d\vec{c}_j = 0. \tag{9}$$

In (4) - (9) $n = \sum_i n_i$; $E_i = \frac{mc_i^2}{2} + \varepsilon_i$. Substituting (3) into (1) we obtain

$$f_i^{(0)} \Big\{ \Big[\frac{E_i}{kT} - \frac{\overline{E}_i}{kT} - 1\Big] \vec{C}_i \cdot \frac{\partial \ln T}{\partial \vec{r}} + \frac{n}{n_i} \vec{C}_i \cdot \vec{d}_i + \\ + \Big[\frac{m_i}{kT} \vec{C}_i \vec{C}_i + \Big(\frac{E_i}{kT} - \frac{\overline{E}_i}{kT} - 1\Big) \frac{kn}{\sum_j n_j C_{vj}} U\Big] : \frac{\partial}{\partial \vec{r}} \vec{c}_0 \Big\} = n_i \sum_j n_j I_{ij} (\Phi_i + \Phi_j), \tag{10}$$

where

$$n_i \sum_j n_j I_{ij} (\Phi_i + \Phi_j) \equiv \\ - \sum_{j,\varepsilon_j,\varepsilon_i',\varepsilon_j'} \int f_i^{(0)} f_j^{(0)} (\Phi_i + \Phi_j - \Phi_i' - \Phi_j')\, K\, dO_j.$$

In deducing the left-hand side of equation (10) the Maxwell transfer equation was used, and also the condition of Φ_i being small. In equation (10)

$$\overline{E}_i = \frac{3}{2} kT + \sum_{\varepsilon_i} \varepsilon_i e^{-\frac{\varepsilon_i}{kT}} \Big(\sum_{\varepsilon_i} e^{-\frac{\varepsilon_i}{kT}}\Big)^{-1}$$

$$dO_j = g_{ij} b\, db\, d\varphi\, d\vec{c}_j.$$

where U is unit tensor; $\frac{\partial}{\partial \vec{r}} c_0$ is the tensor in which the components of the first line and first column, for instance, are respectively equal to:

$$\frac{\partial u_0}{\partial x};\ \frac{\partial v_0}{\partial x};\ \frac{\partial w_0}{\partial x} \text{ and } \frac{\partial u_0}{\partial x};\ \frac{\partial u_0}{\partial y};\ \frac{\partial w_0}{\partial z};$$

u_0, v_0, w_0 are the projections of $\vec{c}_0$ on the x, y, z axes; $U : \frac{\partial}{\partial \vec{r}} \vec{c}_0$ is the biscalar product of the tensors U and $\frac{\partial}{\partial \vec{r}} \vec{c}_0$;

$$\vec{C}_i \cdot \frac{\partial}{\partial \vec{r}} = U_i \frac{\partial}{\partial x} + V_i \frac{\partial}{\partial y} + W_i \frac{\partial}{\partial z}$$

$$\vec{d}_i = \frac{\partial}{\partial \vec{r}} \frac{n_i}{n} + \left\{ \frac{n_i}{n} - \frac{n_i m_i}{\rho} \right\} \frac{\partial p}{\partial \vec{r}}$$

p is the thermodynamic pressure nkT.

The left-hand side of (10) is a linear function of the gradient of macroscopic parameters of the medium, so that Φ_i should have the form

$$\Phi_i = -\vec{A}_i \cdot \frac{\partial \ln T}{\partial \vec{r}} - B_i : \frac{\partial}{\partial \vec{r}} \vec{c}_0 + \frac{n^2}{\rho k T} \sum_{j \neq i} \frac{m_i m_j}{n_i} \vec{D}_{ij} \cdot \vec{d}_j. \quad (11)$$

Here $\vec{A}_i = \vec{C}_i A_i (C_i, \varepsilon_i)$

$$B_i = \overset{\circ}{\vec{C}_i \vec{C}_i} B_i^{(1)} (C_i) + U B_i^{(2)} (C_i, \varepsilon_i)$$

$$\vec{D}_{ij} = \vec{C}_i D_{ij} (C_i).$$

In equations (11)-(12), B_i is a tensor, $\overset{\circ}{\vec{C}_i \vec{C}_i}$ is a tensor the sum of whose diagonal components is zero. For example, the components of the first line of this tensor are equal to $U_i - \frac{1}{3} C_i^2$; $U_i V_i$; $U_i W_i$. Substituting (11) into (10) and equating the right- and left-hand terms in $\frac{d \ln T}{dr}$; $\frac{d}{d\vec{r}} c_0$; d_j we obtain integral equations from which $\vec{A}_i$, B_i, D_{ij} can be determined.

A complete solution for the integral equations for $\vec{A}_i$, B_i and D_{ij} can be obtained from detailed information about the probabilities of different types of molecular collision, calculated from the principles of quantum mechanics. Since the probabilities of different kinds of collision have not yet been satisfactorily worked out for rotational degrees of freedom, we will here consider a gas whose molecules have, in addition to translational, only vibrational degrees of freedom. It is known that as temperature increases the rotational degrees of freedom are excited first, and then the vibrational. But as will be shown below some results obtained for the vibrational degrees of freedom can be applied to any internal degrees of freedom and, in particular, to the rotational ones. Apart from this the results will be of practical interest also if the value of the kinetic coefficient is determined mainly by transfers of translational to vibrational energy in collisions. Of the three kinetic quantities mentioned above, the bulk viscosity is in some conditions determined by these transfers.

Below we will consider the effect of the following types of molecular collision on kinetic coefficients.

1. Elastic without change of the vibrational quantum numbers v of the molecules. These can be described by classical mechanics with a spherically symmetrical interaction potential.

2. Elastic with change of the number v by unity, i.e., collisions leading to an exchange of vibrational energy quanta between

molecules. This sort of collision can only occur between molecules of the same kind. The probabilities of such collisions have been calculated by the method of distorted waves by Schwartz and Slawsky [7] and are given by:

$$K(v, v_1 \to v' v_1') = V^2(v_1 \to v') V^2(v_1 \to v_1') \left(\frac{\pi m g_n}{\alpha h}\right)^2. \tag{13}$$

where

$$V(v \to v \pm 1) = -\alpha h \left(\frac{v + \frac{1}{2} \pm \frac{1}{2}}{2\pi^2 m h \omega}\right)^{\frac{1}{2}}$$

$$V(v \to v) = 1$$

g_n is the normal component of the relative collision velocity of the molecules; and

α is the constant for the potential of molecular interaction $V_0 e^{-\alpha r}$ and can be selected from the Lennard-Jones potential constant.

3. Inelastic with unit change of v. The probabilities of such collisions occurring, according to Schwartz, are given by:

$$K(v, v_1 \to v', v_1') = V^2(v \to v') V^2(v_1 \to v_1') \frac{1}{16\pi^2}(\theta^2 - \theta'^2)^2 \times$$

$$\times \frac{(e^{\theta} - e^{-\theta})(e^{\theta'} - e^{-\theta'})}{(e^{\theta} + e^{-\theta} - e^{\theta'} - e^{-\theta'})^2}, \tag{14}$$

where

$$\theta = \frac{2\pi^2 m g_n}{\alpha h}; \quad \theta' = \frac{2\pi^2 m g_n'}{\alpha h}.$$

Coefficients of Thermal Conductivity

The heat flow vector $\vec{q}$ is

$$\sum_{j, v_j} \int f_j^{(0)} \Phi_j E_j \vec{C}_j \, d\vec{c}_j \tag{15}$$

and is expressed, in the last analysis, in terms of $\vec{A}_i$ and $\vec{D}_{ij}$. The integral equations for $\vec{A}_i$ have the form:

$$f_i^{(0)}\left(\frac{E_i}{kT} - \frac{\overline{E_i}}{kT} - 1\right)\vec{C}_i = n_i \sum_{j, v_j} n_j I_{ij}(\vec{A}_i + \vec{A}_j). \tag{16}$$

It can be shown that equation (16) can be solved by the Ritz variational method [8]. This is known to give an extremely rapidly converging sequence of functions; hence when $\vec{A}_i$ is expanded in series in terms of known functions, only the first terms of the expansion need be retained.

In accordance with the form of the left-hand part of (16) let us express $\vec{A}_i$ in the form:

$$\vec{A}_i = \left(a_i^{(1)} \frac{mC_i^2}{2kT} + a_i^{(2)} \frac{h\omega_i v_i}{kT} + a_i^{(3)}\right)\vec{C}_i, \tag{17}$$

where the coefficients $a_i^{(k)}$ in solving equation (16) by the Ritz method are determined thus: substitute $\vec{A}_i$ into (16), multiply the scalar left- and right-hand parts of (16) in turn by $\frac{m_i C_i^2}{2kT}\vec{C}_i$, $\frac{h\omega_i v_l}{kT}\vec{C}_i$, $\vec{C}_i$, summate and integrate the equations obtained over all possible values of v_i and $\vec{C}_i$; the result is three linear equations for $a_i^{(k)}$. In a similar way $3i-3$ equations can be obtained. One of them is a linear function of the others. The standardizing conditions (7)-(9) give the other equations needed for determining $a_i^{(k)}$. Two of them, equations (7) and (9), are automatically satisfied. Equation (8) is an additional relation between the $a_i^{(k)}$s, which with the $3i-1$ equations obtained above gives a complete system of equations for $a_i^{(k)}$.

For calculating

$$\sum_{v_i}\int \vec{C}_i\cdot\frac{m_i C_i^2}{2kT} I_{ij}(\vec{A}_i+\vec{A}_j)\,d\vec{c}_i$$

$$\sum_{v_i}\int \vec{C}_i\cdot\frac{h\omega_i v_i}{kT} I_{ij}(\vec{A}_i+\vec{A}_i)\,d\vec{c}_i$$

$$\sum_{v_i}\int \vec{C}_i I_{ij}(\vec{A}_i+\vec{A}_j)\,d\vec{c}_i$$

for elastic collisions, the Lennard-Jones potential was used as the interaction potential. For Lennard-Jones functions the integrals for elastic collisions have been tabulated in the form of effective scattering cross-sections, which are temperature-dependent [9]. These will be denoted below as σ_i, $\sigma_{ij}=\frac{\sigma_i+\sigma_j}{2}$. For collisions of the second kind, giving correcting terms in the expression for the thermal conductivity, a model of a hard sphere with diameters of σ_i, σ_{ij} was used for calculating the integrals in (17). Terms covering collisions of the third kind in (17) can be ignored, if $h\omega_i - h\omega_j$ is not too small.

The system of $3i$ equations can be simplified by replacing $a_i^{(3)}$ by $\delta_i^{(3)}$ as follows:

$$a_i^{(3)} = \delta_i^{(3)} - \frac{5}{2}a_i^{(1)} - \frac{\overline{E}_{vi}}{kT}a_i^{(2)}.$$

As a result of this substitution, the system of $3i$ equations for $a_i^{(k)}$, $\delta_i^{(3)}$ takes the form:

$$8n_iR_ia_i^{(1)} + \sum_{j\neq i} n_jR_{ij}\{Q_{ij}a_i^{(1)} + P_{ij}a_j^{(1)} + S_{ij}\delta_i^{(3)} + L_{ij}\delta_j^{(3)}\} = \frac{15}{4}$$

$$a_i^{(2)}\left\{n_iR_i\left[1-\frac{1}{\pi^2}\left(\frac{\alpha_i h}{h\omega_i}\right)^2\frac{kT}{m_i}\right] + \sum_{j\neq i} n_jR_{ij}\right\} = \frac{3}{8}$$

$$\sum_{j\neq i}\{M_j^2a_i^{(1)} + 2M_j\delta_i^{(3)} - M_i^2a_j^{(1)} - 2M_i\delta_j^{(3)}\} = 0$$

$$\sum_j n_j\delta_j^{(3)} = 0,$$

where

$$R_i = \sigma_i^2 \left(\frac{\pi kT}{m_i}\right)^{\frac{1}{2}}; \quad R_{ij} = \sigma_{ij}^2 \left(\frac{2\pi kT}{m_{ij} M_i M_j}\right)^{\frac{1}{2}};$$
$$Q_{ij} = M_j (76 M_i M_j + 55 M_i^2 + 48 M_j^2) - 5 M_j (6 M_j + 5 M_i)$$
$$P_{ij} = -M_i (87 M_i M_j + 30 M_i^2 + 30 M_j^2) + 5 M_i (5 M_i + 6 M_j)$$
$$S_{ij} = 2 M_j (6 M_j + 5 M_i); \quad L_{ij} = -2 M_i (5 M_i + 6 M_j)$$
$$M_i = \frac{m_i}{m_{ij}}; \quad M_j = \frac{m_j}{m_{ij}}; \quad m_{ij} = m_i + m_j.$$

The thermal conductivity of gases was studied experimentally in the steady state, i.e., with the mean velocity of the molecules of any kind zero. To calculate the heat flux for the experimental condition, let us put $\vec{q}$ in the form:

$$\vec{q} = \sum_j n_j \vec{\overline{C}}_j \left(\frac{5}{2} kT - \overline{E}_{vj}\right) + \sum_{j,\, vj} \int f_j^0 \Phi_j \left(E_j - \frac{5}{2} kT - \overline{E}_{vj}\right) \vec{C}_j d\vec{c}_j.$$

Putting $\vec{\overline{C}}_j = 0$, we obtain

$$\vec{q} = -\lambda \frac{\partial T}{\partial \vec{r}},$$

where $\lambda = \lambda_n + \lambda_b$ is the thermal conductivity. λ_n is the thermal conductivity of a mixture of monatomic gases and is calculated in the usual way [8]. λ_b is calculated from $a_i^{(2)}$:

$$\lambda_b = \sum_i \frac{3}{8} n_i \frac{kT}{m_i} C_{vi}^* \left\{ n_i R_i \left[1 - \frac{1}{\pi^2} \left(\frac{\alpha_i h}{h\omega_i}\right)^2 \frac{kT}{m_i}\right] + \sum_{j \neq i} n_i R_{ij} \right\}^{-1}. \qquad (18)$$

Here C_{vi}^* is the heat capacity of the internal degrees of freedom in one molecule. The physical significance of the terms in the expression for λ can be found simply from the case of a single-component gas, for which

$$\lambda = \frac{5}{2} \frac{\mu}{m} \frac{3}{2} k + nDC_v^* \left[1 + \frac{1}{\pi^2} \left(\frac{\alpha h}{h\omega}\right)^2 \frac{kT}{m}\right]. \qquad (19)$$

In this case

$$\lambda_n = \frac{5}{2} \frac{\mu}{m} \frac{3}{2} k,$$
$$\lambda_b = nDC_v^* \left[1 + \frac{1}{\pi^2} \left(\frac{\alpha h}{h\omega}\right)^2 \frac{kT}{m}\right].$$

Here μ is the shear viscosity for the monatomic gas, D the coefficient of self-diffusion [6]. λ_n is determined only by elastic collisions of the first type, those of the second type not affecting it, and the effect of inelastic collisions can be ignored because of their low probability.

λ_b without a correcting term is determined only by elastic collisions of the first type and corresponds to transfer of heat by self-diffusion of excited molecules. The correcting term in the expression for λ_b appears because of elastic collisions of the second type, and is due to an Estafet mechanism of heat transfer by exchanges of internal energy quanta between molecules in collision.

An equation of the type of (19) without correction to λ_b was first deduced by Eucken in the form:

$$\lambda = \frac{5}{2}\frac{\mu}{m}\frac{3}{2}k + \mu\frac{C_v^*}{m}. \qquad (20)$$

which differs from (19) without correction for the Estafet heat transfer mechanism by a constant in the second term, $\frac{\rho D}{\mu} = 1.2$. It was obtained with the approximation that the mean free paths of the molecules in momentum and internal energy transfers are identical. In the deduction of equation (19) it was proved that if second- and third-type collisions are ignored, the internal degrees of freedom give a contribution to λ because of the diffusional mechanism of heat transfer. The correcting term to λ_b in (19) remains additive when allowance is made for molecular rotation if the probability of inelastic collisions is small for rotation. Equation (18) without correction for the Estafet heat-transfer mechanism is a generalized Eucken-type equation for a multicomponent mixture of gases and can be used for calculating thermal conductivities with allowance for any internal degrees of freedom if the probabilities of collisions with a change of the internal state are small.

Coefficients of Viscosity

For a single-component gas the pressure tensor P is:

$$pU + \sum \int m\vec{C}\vec{C} f^{(0)}\,\Phi\, d\vec{C}. \qquad (21)$$

The correcting term in (21) is expressed in the final analysis by the tensor B, whose integral equation is:

$$f^{(0)}\left\{\frac{m}{kT}\overset{\circ}{\vec{C}\vec{C}} = \left[\left(\frac{2}{3} - \frac{k}{C_v}\right)\frac{mC^2}{2kT} - \left(\frac{h\omega v}{kT} - \frac{\overline{E}_v}{kT}\right)\right]U\right\} = n^2 I(B). \qquad (22)$$

In accordance with the form of the left-hand side of equation (22), B can be written

$$B = b_1 \frac{m}{kT}\overset{\circ}{\vec{C}\vec{C}} + \left(b_2\frac{mC^2}{2kT} + b_3\frac{h\omega v}{kT} + b_4\right)U.$$

With the standardizing equations (7) and (9), we can show that:

$$B = b_1 \frac{m}{kT}\overset{\circ}{\vec{C}\vec{C}} + b_3\left[\left(\frac{h\omega v}{kT} - \frac{\overline{E}_v}{kT}\right) - \frac{C_v^*}{C_t}\left(\frac{mC^2}{2kT} - \frac{3}{2}\right)\right]U.$$

To determine b_1, we substitute B into (22), obtain the biscalar product of the left- and right-hand parts of (22) and the tensor $\frac{m}{kT}\overset{\circ}{\vec{C}\vec{C}}$ and summate and integrate the equation obtained over all v s and $\vec{c}$ s. Since $\overset{\circ}{\vec{C}\vec{C}} : U = 0$, the terms with b_3 disappear from the equation. Terms for second-type collisions cancel each other out. Neglecting the small corrections for third-type collisions, we find

$$b_1 = \frac{15}{16}\frac{1}{n\sigma^2}\left(\frac{m}{\pi kT}\right)^{\frac{1}{2}}.$$

To determine b_3 we obtain the biscalar product of the tensor equation (22) and unit tensor:

$$\left[\left(\frac{h\omega v}{kT} - \frac{\overline{E}_v}{kT}\right) - \frac{C_v^*}{C_t}\left(\frac{mC^2}{2kT} - \frac{3}{2}\right)\right] U$$

and summate and integrate the expression obtained over all v s and $\vec{c}$ s. The terms with b_1 disappear from the equation, and those for second- and third-type collisions cancel each other out. As a result, b_3 will be determined only by inelastic collisions

$$b_3 = -\frac{1}{32\pi^{4,5}} \frac{C_t}{C_v} \left(\frac{1}{mkT}\right)^{\frac{1}{2}} \frac{1}{n\sigma^2} \left(\frac{\alpha^* h}{h\omega}\right)^2 \beta^{-\frac{1}{2}} e^{\beta - \frac{h\omega}{2kT}}, \tag{23}$$

where

$$\beta = 3\left[\frac{\pi^4 (h\omega)^2 m}{(\alpha^* h)^2 kT}\right]^{\frac{1}{3}}. \quad C_t = \frac{3}{2}k;$$

and α^* is a function of temperature.

The expression for the pressure tensor [equation (21)] can be written:

$$P = nkT\,U - 2\mu \frac{\partial}{\partial \vec{r}} \overset{\circ}{\vec{c}_0} - \zeta \operatorname{div} \vec{c}_0 U.$$

where μ is the shear and ζ the bulk viscosity.

$$\mu = nkTb_1; \tag{24}$$

$$\zeta = -nkT \frac{C_v^*}{C_t} b_3 \tag{25}$$

$\frac{\partial}{\partial \vec{r}} \overset{\circ}{\vec{c}_0}$ is the symmetrical tensor, the sum of whose diagonals is zero.

The expression for μ coincides with that for a monatomic gas. Since the probabilities of third-type collisions is small right up to the dissociation temperature, the effect of vibrational degrees of freedom on the shear viscosity can be neglected. The rotational degrees of freedom, apparently, change expression (24) to some extent at high temperatures.

The bulk viscosity ζ is determined only by inelastic collisions. For calculating the effect of molecular rotation on it at ordinary temperatures, the phenomenological theory of bulk viscosity developed by Mandel'shtam and Leontovich [10] can be used. Since at ordinary temperatures the probabilities of inelastic collisions with simultaneous change of the vibrational and rotational states of the molecules are considerably less than the probabilities of inelastic collisions in which either the vibrational or the rotational state is changed but not both, we use that part of the theory which gives a generalization of the ideas developed by the authors for the case of the occurrence in the gas of certain independent relaxational processes. It can be shown that with $\omega\tau_n \ll 1$, where τ_n is the relaxation time of any relaxational process, and ω is the ultrasonic frequency,

$$\zeta = \frac{nk^2T}{C_t} \sum_n \tau_n \frac{C_n^*}{C_n}. \tag{26}$$

In equation (26) C_n^* is the heat capacity of the internal degrees of freedom of the nth type for one molecule; $C_n = C_t + C_n^*$.

It follows from (26) that the bulk viscosity is an additive function of terms characterizing the different relaxational processes. If the heat capacity of the vibrational degrees of freedom is not too small and the relaxation time for vibrations considerably exceeds that for rotations, the bulk viscosity is determined practically entirely by inelastic collisions with change of the vibrational states of the molecules. At not excessively high temperatures this is true for most gases.

The applicability of formula (25) for different temperatures, apart from what has been observed above, is limited by the method of solving the Boltzmann equation and the methods of calculating the integrals expressing b_3.

The limit set to its applicability by the method of solving the Boltzmann equation is given by

$$nkT \gg \zeta \, div \, \vec{c}_0 \, . \tag{27}$$

which, for the propagation of ultrasonic vibrations in a gas, becomes:

$$\zeta\omega \ll p.$$

The limits of applicability imposed by the methods of calculating the integrals are determined as follows. The integrals can be reduced to the form:

$$J = \int_0^\infty \int_0^{\frac{\pi}{2}} e^{-\frac{m}{4kT} g^2} \varphi_\pm (g_n) g^3 \sin\psi \cos\psi \, d\psi \, dg,$$

where

$$\varphi_\pm = \frac{K(v, v_1 \to v \pm 1, v_1)}{V^2 (v \to v \pm 1)}.$$

After replacing $\cos\psi$ by x we obtain:

$$J = \int_0^\infty \int_0^1 e^{-\frac{m}{4kT} g^2} \varphi_\pm (gx) \, x dx dg \, .$$

On changeover to the variables $y = gx$, $x = t$, domain I of the (g, x) plane bounded by the lines $g=g_1$, $g=g_2$, $x=0$, $x=1$ transforms into the domain (y, t) bounded by the lines $y=g_1t$, $y=g_2t$, $t=0$ and $t=1$ and

$$J_I' = J_{II} + J_{III},$$

where J_I is the integral over domain I of the (y, x) plane, J_{II} is the integral over the domain of the (y, t) plane, bounded by the lines $y=g_1$, $x=1$ and $y=g_2t$; J_{III} is an integral over the (y_1t) plane domain, bounded by the lines $y=g_2t$, $y=g_1t$ and $y=g_1$. Making in J_{II} the substitutions $z=\frac{1}{t^2}$, $y=y$ and going to the limits $g_1 \to 0$, $g_2 \to \infty$, we find:

$$J_{III} \to 0$$

$$J_{II} \to J = \frac{kT}{m}\int_0^\infty e^{-\frac{m}{4kT}y^2}\,\varphi_\pm(y)dy.$$

This integral was calculated by Schwartz [7] by the method of "steepest descent" on the assumption that:

$$e^{\left(\frac{2\pi^2 m}{\alpha^* h}\right)} \gg 1$$

$$\frac{mg_n^{*2}}{4} \gg h\omega \quad \text{or} \quad \frac{mg_n'^{*2}}{4} \gg h\omega, \tag{28}$$

$$\text{where } g_n^* = \left(\frac{8\pi^2 kTh\omega}{\alpha^* hm}\right)^{\frac{1}{3}} \pm \frac{h\omega}{m}\left(\frac{8\pi^2 kTh\omega}{\alpha^* hm}\right)^{-\frac{1}{3}} \tag{29}$$

$$\alpha^* = \frac{12}{r_0 D}\left[\frac{1}{2} + \frac{1}{2}\left(1+D\right)^{\frac{1}{2}}\right]^{\frac{1}{6}}\left[1 + \left(1+D\right)^{\frac{1}{2}} + D\right]$$

$$D = \frac{\frac{mg_n^{*2}}{4} + \varepsilon}{\varepsilon}\,;\; r_1 = r_0\left[\frac{1}{2} + \frac{1}{2}\left(1+D\right)^{\frac{1}{2}}\right]^{-\frac{1}{6}}. \tag{30}$$

ε and r_0 are the Lennard-Jones potential constants. Condition (28) defines the limits of applicability of formula (25) imposed by the methods of calculating the integrals.

Equation (25) gives the correct order for ζ. Using the Lennard-Jones potential constants for CO_2, $\frac{\varepsilon}{k} = 190$, $r_0 = 3.996$ Å, we find by successive approximations from (29) and (30) for $T' =$ 298°K the value $\alpha^* = 4.98 \times 10^8$ cm/sec. Putting $\sigma = r_1$, where r_1 is the classical distance of closest approach of molecules, we find $\sigma = 3.54$ Å, $\zeta = 1.15$ g/cm.sec., $\frac{\nu}{p} \ll 0.1$ ms/atm, $\alpha_1\lambda = 17.5\,\frac{\nu}{p}$, where $\frac{\nu}{p}$ is in ms/atm; λ, α_1 are respectively the wavelength and absorption coefficient for ultrasonic vibrations. According to Fricke [11], for $\frac{\nu}{p} = 0.01$, $\alpha_1\lambda = 0.1$.

In conclusion, the author thanks Prof. E.V. Stupochenko for useful remarks about this paper.

REFERENCES

1. M. LEONTOVICH, Zh. eksper. teor. fiz., 6, 561 (1936).
2. C.S. WANG-CHANG and G.E. UHLENBECK, University of Michigan Publication CM-681 (1951).
3. P. PIDDUCK, Proc. Roy. Soc., A101, 101 (1922).
4. I. ISHIDA, Phys. Rev., 10, 305 (1917).
5. J.H. JEANS, The Dynamical Theory of Gases, Cambridge University Press (1904).
6. S. CHAPMAN and T.G. COWLING, The Mathematical Theory of Non-uniform Gases, Cambridge (1953).
7. R.N. SCHWARTZ and Z.R. SLAWSKY, J. Chem. Phys., 20, 1591 (1952).
8. C.F. CURTISS and J.HIRSCHFELDER, ibid., 17, 552 (1949).

9. J.O. HIRSCHFELDER, C.F. CURTISS, and R.B. BIRD, Molecular Theory of Gases and Liquids (1954).
10. L. MANDEL'SHTAM and M. LEONTOVICH, Zh. eksper. teor. fiz., 7, 438 (1937).
11. E.F. FRICKE, J. Acoust. Soc. Amer., 12, 245 (1940).

I.B. Rozhdestvenskii

Thermodynamic and Gas-dynamic Properties of Flowing Air Downstream of a Normal Shock Wave with Allowance for Ionization and Dissociation

This paper presents a method for, and the result of, calculating the thermodynamic and gas-dynamic properties of flowing air behind a normal shock wave. The study covered speeds from 4500 to 15,500 m/sec and pressures before shock from 1 to 0.00001 atm. Under these conditions, temperatures of up to 12,000°K and pressures of up to 1000 atm develop behind the shock front. Experimental methods of studying and air flow under these conditions, of course, do not exist, and a theoretical calculation becomes of fundamental importance.

In the temperature and pressure ranges indicated, air is a mixture of reacting gases: oxygen and nitrogen molecules dissociate, NO is formed, and atoms and molecules ionize. Nowadays it is possible by the methods of statistical physics and with spectroscopic data to determine the thermodynamic functions of air as a function of temperature and pressure with great accuracy. On the other hand, the equations of gas dynamics for one-dimensional flow yield values of the temperature T_2, the pressure p_2, the density ρ_2 and the velocity V_2 immediately behind a normal shock wave if the thermodynamic quantities behind the front are known.

A study has been published of the thermodynamic properties of air between 1000° and 12,000°K and 0.001 and 1000 atm [1]. The paper in question describes a programme for calculating all thermodynamic properties of air on an electronic computer as functions of temperature and pressure. To determine the gas-dynamic properties of a normal shock and find the thermodynamic properties behind the shock as a function of the pressure and velocity before the shock a system of algebraic functional equations must be solved, including the continuity equation, the energy and momentum conservation equations and the equation of state. The molecular weights appearing in the equations of conservation of energy [and] enthalpy and the equation of state are functions of temperature and pressure. From the temperature and pressure behind the shock as found in solving the gas-dynamic system all the necessary thermodynamic functions were calculated.

I. Nature of the Problem; System of Thermodynamic and Gas-dynamic Equations for Air*

It is required to find the equation for the change of gas-dynamic and thermodynamic properties of air behind a normal shock as a function of the velocity and pressure of the air before the shock. The air behind the shock is considered to be an equilibrium mixture of reacting gases, subject to the Clapeyron equation of state.

Let us write the complete system of equations for the thermodynamics and gas dynamics of air.

1. System of Thermodynamic Equations

These equations include the Dalton equation, the mass balance equation, the mass action equations and the equation of conservation of charge:

$$\left.\begin{array}{l}
X_N + X_O + X_{Ar} + X_{N_2} + X_{O_2} + X_{NO+} + X_{N+}^{+} X_{O+}^{+} X_{Ar+} + X_{N_2+} + \\
+ X_{O_2+} + X_{NO+} + X_{e-} = 1 \\
\dfrac{X_N + 2X_{N_2} + X_{NO} + X_{N+} + 2X_{N_2+} + X_{NO+}}{X_O + 2X_{O_2} + X_{NO} + X_{O+} + 2X_{O_2+} + X_{NO+}} = 3{,}727^1 \\
\dfrac{X_{Ar} + X_{Ar+}}{X_O + 2X_{O_2} + X_{NO} + X_{O+} + 2X_{O_2+} + X_{NO+}} = 0{,}02315 \\
\dfrac{X_N^2}{X_{N_2}} = \dfrac{K_{pN}}{p} \quad \dfrac{X_{N+}\cdot X_{e-}}{X_N} = \dfrac{K_{pN+}}{p} \quad \dfrac{X_{O_2^+}\cdot X_{e-}}{X_{O_2}} = \dfrac{K_{pO_2^+}}{p} \\
\dfrac{X_O^2}{X_{O_2}} = \dfrac{K_{pO}}{p} \quad \dfrac{X_{O+}\cdot X_{e-}}{X_O} = \dfrac{K_{pO+}}{p} \quad \dfrac{X_{N_2^+}\cdot X_{e-}}{X_{N_2}} = \dfrac{K_{pN_2^+}}{p} \\
\dfrac{X_N\cdot X_O}{X_{NO}} = \dfrac{K_{pNO}}{p} \quad \dfrac{X_{Ar+}\cdot X_{e-}}{X_{Ar}} = \dfrac{K_{pAr+}}{p} \quad \dfrac{X_{NO+}\cdot X_{e-}}{X_{NO}} = \dfrac{K_{pNO+}}{p} \\
X_{N+} + X_{O+} + X_{Ar+} + X_{N_2^+} + X_{O_2^+} + X_{NO+} - X_{e-} = 0\,,
\end{array}\right\} \mathrm{I}$$

where X denotes the fraction of a component and K_p the equilibrium constant of the corresponding reaction.

System I gives the composition of air as a function of temperature and pressure if the equilibrium constants K_p are known.

Knowing the composition we can find the enthalpy and the molecular weight of air.

$$h = \frac{1}{\mu} \sum_{l=1}^{13} H_l X_l$$

$$\mu = \sum_{l=1}^{13} \mu_l X_l,$$

*The composition of air (volumetric) under standard conditions is taken as $X^0_{N_2} = 0.7808$; $X^0_{O_2} = 0.2095$; $X^0_{Ar} = 0.0097$.

where H_l are the molar enthalpies of the components and μ_l their molecular weights.

For calculating heat capacities at constant pressure and volume, and also for calculating the sonic velocity, system I is insufficient. The equations for these quantities c_p, c_v and a are [2]:

$$c_p = \frac{1}{\mu}\left[\sum_{l=1}^{13} c_{pl}X_l + \sum_{l=1}^{13} H_l \frac{1}{N}\left(\frac{\partial N_l}{\partial T}\right)_p\right]$$

$$c_v = \frac{1}{\mu}\left[\sum_{l=1}^{13} c_{pl}X_l - R + \sum_{l=1}^{13} H_l \frac{1}{N}\left(\frac{\partial N_l}{\partial T}\right)_v - RT\sum_{l=1}^{13}\frac{1}{N}\left(\frac{\partial N_l}{\partial T}\right)_v\right]$$

$$a = \sqrt{\frac{\gamma RT}{\mu}\frac{1+T\frac{1}{N}\left(\frac{\partial N}{\partial T}\right)_v}{1+T\frac{1}{N}\left(\frac{\partial N}{\partial T}\right)_p}}.$$

It will be seen that to find heat capacities and the sonic velocity, we need to know, besides the ordinary quantities μ, c_{pl}, X_l, H_l, the partial differentials with respect to T of the numbers of moles of components at constant pressure and volume $\frac{1}{N}\left(\frac{\partial N_l}{\partial T}\right)_p$, $\frac{1}{N}\left(\frac{\partial N_l}{\partial T}\right)_v$ and $\frac{1}{N}\left(\frac{\partial N}{\partial T}\right)_p = \sum_{l=1}^{13}\frac{1}{N}\left(\frac{\partial N_l}{\partial T}\right)_p$ and $\frac{1}{N}\left(\frac{\partial N}{\partial T}\right)_v = \sum_{l=1}^{13}\frac{1}{N}\left(\frac{\partial N_l}{\partial T}\right)_v$.

These quantities are easily obtained from the condition that the number of atoms of nitrogen, oxygen and argon does not change and from the mass action equations, if in the latter we change over from X_l to N_l and use the thermodynamic relations

$$\left(\frac{\partial \ln K_p}{\partial T}\right)_p = \frac{d \ln K_p}{dT} = \frac{Q}{RT^2},$$

where Q is the heat of reaction, $Q = \sum_{l=1}^{k} \nu_l H_l$;
k is the number of components in the reaction, and
ν_l is the stoichiometric coefficient.

The equations for constancy of the numbers of atoms are:

$$N_N + 2N_{N_2} + N_{NO} + N_{N^+} + 2N_{N_2^+} + N_{NO^+} = \text{const},$$
$$N_O + 2N_{O_2} + N_{NO} + N_{O^+} + 2N_{O_2^+} + N_{NO^+} = \text{const},$$
$$N_{Ar} + N_{Ar^+} = \text{const}.$$

We thus obtain two further systems of equations for determining c_p, c_v and a.

$$\frac{1}{N}\left(\frac{\partial N_N}{\partial T}\right)_p + \frac{2}{N}\left(\frac{\partial N_{N_2}}{\partial T}\right)_p + \frac{1}{N}\left(\frac{\partial N_{NO}}{\partial T}\right)_p + \frac{1}{N}\left(\frac{\partial N_{N^+}}{\partial T}\right)_p + \frac{2}{N}\left(\frac{\partial N_{N_2^+}}{\partial T}\right)_p + \frac{1}{N}\left(\frac{\partial N_{NO^+}}{\partial T}\right)_p = 0$$

$$\left.\begin{array}{l}
\frac{1}{N}\left(\frac{\partial N_{O}}{\partial T}\right)_p+\frac{2}{N}\left(\frac{\partial N_{O_2}}{\partial T}\right)_p+\frac{1}{N}\left(\frac{\partial N_{NO}}{\partial T}\right)_p+\frac{1}{N}\left(\frac{\partial N_{O^+}}{\partial T}\right)_p+\frac{2}{N}\left(\frac{\partial N_{O_2^+}}{\partial T}\right)_p+ \\
\qquad +\frac{1}{N}\left(\frac{\partial N_{NO^+}}{\partial T}\right)_p=0 \\
\frac{1}{N}\left(\frac{\partial N_{Ar}}{\partial T}\right)_p+\frac{1}{N}\left(\frac{\partial N_{Ar^+}}{\partial T}\right)_p=0 \\
\frac{2}{X_N}\frac{1}{N}\left(\frac{\partial N_{N}}{\partial T}\right)_p-\frac{1}{X_{N_2}}\frac{1}{N}\left(\frac{\partial N_{N_2}}{\partial T}\right)_p-\frac{1}{N}\left(\frac{\partial N}{\partial T}\right)_p=\frac{Q_N}{RT^2} \\
\frac{2}{X_O}\frac{1}{N}\left(\frac{\partial N_{O}}{\partial T}\right)_p-\frac{1}{X_{O_2}}\frac{1}{N}\left(\frac{\partial N_{O_2}}{\partial T}\right)_p-\frac{1}{N}\left(\frac{\partial N}{\partial T}\right)_p=\frac{Q_O}{RT^2} \\
\frac{1}{X_N}\frac{1}{N}\left(\frac{\partial N_{N}}{\partial T}\right)_p+\frac{1}{X_O}\frac{1}{N}\left(\frac{\partial N_{O}}{\partial T}\right)_p-\frac{1}{X_{NO}}\frac{1}{N}\left(\frac{\partial N_{NO}}{\partial T}\right)_p-\frac{1}{N}\left(\frac{\partial N}{\partial T}\right)_p=\frac{Q_{NO}}{RT^2} \\
\frac{1}{X_{N^+}}\frac{1}{N}\left(\frac{\partial N_{N^+}}{\partial T}\right)_p+\frac{1}{X_{e^-}}\frac{1}{N}\left(\frac{\partial N_{e^-}}{\partial T}\right)_p-\frac{1}{X_N}\frac{1}{N}\left(\frac{\partial N_{N}}{\partial T}\right)_p-\frac{1}{N}\left(\frac{\partial N}{\partial T}\right)_p=\frac{Q_{N^+}}{RT^2} \\
\frac{1}{X_{O^+}}\frac{1}{N}\left(\frac{\partial N_{O^+}}{\partial T}\right)_p+\frac{1}{X_{e^-}}\frac{1}{N}\left(\frac{\partial N_{e^-}}{\partial T}\right)_p-\frac{1}{X_O}\frac{1}{N}\left(\frac{\partial N_{O}}{\partial T}\right)_p-\frac{1}{N}\left(\frac{\partial N}{\partial T}\right)_p=\frac{Q_{O^+}}{RT^2} \\
\frac{1}{X_{Ar^+}}\frac{1}{N}\left(\frac{\partial N_{Ar^+}}{\partial T}\right)_p+\frac{1}{X_{e^-}}\frac{1}{N}\left(\frac{\partial N_{e^-}}{\partial T}\right)_p-\frac{1}{X_{Ar}}\frac{1}{N}\left(\frac{\partial N_{Ar}}{\partial T}\right)_p-\frac{1}{N}\left(\frac{\partial N}{\partial T}\right)_p= \\
\qquad =\frac{Q_{Ar^+}}{RT^2} \\
\frac{1}{X_{N_2^+}}\frac{1}{N}\left(\frac{\partial N_{N_2^+}}{\partial T}\right)_p+\frac{1}{X_{e^-}}\frac{1}{N}\left(\frac{\partial N_{e^-}}{\partial T}\right)_p-\frac{1}{X_{N_2}}\frac{1}{N}\left(\frac{\partial N_{N_2}}{\partial T}\right)_p-\frac{1}{N}\left(\frac{\partial N}{\partial T}\right)_p= \\
\qquad =\frac{Q_{N_2^+}}{RT^2} \\
\frac{1}{X_{O_2^+}}\frac{1}{N}\left(\frac{\partial N_{O_2^+}}{\partial T}\right)_p+\frac{1}{X_{e^-}}\frac{1}{N}\left(\frac{\partial N_{e^-}}{\partial T}\right)_p-\frac{1}{X_{O_2}}\frac{1}{N}\left(\frac{\partial N_{O_2}}{\partial T}\right)_p-\frac{1}{N}\left(\frac{\partial N}{\partial T}\right)_p= \\
\qquad =\frac{Q_{O_2^+}}{RT^2} \\
\frac{1}{X_{NO^+}}\frac{1}{N}\left(\frac{\partial N_{NO^+}}{\partial T}\right)_p+\frac{1}{X_{e^-}}\frac{1}{N}\left(\frac{\partial N_{e^-}}{\partial T}\right)_p-\frac{1}{X_{NO}}\frac{1}{N}\left(\frac{\partial N_{NO}}{\partial T}\right)_p-\frac{1}{N}\left(\frac{\partial N}{\partial T}\right)_p= \\
\qquad =\frac{Q_{NO^+}}{RT^2},
\end{array}\right\} \text{II}$$

where

$$\frac{1}{N}\left(\frac{\partial N}{\partial T}\right)_p=\sum_{l=1}^{13}\frac{1}{N}\left(\frac{\partial N_l}{\partial T}\right)_p,$$

$$\frac{1}{N}\left(\frac{\partial N_{e^-}}{\partial T}\right)_p=\frac{1}{N}\left(\frac{\partial N_{N^+}}{\partial T}\right)_p+\frac{1}{N}\left(\frac{\partial N_{O^+}}{\partial T}\right)_p+\frac{1}{N}\left(\frac{\partial N_{Ar^+}}{\partial T}\right)_p+\frac{1}{N}\left(\frac{\partial N_{N_2^+}}{\partial T}\right)_p+ +\frac{1}{N}\left(\frac{\partial N_{O_2^+}}{\partial T}\right)_p+\frac{1}{N}\left(\frac{\partial N_{NO^+}}{\partial T}\right)_p$$

System of equations III with V = const is, in view of its cumbrousness, not reproduced. Systems I, II and III permit calculation of the thermodynamic functions of air as a function of temperature and pressure [1].

2. System of Equations for a Normal Shock

We will denote all quantities before the shock by the subscript 1, and quantities after it by the subscript 2.

The enthalpy h_2 and the molecular weight after the shock μ_2 will be functions of temperature T_2 and pressure p_2 behind the shock $h_2 = h_2\ (T_2,\ p_2)$ and $\mu_2 = \mu_2(T_2,\ p_2)$. The system of gas-dynamic equations for our case is:

$$\left.\begin{array}{ll} \rho_1 V_1 = \rho_2 V_2 & \text{(1) equation of continuity;} \\ h_1 + \frac{V_1^2}{2J} = h_2(T_2,\ p_2) + \frac{V_2^2}{2J} & \text{(2) equation of conservation of energy;} \\ p_1 + \rho_1 V_1^2 = p_2 + \rho_2 V_2^2 & \text{(3) equation of conservation of momentum;} \\ p_1 = \frac{R}{\mu_1}\rho_1 T_1 & \text{(4) equation of state before the shock} \\ p_2 = \frac{R}{\mu_2(T_2,\ p_2)}\rho_2 T_2 & \text{(5) equation of state after the shock} \end{array}\right\} \text{IV}$$

where R is the universal gas constant, 8.31436×10^7 ergs/g.mole °K and J is the mechanical equivalent of heat (1 g.cal = 4.1855×10^7 ergs).

The air will be considered as non-radiating before and immediately after the shock. The enthalpy and molecular weight before the shock are calculated in the classical approximation:

$$h_1 = \frac{1}{\mu_1}\left(\frac{7}{2}X^0_{O_2} + \frac{7}{2}X^0_{N_2} + \frac{5}{2}X^0_{A_r}\right)RT_1$$

$$\mu_1 = \mu_{O_2}X^0_{O_2} + \mu_{N_2}X^0_{N_2} + \mu_{Ar}X^0_{Ar}.$$

System IV makes it possible to calculate, from known values before the shock, all the gas-dynamic quantities after the shock, if $h_2(T_2,\ p_2)$ and $\mu_2(T_2,\ p_2)$ are known.

II. Solution of the Gas-dynamic Problem

The values of the required quantities behind the shock can be found from the solution of system IV for known values in front of the shock. However, this is only possible if $h_2 = h_2(T_2,\ p_2)$ and $\mu_2 = \mu_2(T_2,\ p_2)$ are known. In our case h_2 and μ_2 are determined from numerical solution of system I, which is equivalent to specifying a table of values of h_2 and μ_2 as functions of T_2 and p_2. Linear interpolation for T_2 and p_2 in the functions for h_2 and μ_2 by a Taylor series expansion makes the problem very extensive and complicates the programming of it for a computing machine, since in view of the non-linearity of the thermodynamic functions it is impossible to select in advance the same minimum range for temperature and pressure, inside which interpolation with sufficient accuracy is possible.

The problem can be solved in another way, by specifying the

temperature behind the shock T_2. The solution is in two stages.

I. We specify the temperature behind the shock T_2 and for a certain pressure behind the shock p_2 we determine h_2 and μ_2 with system I. Let us find the pressure before the shock p_1. From the equation of continuity we have $V_1 = \frac{\rho_2}{\rho_1} V_2$. Putting V_1 into equations (2) and (3) we obtain:

$$h_1 + \alpha\left(\frac{\rho_2}{\rho_1}\right)^2 V_2^2 = h_2 + \alpha V_2^2,$$
$$p_1 + \rho_1\left(\frac{\rho_2}{\rho_1}\right)^2 V_2^2 = p_2 + \rho_2 V_2^2,$$

where

$$\alpha = \frac{1}{2J}$$

or

$$h_2 - h_1 = \alpha\left[\left(\frac{\rho_2}{\rho_1}\right)^2 - 1\right] V_2^2, \qquad (6)$$
$$p_2 - p_1 = \rho_2\left(\frac{\rho_2}{\rho_1} - 1\right) V_2^2 .$$

Division yields:

$$\frac{h_2 - h_1}{p_2 - p_1} = \frac{\alpha}{\rho_2}\left(\frac{\rho_2 + \rho_1}{\rho_1}\right).$$

We discard the trivial solution $\rho_2 = \rho_1$. Eliminating ρ_1 and ρ_2 from equations (4) and (5), and collecting up similar terms, we obtain a quadratic in p_1:

$$\frac{T_2}{\mu_2}\,\frac{1}{p_2}\,p_1^2 + \left(\frac{h_2 - h_1}{\alpha R} - \frac{T_2}{\mu_2} + \frac{T_1}{\mu_1}\right) p_1 - \frac{T_1}{\mu_1}\,p_2 = 0 . \qquad (7)$$

which can be written in the dimensionless form:

$$a\pi^2 + b\pi + c = 0 , \qquad (7')$$

where

$$\pi = \frac{p_1}{p_2}$$
$$a = \frac{T_2}{\mu_2}$$
$$b = \frac{h_2 - h_1}{\alpha R} + \frac{T_1}{\mu_1} - \frac{T_2}{\mu_2}.$$
$$c = -\frac{T_1}{\mu_1}.$$

The discriminant of the equation, $\Delta = 4ac - b^2$, is negative, so that (7') has two real different roots. Since the pressure is decidedly positive, we take the positive root. Thus, by specifying the pressure behind the shock for a given temperature T_2 behind the shock, we find the pressure p_1 before the shock:

$$p_1 = p_2 \frac{b}{2a}\left(\sqrt{1 - \frac{4ac}{b^2}} - 1\right). \qquad (8)$$

2. Let the pressure before the shock be p_1^0. Then, specifying for T_2 some values of p_2, we find from (8) a pair of values $p_1^{(1)}$ and $p_1^{(2)}$ satisfying the condition

$$p_1^{(1)} < p_1^0 < p_1^{(2)}. \quad (9)$$

If $|p_1^{(1)} - p_1^{(0)}| \leqslant \varepsilon$, where ε is the standard error, we find the pressure p_1, differing from the specified pressure p_1^0 by not more than $\frac{\varepsilon}{2}$. The pressure behind the shock p_2 corresponding to the pressure in front of the shock thus found, p_1, makes it possible to determine for a given T_2 all the thermodynamic functions for air behind the shock with systems I, II, and III. The velocity V_2 is obtained from equation (6) and the velocity v_1 from the equation of continuity (I). The entropy behind the shock is calculated from:

$$s = \frac{R}{\mu}\left[-2,665 + \ln\frac{T^{\frac{5}{2}}}{P} + \sum_{l=1}^{13}\ln\left(\frac{\mu_l^{\frac{3}{2}}\cdot Q_l}{X_l}\right)\cdot X_l + \frac{U - \sum\limits_{l=1}^{13} U_l^0 X_l}{RT}\right],$$

where Q_l are the statistical sums of the internal degrees of freedom, and $U_l{}^0$ are the constant internal energies of the components.

The numerical method for finding the parameters of a normal shock and the thermodynamic functions of air behind a normal shock can be used for calculating the gas-dynamic properties for an oblique shock in the same way as for a normal shock. We shall not deal with this here.

III. Results of Calculations

Calculations by the method outlined were made on the high-speed electronic computer (BESM) of the USSR Academy of Sciences. The temperature T_2 behind the shock was changed in 100-degree steps, with 61 points in all from 6000° to 12,000°K. For each T_2 calculations were made for three temperatures before the shock (T_1 = 200°, 300° and 400°K) and for 21 values of the pressure p_1 before the shock (0.1×10^{-4}, 0.25×10^{-4}, 0.5×10^{-4} ...... 0.75×10^0, 1). Hence 3843 points in all were calculated. For each pair of temperature and pressure values before the shock, calculations were made of air velocities in front of and behind the shock, the Mach number $\frac{V_1}{a_1}$ for the flow, the temperature, pressure and density of the air behind the shock, and also of the molecular weight, enthalpy, entropy, specific heat at constant pressure and volume, and sonic velocity behind the normal shock. The relative error of the calculations was 0.01 per cent. From Figs. 1-6 we see that T_2, p_2 and V_2 increase with V_1 at all values of p_1. The molecular weight μ_2 decreases as V_1 increases. ρ_2 increases with M_1 and passes through a maximum, but at $p_1 = 0.0001$ and $p_1 = 0.00001$ density continues to increase with M_1. The specific heat c_{p_2} passes through two maxima as a function of V_1 with p_1 as parameter. The first left maximum for all p_1s corresponds to the region of maximum dissociation of air, the following maximum for $p_1 = 0.00001$ corresponds to maximum ionization.

Fig. 2 shows the relation between the pressure ratio $\frac{p_2}{p_1}$ and M_1 for T_1 = 200°, 300° and 400°K and for all pressures p_1. This relation in our case, as in the classical case, i.e., without correction for chemical processes behind the shock, is practically a function of M_1 only. The lower curve, given for comparison, is for the classical case [3].

From the plots for T_2 and $\frac{\rho_2}{\rho_1}$ it can easily be seen that the ratio of temperatures and densities in our case are not only functions of M_1, but also of the pressure and temperature in front of the shock wave.

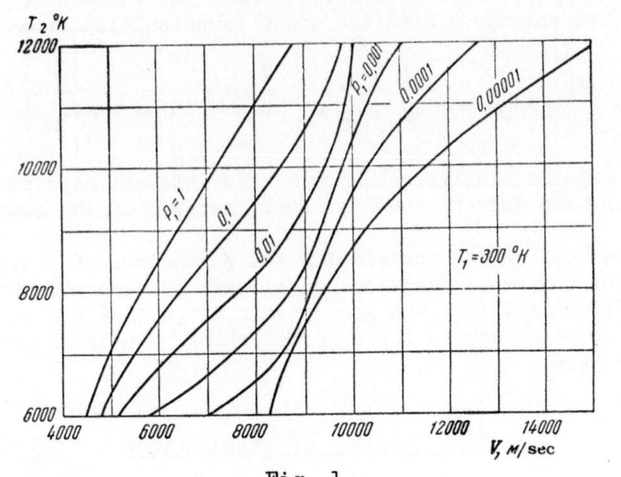

Fig. 1
Variation of temperature T_2 behind the shock with the air velocity V_1.

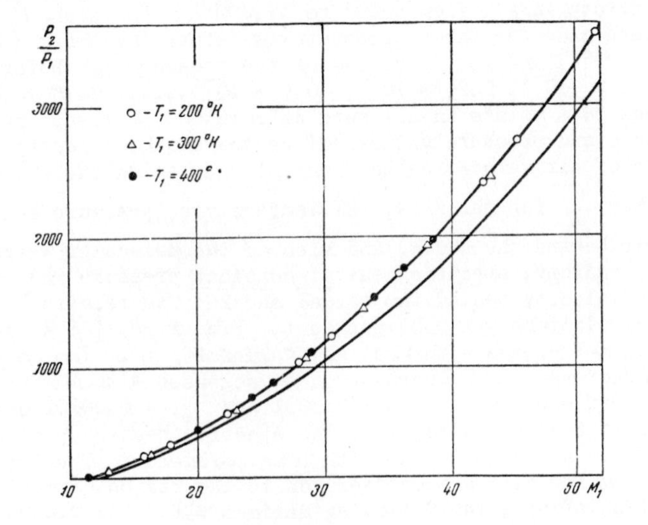

Fig. 2
Pressure ratio $\frac{p_2}{p_1}$ as a function of M_1. The lower curve from classical data [3].

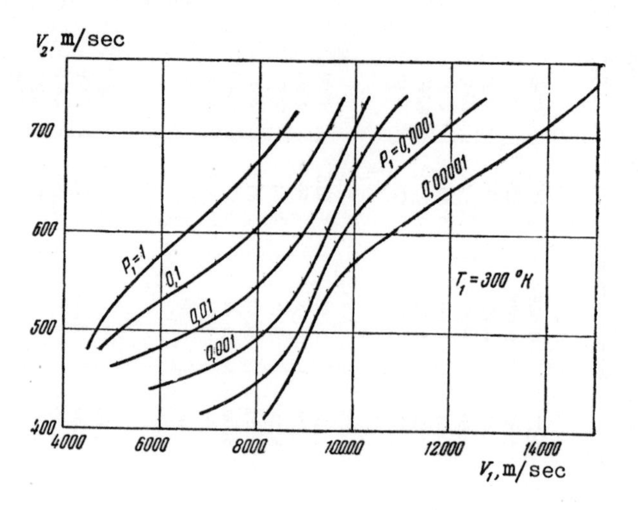

Fig. 3
Velocity V_2 behind the shock as a function of that before the shock, V_1.

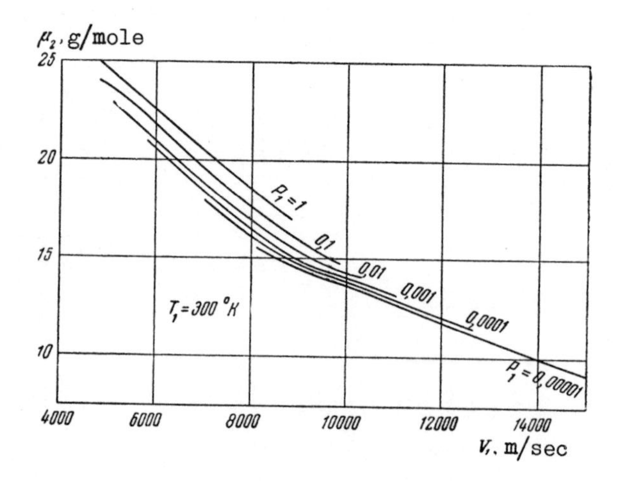

Fig. 4
Variation of molecular weight μ_2 behind the shock with V_1.

$V_1 \frac{m}{sec}$	M_1	T_2 °K	atm	$\rho_2 \frac{g}{cm}$	$V_2 \frac{m}{sec}$	$\mu_2 \frac{g}{mole}$	$h_2 \frac{cal}{g}$	$S_2 \frac{cal}{g\ °K}$	$C_{p_2} \frac{cal}{g\ °K}$	$C_{V_2} \frac{cal}{g\ °K}$	$a_2 \frac{m}{sec}$
$T_1 = 200$ $P_1 = 1$											
4470	15.8	6000	312	$0.164 \cdot 10^{-1}$	482	25.9	2410	2,27	0.589	0.462	1540
4990	17.6	7000	389	$0.168 \cdot 10^{-1}$	523	24.8	2990	2,33	0,688	0,529	1690
5620	19.8	8100	497	$0.176 \cdot 10^{-1}$	563	23.6	3790	2,41	0,922	0.736	1850
6230	22,0	9000	613	$0.185 \cdot 10^{-1}$	593	22.3	4650	2,48	1.21	0,958	2000
6990	24.7	10000	776	$0.196 \cdot 10^{-1}$	629	20.7	5840	2.57	1,53	1,18	2190
7790	27,5	11000	966	$0.205 \cdot 10^{-1}$	670	19.2	7240	2.67	1.72	1.30	2390
8550	30.1	12000	1170	$0.210 \cdot 10^{-1}$	717	17,8	8720	2,78	1.72	1.29	2610
$T_1 = 200$ $P_1 = 0.01$											
5080	17.9	6000	4,09	$0.192 \cdot 10^{-3}$	467	23.1	3100	2,73	1,10	0.915	1590
6120	21,6	7000	6.01	$0.219 \cdot 10^{-3}$	493	20,9	4500	2,88	2.08	1.70	1790
7550	26.6	8100	9,23	$0.249 \cdot 10^{-2}$	534	18.0	6820	3,14	2.71	2,14	2090
8560	30.2	9000	11,9	$0.260 \cdot 10^{-3}$	581	16.1	8760	3,34	2,18	1.71	2350
9300	32,8	10000	14.1	$0.258 \cdot 10^{-3}$	637	15.1	10300	3,50	1.35	1.06	2600
9790	34.5	11000	15.5	$0.251 \cdot 10^{-3}$	690	14.6	11400	3,59	1.04	0.818	2800
10200	36,0	12000	16,9	$0.244 \cdot 10^{-3}$	739	14,2	12500	3,65	1.09	0.866	2950
$T_1 = 200$ $P_1 = 0,00001$											
8040	28.3	6000	$0.107 \cdot 10^{-1}$	$0.344 \cdot 10^{-6}$	413	15.8	7750	4.09	3.45	2.87	1890
8880	31,3	7000	$0.130 \cdot 10^{-1}$	$0.331 \cdot 10^{-6}$	473	14,6	9440	4.34	0.929	0.74	2230
9370	33.0	8100	$0.144 \cdot 10^{-1}$	$0.310 \cdot 10^{-6}$	534	14.3	10500	4.45	1.28	1,06	2370
10000	35.4	9000	$0.165 \cdot 10^{-1}$	$0.306 \cdot 10^{-6}$	578	13.7	12000	4.57	2.41	2,03	2510
11200	39.6	10000	$0.208 \cdot 10^{-1}$	$0.317 \cdot 10^{-6}$	626	12.5	15100	4.78	4.41	3,63	2750
12900	45.4	11000	$0.273 \cdot 10^{-1}$	$0.333 \cdot 10^{-6}$	682	11.0	19800	5.10	6,52	5,16	3080
14700	51.7	12000	$0.356 \cdot 10^{-1}$	$0.345 \cdot 10^{-6}$	751	9.54	25700	5.50	7.31	5,65	3470

$T_1 = 400 \quad P_1 = 1$

4520	11.3	6000	160	$0.822 \cdot 10^{-2}$	485	25.4	2500	2.33	0.606	0.477	1560
5060	12.6	7000	201	$0.850 \cdot 10^{-2}$	526	24.3	3120	2.40	0.743	0.594	1700
5770	14.4	8100	263	$0.905 \cdot 10^{-2}$	563	22.9	4040	2.49	1.10	0.882	1870
6470	16.1	9000	332	$0.964 \cdot 10^{-2}$	592	21.4	5050	2.57	1.46	1.15	2030
7320	18.3	10000	428	$0.103 \cdot 10^{-1}$	630	19.7	6450	2.69	1.78	1.37	2240
8170	20.4	11000	535	$0.107 \cdot 10^{-1}$	674	18.1	8020	2.81	1.87	1.41	2470
8940	22.3	12000	640	$0.109 \cdot 10^{-1}$	724	16.7	9570	2.92	1.70	1.28	2690

$T_1 = 400 \quad P_1 = 0.01$

5190	12.9	6000	2.14	$0.987 \cdot 10^{-4}$	464	22.7	3280	2.81	1.36	1.14	1590
6410	16.0	7000	3.31	$0.116 \cdot 10^{-3}$	488	20.1	4970	3.00	2.52	2.04	1820
7930	19.7	8100	5.11	$0.131 \cdot 10^{-3}$	535	17.0	7560	3.30	2.74	2.17	2150
8840	22.0	9000	6.36	$0.133 \cdot 10^{-3}$	584	15.5	9390	3.50	1.81	1.44	2400
9450	23.5	10000	7.26	$0.130 \cdot 10^{-3}$	639	14.7	10700	3.62	1.13	0.889	2640
9890	24.6	11000	7.93	$0.126 \cdot 10^{-3}$	691	14.4	11700	3.70	1.04	0.825	2810
10300	25.8	12000	8.66	$0.123 \cdot 10^{-3}$	739	14.0	12800	3.77	1.25	1.00	2950

$T_1 = 400 \quad P_1 = 0.00001$

8280	20.6	6000	$0.568 \cdot 10^{-2}$	$0.177 \cdot 10^{-6}$	414	15.3	8260	4.26	2.61	2.18	1930
8910	22.2	7000	$0.655 \cdot 10^{-2}$	$0.166 \cdot 10^{-6}$	474	14.5	9540	4.45	0.853	0.676	2240
9450	23.6	8100	$0.735 \cdot 10^{-2}$	$0.156 \cdot 10^{-6}$	534	14.1	10700	4.57	1.58	1.33	2360
10300	25.6	9000	$0.869 \cdot 10^{-2}$	$0.157 \cdot 10^{-6}$	577	13.4	12700	4.71	3.12	2.63	2530
11700	29.2	10000	$0.114 \cdot 10^{-1}$	$0.165 \cdot 10^{-6}$	626	12.0	16500	4.99	5.61	4.57	2810
13600	33.9	11000	$0.153 \cdot 10^{-1}$	$0.175 \cdot 10^{-6}$	687	10.3	22200	5.39	7.64	5.99	3180
15500	38.6	12000	$0.198 \cdot 10^{-1}$	$0.179 \cdot 10^{-6}$	762	8.89	28600	5.85	7.30	5.67	3600

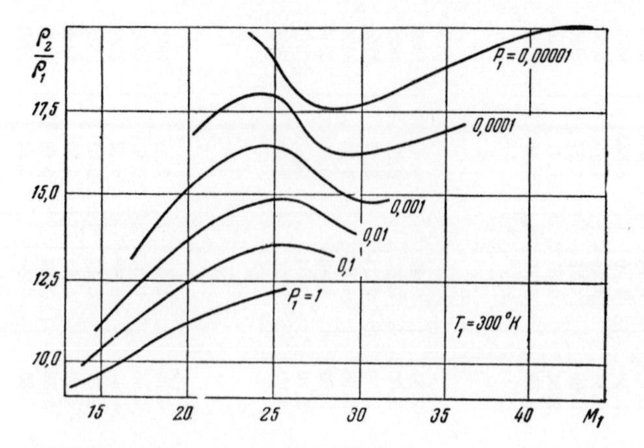

Fig. 5
Density ratio $\frac{\rho_2}{\rho^1}$ as a function of M_1 .

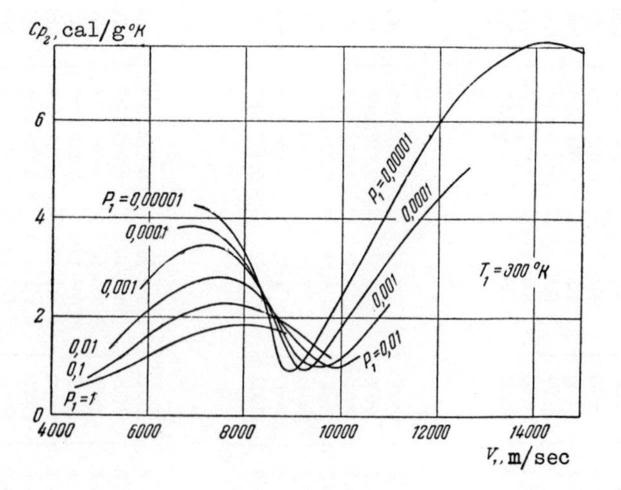

Fig. 6
Variation of specific heat at constant pressure c_{p_2} with V_1 .

The foregoing table is of thermodynamic and gas dynamic values for a normal shock as a function of the velocity for $T_1 = 200°$ and 400°K and three pressures in front of the shock.

REFERENCES

1. Thermodynamic properties of air between 1000° and 12,000°K and 0.001 to 1000 atm. First paper in this book.
2. P.S. EPSTEIN, Kurs termodinamiki (Course of Thermodynamics) (Translation into Russian).
3. R. SAUER, Techeniya szhimayemoi zhidkosti (Flow of Compressible Liquids) (Translation into Russian) (1954).

N.F. Gorban

Determination of Gas-dynamic Properties of Flow Behind a Normal Shock Wave with Correction for Variable Specific Heats and Dissociation of Air

1. Statement of the Problem

It is required to determine the equation for the pressure p_2, the density ρ_2 the temperature T_2, the speed V_2, the Mach number M_2, the sonic velocity a_2 and the ratio $\frac{C_{p_2}}{C_{v_2}} = \gamma_2$ in the flow directly behind a normal shock in air with variable specific heats and dissociation, as a function of the speed V_1 before the shock and the flight altitude H.

In solving this problem it was assumed that the state of the gas behind the shock is that of thermodynamic equilibrium, the change from the equilibrium state before the shock to that after it being instantaneous. Heat loss from the air by radiation was not allowed for in calculating the temperature of the air behind the shock.

2. Method of Solution

At present only graphical methods are known for determining gas-dynamic quantities of flow directly behind a normal shock, with correction for variable specific heats and dissociation. This procedure is not always rational. Thus, for instance, an enormous number of graphs would have to be plotted for solving the problem over a wide range of speeds and heights. This would take a lot of time, and the accuracy of the results might in certain cases not be high enough. The graphical method also represents a failure to take advantage of the high-speed electronic computing machines available in the U.S.S.R.

In view of this, we devoted our attention to working out an analytical method of calculating gas-dynamic quantities for the flow behind a shock wave with which it would be possible to use present computing aids.

Various methods of solving the problem analytically were investigated. From the theoretical studies a method was selected, giving a simple solution of the problem.

For determination of the ratio between the gas-dynamic properties before and behind a normal shock the following equations can be written:

$\rho_1 v_1 = \rho_2 v_2$ (1) Continuity

$i_1 + \frac{V_1^2}{2gJ} = i_2 + \frac{V_2^2}{2gJ}$ (2) conservation of energy

$\rho_1 V_1^2 + p_1 = \rho_2 V_2^2 + p_2$ (3) conservation of momentum

$\frac{\rho_1 \mu_1}{\rho_1 T_1} = R_{univ} g$ (4) Clapeyron equation

$\frac{\rho_2 \mu_2}{\rho_2 T_2} = R_{univ} g$ (5) Clapeyron equation

$\left.\begin{array}{l} i = f(p, T) \\ \mu = F(p, T) \end{array}\right\}$ (6) thermodynamic dependences of the enthalpy and molecular weight of air on pressure and temperature.

A solution of the problem of determination of the gas-dynamic quantities in a flow directly behind a shock wave from specified gas-dynamic quantities in the flow in front of the shock leads to functional equations the solution of which is extremely laborious. Hence to determine the ratio of the gas-dynamic quantities before a shock to those after it, it is most rational to determine ρ_1, p_1, V_1, ρ_2 and V_2 from specified values of $p_2, T_2, T_1, \mu_1, i_1, \mu_2, i_2$ by analytical solution of equations (1)-(5). The enthalpy and molecular weight are determined from tables for specified T_2 and p_2. The values of the molecular weight and enthalpy of air before a shock can be taken as constant for a specified temperature T_1 before the shock. From (1)-(5) we see that the number of unknowns is equal to the number of equations and hence the quantities sought, ρ_1; p_1; V_1, ρ_2; V_2 can easily be found from these equations. The simplest solution of the equations is obtained for V_1, corresponding to the specified temperature and pressure behind the shock wave. By simple transformations we can easily obtain the following system of equations from (1)-(5):

$$V_1 + \frac{p_1}{\rho_1 V_1} = V_2 + \frac{p_2}{\rho_2 V_2} \tag{8}$$

$$\frac{p_1}{\rho_1} = \frac{R^* T_1}{\mu_1}, \quad \text{where. } R^* = gR_{univ}. \tag{9}$$

$$\frac{p_2}{\rho_2} = \frac{R^* \cdot T_2}{\mu_2} \tag{10}$$

$$i_1 + \frac{1}{k} V_1^2 = i_2 + \frac{1}{k} V_2^2, \quad \text{where } k = 2gJ \tag{11}$$

$$\begin{gathered} V_2^2 = k(i_1 - i_2) + V_1^2 \\ V_2 = \sqrt{k(i_1 - i_2) + V_1^2} \\ V_1 + \frac{R^* \cdot T_1}{\mu_1 V_1} = V_2 + \frac{R^* T_3}{\mu_2 V_2}, \end{gathered} \tag{12}$$

where

$$V_1 + \frac{R^* T_1}{\mu_1 V_1} = \sqrt{V_1^2 = k(i_1 - i_2)} + \frac{R^* \cdot T_2}{\mu_2 \sqrt{V_1^2 + k(i_1 - i_2)}}$$

Solving this system for the speed before the shock V_1, we obtain:

$$\mu_1\mu_2V_1^2\sqrt{V_1^2+k(i_1-i_2)}+R^*T_1\mu_2\sqrt{V_1^2+k(i_1-i_2)}=$$
$$=\mu_1\mu_2V_1[V_1^2+k(i_1-i_2)]+R^*T_2\mu_1V_1;$$

$$\mu_1^2\mu_2^2V_1^4[V_1^2+k(i_1-i_2)]+2R^*T_1\mu_1\mu_2^2V_1^2[V_1^2+k(i_1-i_2)]+$$
$$+R^{*2}T_1^2\mu_2^2[V_1^2+k(i_1-i_2)]=\mu_1^2\mu_2^2V_1^2[V_1^2+k(i_1-i_2)]^2+$$
$$+2R^*T_2\mu_1^2\mu_2^2V_1^2[V_1^2+k(i_1-i_2)]+R^{*2}T_2^2\mu_1^2V_1^2;$$
$$\mu_1^2\mu_2^2V_1^6+[\mu_1^2\mu_2^2k(i_1-i_2)+2R^*T_1\mu_1\mu_1^2]V_1^4+$$
$$+[2R^*T_1\mu_1\mu_2^2k(i_1-i_2)+R^{*2}T_1^2\mu_2^2]V_1^2+R^{*2}T_1^2\mu_2^2k(i_1-i_1)=\mu_1^2\mu_2^2V_1^6+$$
$$+[2\mu_1^2\mu_2^2+k(i_1-i_2)+2R^*T_2\mu_1^2\mu_2]V_1^4+[\mu_1^2\mu_2^2k^2(i_1-i_2)^2+$$
$$+2R^*T_2\mu_1^2\mu_2k(i_1-i_2)+R^{*2}T_2^2\mu_1^2]V_1^2;$$
$$[\mu_1^2\mu_2^2k(i_1-i_2)+2\mu_1\mu_2R^*(\mu_1T_2-\mu_2T_1)]V_1^4+[\mu_1^2\mu_2^2k^2(i_1-i_2)^2+$$
$$+2\mu_1\mu_2R^*k(i_1-i_2)(\mu_1T_2-\mu_2T_1)+R^{*2}(\mu_1^2T_2^2-\mu_2^2T_1^2)]V_1^2-$$
$$-R^{*2}T_1^2\mu_2^2k(i_1-i_2)=0$$

Putting

$$A=\mu_1^2\mu_2^2k(i_1-i_2)+2\mu_1\mu_2R^*(\mu_1T_2-\mu_2T_1)$$
$$B=\mu_1^2\mu_2^2k^2(i_1-i_2)^2+2\mu_1\mu_2R^*k(i_1-i_2)(\mu_1T_2-\mu_2T_1)+R^{*2}(\mu_1^2T_2^2-\mu_2^2T_1^2)$$
$$C=R^{*2}T_1^2\mu_2^2k(i_1-i_2),$$

the equation for V_1 becomes

$$AV_1^4+BV_1^2+C=0,$$
$$V_1^2=y,\quad AC^2+By+C=0,$$
$$y=\frac{-B\pm\sqrt{B^2-4AC}}{2A}$$

Knowing V_1, it is easy to determine

$$V_2=\sqrt{V_1^2+k(i_1-i_2)}\qquad \rho_2=\frac{p_2\mu_2}{R^*T_2},$$
$$\rho_1=\rho_2\frac{V_2}{V_1}\text{and}\,p_1=\rho_1\frac{R^*T_1}{\mu_1}.$$

If the system of equations (8)-(12) is solved for the speed after the shock V_2, we obtain a biquadratic equation of the same type

$$AV_2^4+BV_2^2+C=0,$$

where

$$A=\mu_1^2\mu_2^2k(i_1-i_2)+2\mu_1\mu_2R^*(T_1\mu_2-T_2\mu_1)$$
$$B=\mu_1^2\mu_2^2k^2(i_1-i_2)^2+2R^*\mu_1\mu_2k(i_2-i_1)(T_1\mu_2-T_2\mu_1)+R^{*2}(T_1^2\mu_2^2+T_2^2\mu_1^2)$$
$$C=-R^{*2}T_2^2\mu_1^2k(i_2-i_1).$$

Thus A, B and C for the solution of the equations for V_2 differ from the A, B and C for their solution for V_1 only in a change in the subscripts for enthalpy, temperature and molecular weight of air. Solution of the systems of equations (8)-(12) for air pressure before the shock gives

$$Ap_1^3+Bp_1^2+Cp_1+D=0,$$

where

$$A = R^*T_1T_2(\mu_1T_2)^2$$
$$B = [\mu_2k(i_2 - i_1) - R^*T_1T_2]\,p_2(\mu_1T_2)^2$$
$$C = [\mu_1k(i_2 - i_1) + R^*T_1T_2]\,p_2(\mu_1T_2)^2$$
$$D = R^*T_1T_2(p_2\mu_2)^2T_1^2p_2 .$$

In the solution of the system of equations (8)-(12) for air density before the shock, ρ_1, we obtain an equation of the type

$$A\rho_1^3 + B\rho_1^2 + C\rho_1 + D = 0 ,$$

where

$$A = R^*T_1\mu_2 ,$$
$$B = [k(i_2 - i_1)\mu_1\frac{R^*T_2}{p_2} - R^*T_1\mu_2] ,$$
$$C = \frac{R^*T_2}{p_2}[k(i_2 - i_1)\mu_1 + R^*T_1] ,$$
$$D = R^*T_2\mu_1\frac{p_1T_2}{p_2\mu_2} .$$

From an analysis of the equations for V_1; V_2; $p_1$and ρ_1 we can conclude that to solve the problem we must use the equation for V_1 as the simplest and most characteristic initial quantity. The biquadratic equation for V_1 can easily be solved. With a large number of systems of equations, for a wide range of heights and speeds, the problem for determining the ratio between the gas-dynamic quantities before and after the shock can be successfully solved by a computing machine. The use, in the present work, of the above method of calculating the flight velocity V_1 for calculating the relations of gas-dynamic flow quantities, in the case of a normal shock, made it possible to increase the accuracy in determining the unknown quantities, to reduce considerably the time needed for working out the problem, and to reduce considerably the cost of the calculations. The calculations in our work were made for two mean temperatures of the air T_1 before the shock, 220° and 350°K, selected as the averages from the variations of the minimum and maximum temperature of air with height (Fig. 1). Since at the flight speeds of

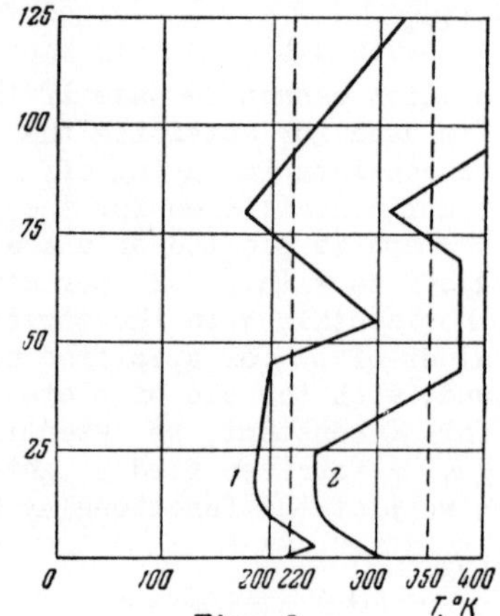

Fig. 1

Variation of air temperature with height: 1 - probable minimum; 2 - probable maximum.

interest the effect of T_1 on the values of T_2; V_2; ρ_2; V_1 is small, these quantities were calculated only for T_1 = 220°K. For T_1 = 350°K, the corresponding value of p_1 was determined by simple proportion:

$$(p_1)_{350} \cong (p_1)_{220} \frac{350}{220}.$$

The values of T_2;V_2; V_1;ρ_2;ρ_1 at T_1 = 350°K were taken as equal to the values of the same quantities for 220°K. The calculations yielded the upper limit of the after-shock pressure, corresponding to the selected pre-shock temperature at which p_1 did not exceed one atm. The ratios between the pre- and after-shock gas-dynamic quantities were determined from the thermodynamic equations $\mu = f(p; T)$ and $i = F(p; T)$ found from 2000° to 8000°K and from 0.0001 to 420 atm.

With the aid of tables of the ratios of pre- and after-shock gas-dynamic quantities, the following functions were plotted

1. $p_1 = f(V_1)$
2. $V_2 = f(V_1)$
3. $T_2 = f(V_1)$
4. $\rho_2 = f(V_1)$ at $p_2 = \text{const}$.
5. $a_2 = f(V_1)$
6. $\gamma_2 = f(V_1)$

for constant after-shock pressure p_2. Graphs of p_1 against V_1 were plotted for T_1=220° and T_1=350°K. It is difficult to use the indicated correlations for practical calculations. It is desirable to know the dependence of the gas-dynamic quantities for the flow immediately after the shock on the same quantities before it, and they can be found in two ways.

In the first, with the tables obtained the value of V_1 is found by linear interpolation for the selected values of p_1 for specified pressures after the shock, and from this value the corresponding values of T_2; ρ_2; V_2; α_2; γ_2 are found from tables. This interpolation method makes it unnecessary to use graphs, so that the problem is solved purely analytically.

However, this interpolation cannot be made if the second method of solving the problem is used for obtaining the required correlations. The second method consists in laying off on the graph of $p_1 = f(V_1)$ for p_2 = const horizontal lines for the pressure of the undisturbed flow. This graph is plotted on a scale which enables values of V_1 to be read off to within 0.25 per cent from the points of intersection of the horizontals with the curve; from these V_1s we can determine the values of p_2 for specified heights. From the values of V_1 and p_2 found, with the aid of plots of γ_2, T_2, ρ_2, V_2 and a_2 against V_1 for p_2 constant, we determine the corresponding values of T_2; ρ_2; V_2; a_2; γ_2 for specified heights. Having determined these quantities, we plot the functions (at H and ρ_1 constant)

1. $p_2 = f(V_1)$
2. $T_2 = f(V_1)$
3. $V_2 = f(V_1)$
4. $\rho_2 = f(V_1)$
5. $a_2 = f(V_1)$

6. $\gamma_2 = f(V_1)$
7. $M_2 = f(V_1)$
8. $\frac{p_2}{p_1} = f(V_1)$
9. $\rho_2/\rho_1 = f(V_1)$
10. $V_2/V_1 = f(V_1)$

The second method is used at present, since the accuracy of the values thus obtained is sufficient for practical calculations, with appropriate choice of the scales for the plots of p_1, T_2, etc., against V_1 for ρ_2 constant, and the solution of the problem is greatly simplified. The value of p_1 for the height selected was determined from Fig. 2, representing $\log \frac{p_H}{p_{H=0}}$ against H.

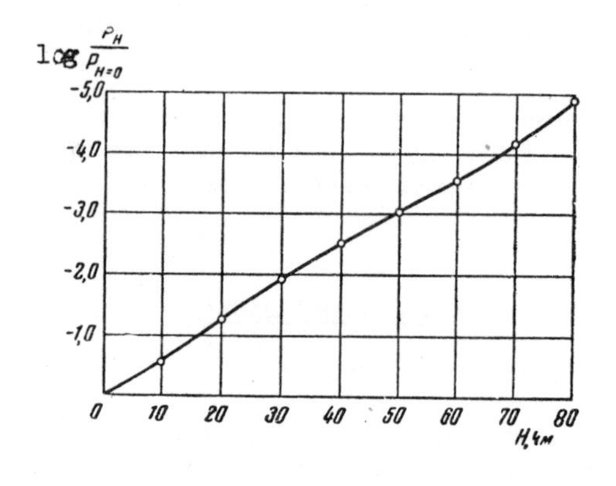

Fig. 2
Variation of log of the ratio of air pressure at height H to pressure at zero height, with the height.

To determine the gas-dynamic properties of throttled flow T_{00}, p_{00} and ρ_{00} to a first approximation the following equations can be used

$$1.\ \frac{p_{00}}{p_2} = \left(1 + \frac{\gamma_2 - 1}{2} M_2^2\right)^{\frac{\gamma_2}{\gamma_2 - 1}} \tag{13}$$

$$2.\ \frac{T_{00}}{T_2} = \left(1 + \frac{\gamma_2 - 1}{2} M_2^2\right) \tag{14}$$

$$3.\ \frac{\rho_{00}}{\rho_2} = \left(1 + \frac{\gamma_2 - 1}{1} M_2^2\right)^{\frac{1}{\gamma_2 - 1}} \tag{15}$$

Since M_2 is small, and the variations in γ_2 with temperature and pressure are small also, equations (13)-(15) can be used for practical calculations. After the variations of T_{00}, etc., with V_1 for each selected altitude were determined, plots were made of the variations of these quantities with T_1 for constant altitude.

3. Results of Calculations

The gas-dynamic properties of air after a normal shock were determined by the method of calculation proposed over a range of flight speeds from 2000 to 8500 m/sec, and for heights of 0, 2.5, 5, 10, 15, 20, 25, 30, 35, 45, 50, 60, 70 and 80 km. These calculations yielded tables of the relations between the gas-dynamic quantities before and after a normal shock for constant p_2.

Each table was obtained for a single constant value of p_2, and with T_2 varying from 2000 to 8000°K, and for the following values of p_1 in atmospheres: 0.0001; 0.001; 0.002; 0.006; 0.008; 0.01; 0.02; 0.04; 0.06; 0.08; 0.1; 0.2; 0.3; 0.4; 0.5; 0.6; 0.7; 0.8; 0.9; 1; 2; 3; 4; 5; 6; 7; 8; 9; 10; 11; 13; 15; 17; 19; 20; 22; 30; 32; 40; 42; 50; 60; 70; 80; 90; 100; 110; 120; 130; 140; 150; 160; 170; 180; 190; 200; 210; 220; 230; 240; 250; 260; 270; 280; 290; 300; 310; 320; 330; 340; 350; 360; 370; 380; 390; 400; 410; 420.

The tabulated results made it possible to calculate the dependence of the gas-dynamic properties of the flow after a normal shock on the flight speed for all selected heights, for $T_1 = 220$°K and $T_1 = 350$°K.

4. Conclusions

The following conclusions emerge:

1. The effects of dissociation and variable specific heat of air are very considerable for flight speeds of 2500 m/sec and above.

2. The temperature of the air before the shock substantially affects only the pressure and density of air after the shock.

3. The temperature of the air before the shock, between 220 and 350°K, does not substantially affect T_2, a_2 and M_2 after the shock.

5. Comparative Analysis of the Gas-Dynamic Properties of Flow after a Normal Shock as Obtained by Different Methods, Allowing for Variable Specific Heat and Air Dissociation

For calculating gas-dynamic properties of flow after a normal shock at the Energy Institute of the U.S.S.R. Academy of Sciences we used the thermodynamic relations $\mu = F(p; T)$ and $i = f(p, T)$ obtained on the assumption that the energy of dissociation of NO is 6.49 eV and that of nitrogen (N_2) 9.76 eV. In his calculations about normal shocks Vanichev assumed that the vibrational, rotational and electronic statistical sums have multiplicity and that the energy of dissociation of N_2 is 7.38 eV and that of NO 5.29 eV. Moore's data, as we succeeded in finding out, are based on the same values for dissociation energies (7.38 and 5.29 eV).

Figs. 3 and 4 show the variations of the pressure ratios $\frac{p_2}{p_1}$ with V_1 for constant $p_2 = 1.033 \times 10^4$ kg/m^2 (one standard atmosphere) for $T_1 = 220°K$ and $T_1 = 350°K$. Differences in the values of the dissociation energies of nitrogen and NO, adopted for calculating

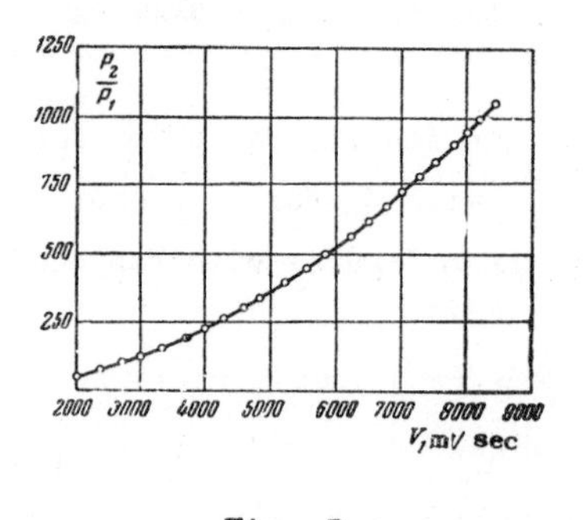

Fig. 3
Variation of ratio of pressure after to pressure before a normal shock with the flight speed

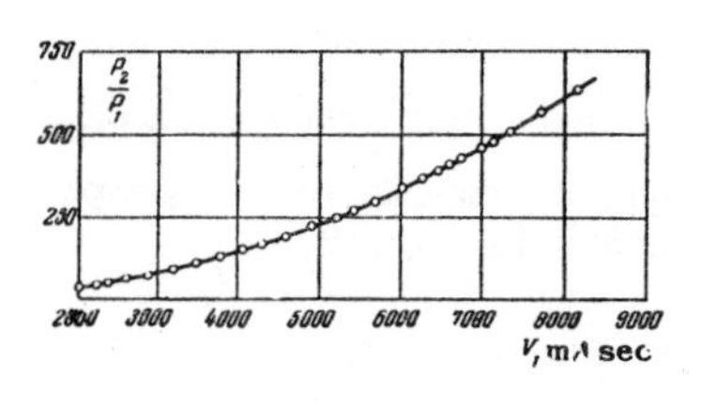

Fig. 4
Variation of $\frac{p_2}{p_1}$ with flight speed

the thermodynamic properties of air, do not affect the variation of the pressure ratio with V_1 at constant p_2.

Fig. 5 shows the variation of T_2 with V_1 for $p_2 = 1$ standard atmosphere at $T_1 = 220°K$.

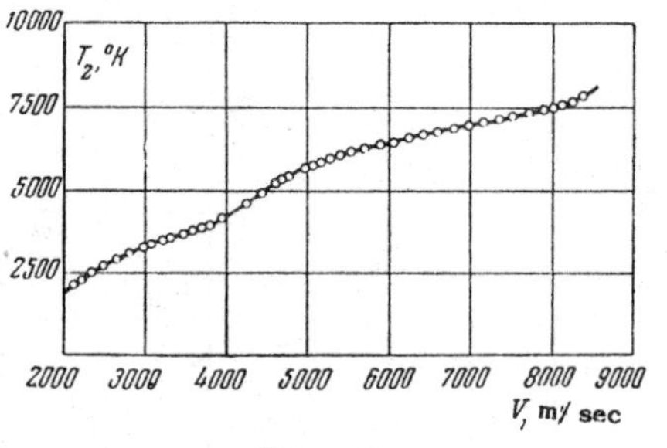

Fig. 5
Variation of T_2 with V_1

We used the thermodynamic variations of μ and i with p and T obtained for the higher values of the dissociation energies, and our plot of T_2 against V_1 lies 6-8 per cent above that given by other authors between 2000 and 4000 m/sec, and about 25 per cent above it in the range 5000-7000 m/sec. The reason is that with the higher values of the dissociation energies of nitrogen and NO the degrees of dissociation are smaller, and therefore the temperature of the air will be higher. Between 2000 and 4000 m/sec before the shock, only the dissociation energy of NO is important, so that in this region the difference in temperatures T_2 is small.

Between 5000 and 7000 m/sec before the shock nitrogen dissociation is important. In this range the difference in temperatures will be greater, since the nitrogen dissociation energies we used are 2.38 eV greater than those used by Moore, and nitrogen is the main constituent of air. It is now known from published information that the energies we used are closer to the truth than Moore's figures.

Figs. 6 and 7 show the variations of the density ratio $\frac{\rho_2}{\rho_1}$ for air before and after a shock, and of $\frac{V_2}{V_1}$ with V_1 for p_2 = one standard atmosphere. A comparison of these figures with Vanichev's is shown in Fig. 8.

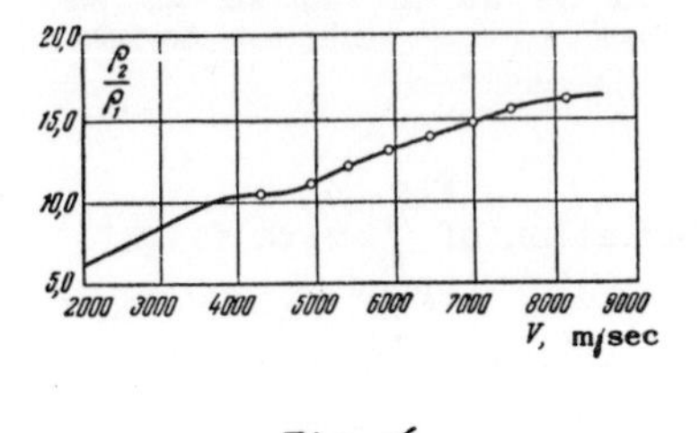

Fig. 6
Variation of the ratio of densities before and after a normal shock with the flight speed.

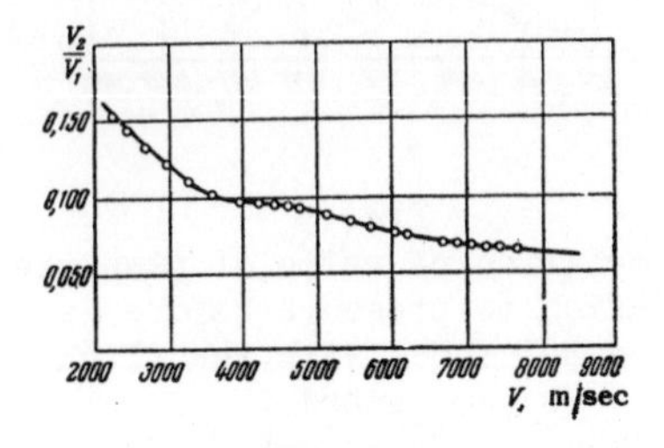

Fig. 7
Variation of the ratio of flight speeds before and after a normal shock with the flight speed.

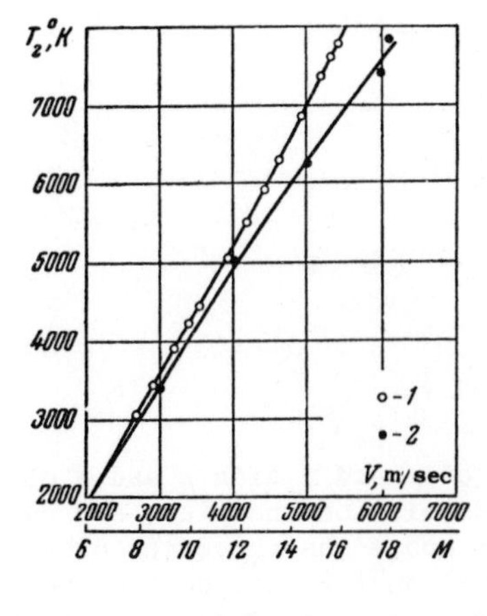

Fig. 8
Temperature after a normal shock: variation with V_1, as calculated by (1) the author, (2) Vanichev.

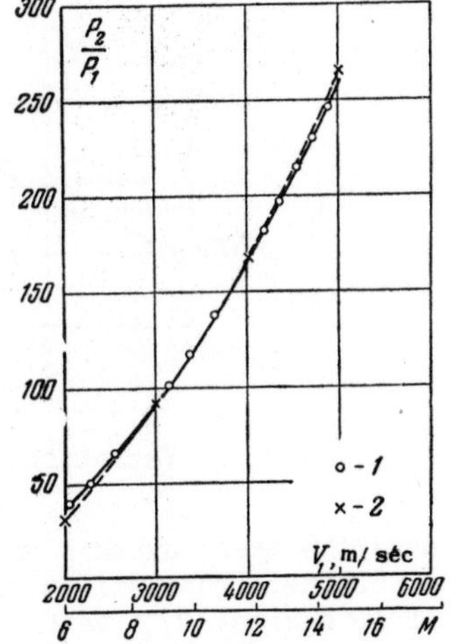

Fig. 9
Ratio of air pressure after a normal shock to that before it: variation with flight speed as calculated by (1) the author, (2) Vanichev.

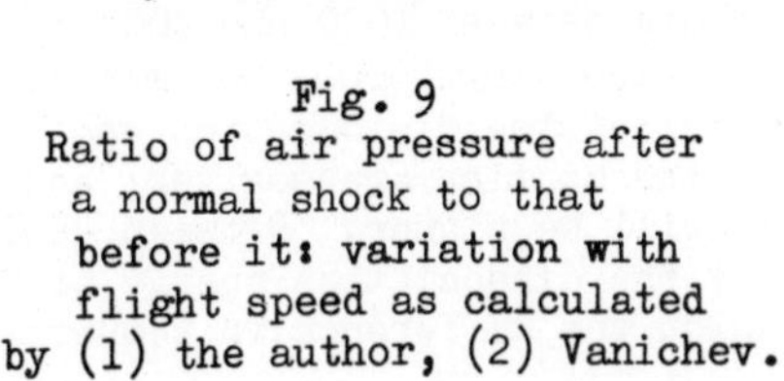

Fig. 8 shows the variation of T_2 with V_1 at zero height and $T_1 = 300°$ K. The T_2 obtained by the present author is higher than Vanichev's, mainly because the latter in his calculations used thermodynamic properties of air based on lower values of the dissociation energies of nitrogen and NO.

Fig. 9 shows the variation of $\frac{p_2}{p_1}$ with V_1 at zero height and $T_1 = 300°$K as calculated by the author and by Vanichev respectively. As would be expected, the differences in the dissociation energies adopted in the calculations do not affect matters here.

The data obtained by the author and by Vanichev, in Fig. 7, are practically the same.

Fig. 10 shows the variation of M_2 with V_1 for constant p_2 of 1 atm and $T_1 = 220°$K, as calculated by the author.

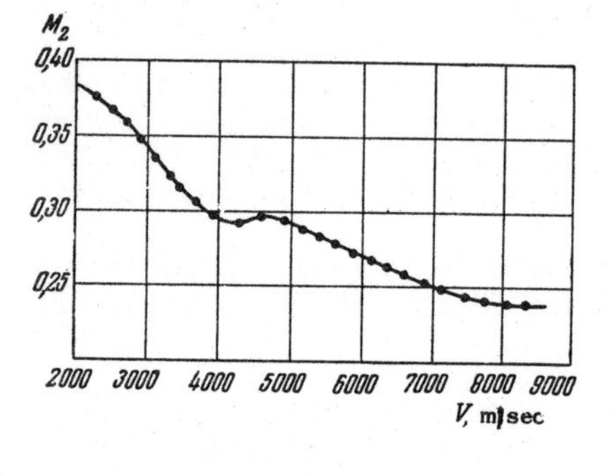

Fig. 10
Variation of M_2 with V_1.

The comparison of the author's and Vanichev's calculations shows that in some cases the selected values of the dissociation energies of nitrogen and NO can substantially affect the results. At 4000°K and above, a more accurate method must also be used for calculating statistical sums, a point which Vanichev, for instance, did not always observe.

V.P. Motulevich

Flow of Gas from a Nozzle Cut in an Oblique Plane

I. Optical Study of the Process

It is well known that oblique cutting is constructionally unavoidable in the nozzles of all turbines.

The striving to reduced weight and size of machines, which is particularly marked in transport turbines, increases the pressure drops in single-stage turbines. By virtue of this the gas can partially expand in the region of the oblique cut.

The flow of a gas from an oblique cut has many special features, strongly affecting the form of the gas flow in front of the blade wheel.

Before we attempt to give a quantitative analysis of the phenomenon studied, we should attentively study its basic qualitative characteristics. It is more sensible to solve this part of the problem with the Toepler optical apparatus. This paper briefly describes the experimental method and results.

All experiments on flow from an oblique-cut grating were made on a gas-dynamic stand [1], [2] with the aid of a universal nozzle fixed to the convergent part of the inlet pipe from the pressure chamber.

Fig. 1 illustrates the nozzle. The channel in which the blade is fixed consists of two symmetrical steel parts with carefully ground working surfaces, forming a convergent nozzle when assembled. The inlet part of the latter, to simplify technique, was made an arc of a circle of radius 25 mm, and the working part was a flat channel, 12 mm high and about 38 mm wide. The comparatively small height of the channel, which increased the relative end errors in studying flow by the Toepler method, was due to the insufficient power of the pumps used.

The outlet section of the nozzle was inclined at 45° to the nozzle axis, which made it possible, with a working blade length of 45 mm, to change the anglè of cut of the grating from 90° to 19° using the whole width of the channel, and to still lower values when only part of it was used.

The experiments were made with steel plates measuring 45 × 12 × × 0.5 mm, placed in the channel in any particular order which made it possible to study flow from one, two or three channels over a fairly wide range of cut angles at the outlet from the grating. The leading ends of the plates, in the core of the flow, were centred symmetrically, while the extreme end blades were displaced to one side, practically flush with the side walls of the nozzle.

The width of the individual channels was kept unchanged (at about 12 mm) irrespectively of their number. The unused part of the nozzle was closed with a flange around which flow could be smooth.

The blades were fixed in the channel by friction. The compression applied to them was small enough not to create appreciable warping of the sides.

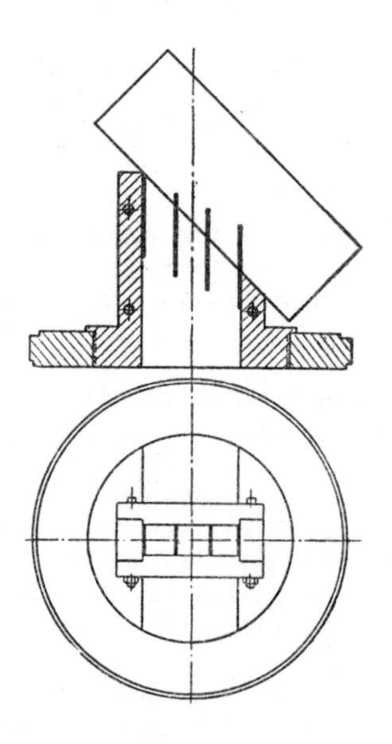

Fig. 1
Diagram of nozzle

The necessary accuracy of assembly was ensured by using a set of end gauges.

The ends of the blades and plates projecting beyond the oblique-cut base of the nozzle were flexibly clamped between two plates of optical glass. These plates on the one hand ensured that the configuration of the channel remained constant during the experiment (their shape may be upset by bending of the blades by the gas flow) and on the other hand made it possible to observe the flow and to make photographs with the Toepler apparatus.

Points of possible ingress of gas in the joints between the end surfaces of glass and metal, and between the glass and the ends of the extreme blades forming the channels were carefully sealed with vacuum wax, which was found to seal satisfactorily.

A flat model of an annular nozzle for a turbine is a lattice with an infinite number of channels, which also should be investigated. To do this by experiment is obviously impossible, but it was found that as the number of channels in a grating with a finite number of channels increases, a point comes at which the flow pattern in the middle filaments practically ceases to change. This makes it possible to get an idea about the special features of gas flow in an infinitely large grating from the flow pattern in the central channel of a fairly large, though finite, lattice.

The maximum number of channels in our experiments was only three, because the pumps used were of low power. But even here the flow pattern in the central filament gave important information about the behaviour of gas in flowing from an infinite lattice.

The object of our work was to explain the qualitative aspects of the phenomenon by isolating the physical factors which determine the pattern of the flow from an oblique-cut lattice of a nozzle apparatus.

To find out the flow pattern for supercritical pressure drops with the oblique section, tests were made with lattices consisting of one and two adjacent channels as well as with a three-channel one.

Let us analyse the experimental results, starting with the experiments made with a single jet.

It is extremely desirable to examine the behaviour of a single jet with different angles of cut and the same pressure ratio in a study of lattices consisting of two or more channels. To analyse the effect of pressure ratio, let us consider the flow of gas from a channel with a section angle α of 35°.

Fig. 2 shows a series of photographs from the right of the blade (left column) and from above it (right column), the letter δ denoting the ratio of the pressure in the pressure chamber to the pressure in front of the nozzle. As would be expected, disturbance lines first of all appear at the critical pressure ratio of 0.528 (frame 2). Starting from $\delta = 0.461$ (frames 5 and 6) the wedge-shaped expansion wave at the end of the lower blade (Meyer type flow) becomes quite clear. As δ decreases, the wedge includes a larger and larger amount of the upper blade, until finally at δ 0.265 (frames 11 and 12) the rarefaction wave does not go outside it. At this time the gas flowing along the upper boundary is over-expanded to a pressure below that in the chamber, so that a shock forms, running from the edge of the upper blade downwards along the flow to intersection with the lower boundary of the latter. From the lower boundary the compression wave is reflected as a new cuneiform rarefaction wave, etc. As δ decreases, the deviation of

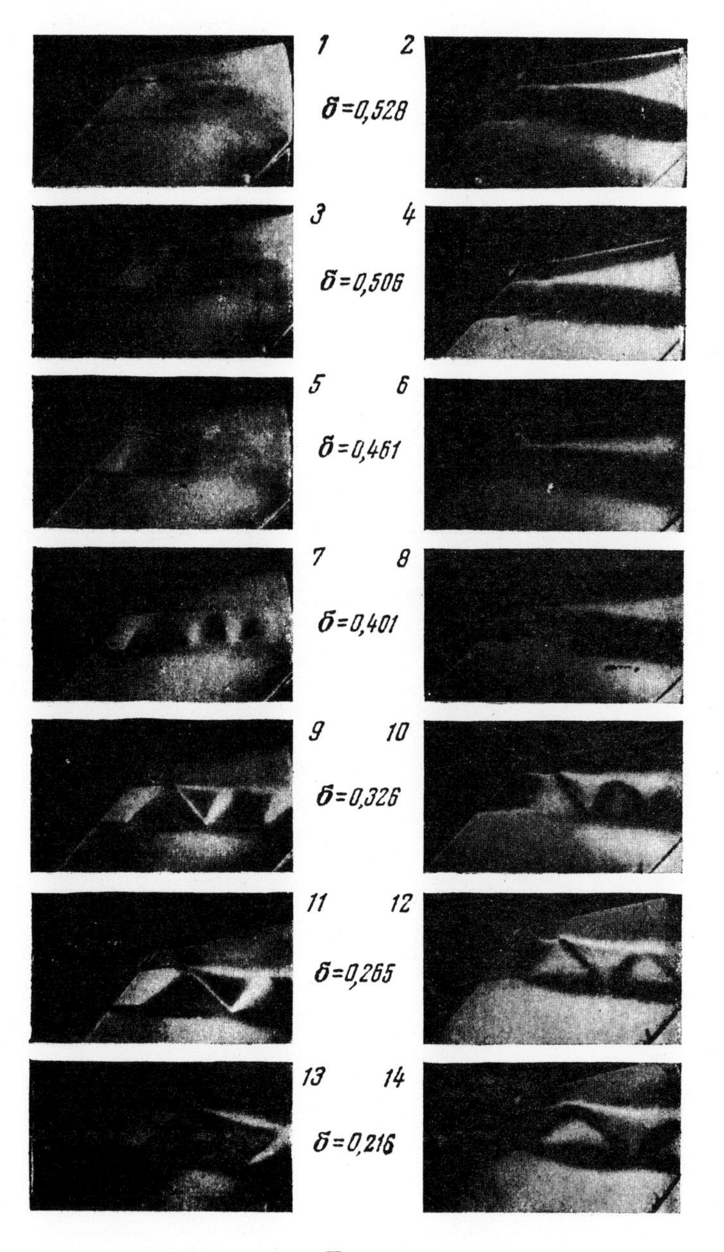

Fig. 2
Flow of gas from a channel with $\alpha = 35°$

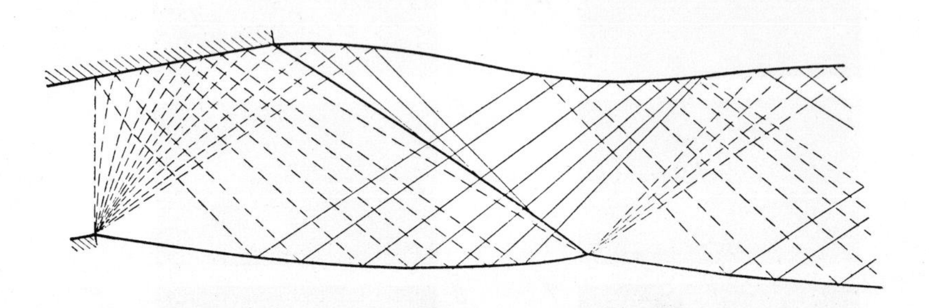

Fig. 3
Results of calculations, by the characteristic method, relating to flow of gas from a channel with $\alpha = 35°$

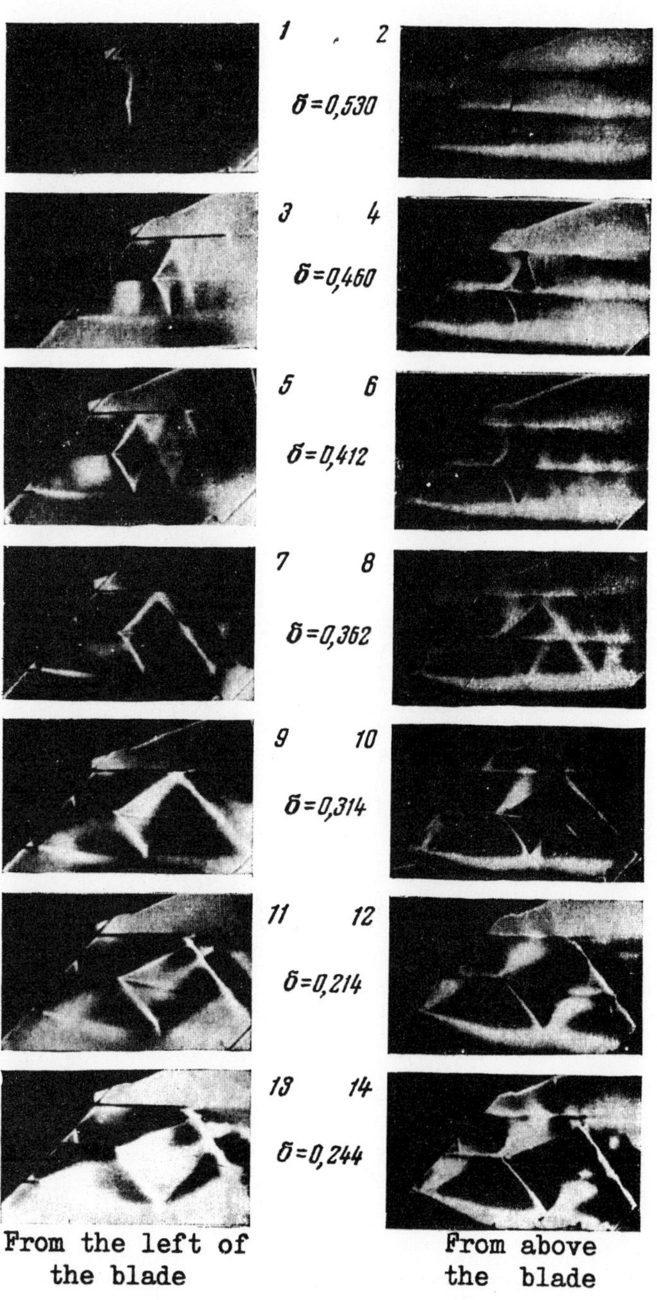

Fig. 4
Flow of gas from two adjacent channels with $\alpha = 25°$

the filament from the axis of the nozzle increases. To get a clearer idea of the behaviour of a jet with different pressure ratios, calculations were made by the characteristics method [3] for δ = 0.216, and the results of these fairly satisfactorily agree with experiment (Fig. 3). The calculation had as its sole object to get a qualitative picture, and therefore, to speed it up, the characteristics of the shock, shown in the pictures by heavy lines, were calculated in a simplified way from the characteristic diagram without using a shock polar. This of course reduces the accuracy. In Fig. 3 the compression lines are shown as continuous, the rarefaction lines as broken, lines.

The dimensions of the channels used for studying the interaction of two jets were made equal to those of the channel for one jet. Fig. 4 shows photos of the flow of two adjacent jets with a cut angle of 25°. As for $\alpha = 90°$, starting from the critical pressure drop, a shock starts from the middle of the blade; it is reflected from the solid wall also as a shock, and from the free surface as a cuneiform expansion wave. Starting from $\delta = 0.460$ (frames 3 and 4) it will be seen that a compression line proceeds downwards along the flow from the edge of the uppermost projecting blade, and gradually transforms into a shock wave as the pressure drop increases. This initially blends with the reflected shock wave, starting from the middle of the blade (frames 9 and 10), and with further fall of δ exists independently; at a δ of 0.314 and below, its start is displaced from the edge of the blade upwards along the flow. This is of course due to breakaway of the boundary layer. The reasons for the formation of this compression wave are the same as in a single jet. Formed in the upper jet, this wave, refracted at the boundary, goes over into the second jet and only from the free boundary of the latter is it reflected as a cuneiform rarefaction wave. As in the case of a single jet, the deflection of the flow increases as the pressure drop increases.

There is nothing novel in the behaviour of three jets by comparison with that of two and one. Here also at the edges of a blade with a flow on both sides thereof, two shocks form, which appreciably affect the pattern of the rest of the jet. Change of the pressure drop, as before, increases the deflection of the flow, which in the case in point was not so noteworthy in view of the extremely large value of the minimum δ.

From our study of the behaviour of the middle of the jet we can already get an idea about how the jet should behave in an infinite lattice.

Let us analyse in somewhat greater detail the flow in the middle of the jet. The fan-shaped rarefaction wave, starting from the short side of the channel, is reflected as a line of elementary rarefaction from the opposite wall and strikes the boundary between two adjacent jets.

At the end of the blade with a flow on both sides two tail shocks are formed. One of them is reflected from the solid wall again as a shock, and the other strikes the eddy trace formed by the blade and, interacting with it, is partially reflected and partially transmitted into the adjacent jet.

From this purely qualitative analysis of the intensity of the perturbations arising in the flow, based on its appearance, it can be concluded that the following are the factors that exert the basic influence on the flow pattern close to the plane of the cut:

a) a primary fan-shaped rarefaction wave, starting from the short wall of the channel (let us call this wave a);
b) a secondary rarefaction wave, formed by reflection of wave a from the solid wall (wave b);
c) part of the tail shock, intersecting the region of oblique cut (shock c);
d) a shock produced by reflection of shock c from the solid wall (shock d);
e) part of the tail shock, going outside the region of the oblique cut (shock e).

All other perturbations arising in the interaction of shocks with solid walls, with jet boundaries and with one another are of subordinate importance.

This qualitative conclusion is fairly well supported by quantitative experiments reported in [4].

Let us analyse how all the above factors affect the direction of the streamline in flow. Starting from the general principle that the components of the vector of increase of speed by the corresponding perturbation lines (small and large) are perpendicular and that it is directed to the low pressure region, we can conclude that the rarefaction wave a and the shocks d and e can deflect the flow towards the normal to the plane of the cut, while rarefaction wave b and shock c act in the opposite direction. On this basis, it is easy to see what should be the form of the streamline in the oblique cut region.

In view of the experimental discovery that only the primary and reflected rarefaction waves exert a basic influence on the flow pattern, apart from the shocks, and also arguing from a visual study of the boundary between adjacent jets, we can conclude that as an approximation it is permissible to assume that there is no reflection of wave b from the boundary between adjacent jets. The latter should in outline coincide with the form of the walls of the supersonic part of the ideal Laval nozzle.

Thus even a purely qualitative analysis shows that the flow at the outlet from an oblique cut is quite heterogeneous. This once again shows that most of the normal methods of calculation, based on one-dimensional flow, are inherently defective. With them it is impossible to estimate sufficiently reliably even the deflection of the flow, to say nothing of the complete impossibility of determining the character of the losses which arise in the flow, and methods of decreasing them.

From our qualitative experimental-cum-theoretical analysis we may conclude that the expansion of a gas in an oblique cut of the nozzle equipment of a turbine is a fairly complicated process, and one which must be analysed by its separate elements. A successive solution of the problem therefore appears rational.

Firstly, it is interesting, on the basis of what is at present known about the flow of an ideal compressible fluid, to try to make calculations about the flow of an ideal gas from a plane-parallel lattice with an oblique cut, consisting of blades with infinitely thin edges. Apart from its independent theoretical interest, a solution of this problem would permit a more detailed analysis of the phenomena in the flow of a gas from an oblique cut, and a calculation of the minimum losses in the gas flow of interest to us.

Secondly, we should analyse the flow of a real gas around the edges of blades of finite thickness, since this produces tail shocks, and the latter, as experiment shows, substantially affect matters.

Thirdly, having solved in some way the second problem we should analyse the interaction of these shocks with a heterogeneous flow in an oblique cut, with one another, with the solid walls and with the eddy traces which they encounter.

Fourthly and finally, since the nozzle apparatus of a turbine works immediately adjacent to the moving blades of the rotor, consideration must be given to non-stationary perturbations which they create, which, superimposed on the main field of flow in the oblique-cut region, deform it to some extent.

Only when all these problems have been solved can one answer with reasonable accuracy the questions which interest engineers regarding the distribution of flow parameters in front of a turbine rotor, the losses and the methods of decreasing them.

II. Flow of an Ideal Gas from a Lattice of Oblique-cut Nozzles with Straight Infinitely Thin Walls

Let us consider an infinite lattice of plane nozzles, whose walls are infinitely thin semi-infinite plates, arranged as shown in Fig. 5. The distance between the plates is h, and the cut angle α_{cut}. Let us assume that the rate of flow in the section AB is uniform and exactly equal to the sonic velocity (the differences in the case of supersonic flows will not be great). It is required to determine the parameters of the flow to the right of the section AB.

Since the number of channels is infinite, all the jets are completely identical, and therefore instead of analysing the whole lattice we can analyse one jet with defined boundary conditions.

The geometry of an oblique cut of the lattice in question is completely defined by h and a_{cut}. The boundary (edge) conditions are arrived at as follows:

a) the width of the jet parallel to the plane of the cut AC should not exceed $h/\sin \alpha_{cut}$.
b) If M and N are the points of intersection of the boundaries of the streamlines parallel to AC, the pressures in them should be identical, and the direction of the velocity vectors should be such that the jets do not intersect.

For an exact solution of the problem the energy, continuity and state equations should be satisfied, in the light of the boundary conditions and the existence of finite discontinuities.

In this way we should find not only the flow parameters inside the jets, but also the configurations of the extreme streamlines and of the shock fronts.

However, it is difficult to solve such a problem in a general form with existing mathematical equipment. Hence we resort to different assumptions which, while little affecting the physical essence of the phenomenon, and the results, considerably simplify calculations.

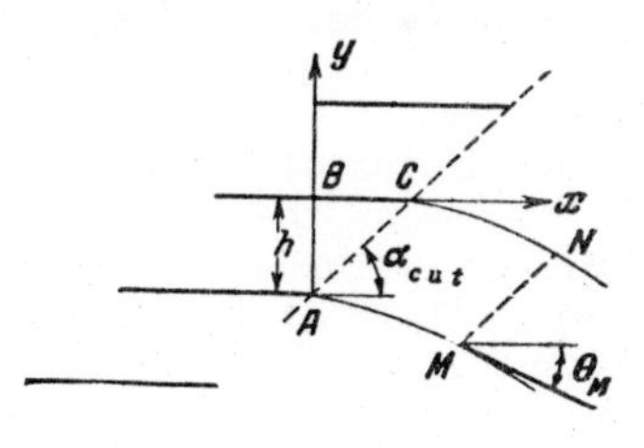

Fig. 5

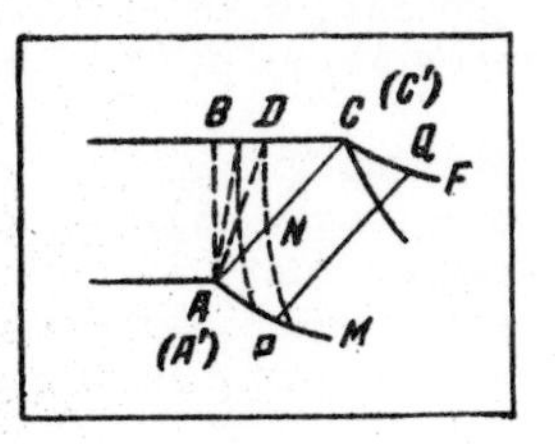

Fig. 6

In the flow of an ideal fluid in the general case the jet can retain a "structure", i.e., a non-uniform distribution of velocities and pressures across the section at an infinite distance downwards from the plane AB. In the real case, by virtue of viscosity forces, the parameters of the accompanying jets equalize more or less rapidly. The final object of further study is the solution of the general problem for the section AC (Fig. 5).

Let us denote by D the point of intersection of the extreme rarefaction wave in the flow from the point A with the surface BC (Fig. 6), and let us examine separately three cases:

1) D coincides with C (which we will call the critical expansion condition);
2) D falls outside BC (supercritical expansion);
3) D falls between B and C (subcritical expansion).

1. Critical Expansion

This name derives from the fact that with further fall of pressure in the plane AC, the parameters of the flow in the ABC region do not change (Fig. 6).

From an examination of Fig. 6 we conclude there is a single-valued relation between $M_{A'}$ (see below) and the cut angle of the nozzle, at which there will be critical expansion. The correlation, plotted by the characteristic method, is shown in Fig. 7.

Analysis of this scheme shows that the direction and magnitude of the velocity of flow in the cut region does not depend, in the present case, on the configuration of the streamline AM.

Let A' be the point corresponding to the parameters of the gas after rotation of the extreme streamlines of the gas around the point A in expansion from $p_A = p_*$ to $p_{A'} < p_A$, where p_* is the pressure in the critical section. Let us show that in the plane of the hodograph this process is represented by the part AA' of an epicycloid (Fig. 8).

For this we will consider how the characteristic of the second set of streamlines, starting from the point B, proceeds in the physical surface. Obviously, in the region lower down the flow than this, the above-mentioned type of flow will occur, and its characteristic is the above one. Let r and ω be polar co-ordinates of the characteristic, where r is measured off from the point A (Fig. 6) and ω is the angle between the section AB and r.

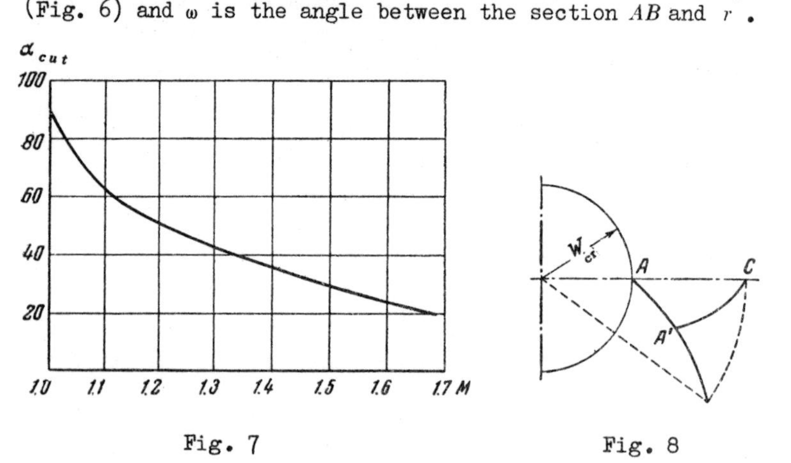

Fig. 7 Fig. 8

Let us denote by r^* the radius vector corresponding to any definite value ω, for example $\omega = \frac{\pi}{4}\sqrt{\frac{\gamma+1}{\gamma-1}}$. The equation of the characteristic is then:

$$r = \frac{r^*}{\sqrt{2^{\frac{\gamma}{\gamma-1}} \cos^{\frac{\gamma+1}{\gamma-1}}\left(\sqrt{\frac{\gamma-1}{\gamma+1}}\,\omega\right) \sin\left(\sqrt{\frac{\gamma-1}{\gamma+1}}\,\omega\right)}} \qquad (1)$$

It will be seen that for any finite value of r^*, r tends to infinity as ω approaches zero. Hence if we assume that the characteristic starts at a certain finite distance from the point of flow rotation, as it does in our case, it envelops the latter within the confines of some infinitely small circle. We can therefore take it as proved that one extreme streamline (and only one) can be described by the Prandtl-Meyer flow equation.

Gas flowing along the wall BC is overexpanded to a pressure below $p_{A'}$ (Fig. 8). Hence to satisfy the condition of equality of pressure there should be a shock directed from the corresponding points of the jet interface from C downwards, this shock ensuring that $p_{A'} = p_{C'}$, where C' means parameters after the shock. In the general case the directions of the velocity vectors at A' and C' will not coincide.

Let us denote the difference between the numerical values of the angles of flow direction at C' and A' as the angle of the stagnation zone θ_{stag}(Fig. 9):

(2)

and let us find its dependence on the pressure ratio:

$$p_{A'}/p_A = p_{A'}/p_* = p_{C'}/p_*.$$

In flow around a sharp edge at the point A we shall have:

$$-\theta_{A'} = \arccos\left[\frac{\gamma+1}{\gamma-1}\left(\frac{p_*}{p_{A'}}\right)^{\frac{\gamma-1}{\gamma}} - \frac{2}{\gamma-1}\right]^{-\frac{1}{2}} + \frac{1}{2}\sqrt{\frac{\gamma+1}{\gamma-1}}\arccos\left[1 - 2\left(\frac{p_{A'}}{p_*}\right)^{\frac{\gamma-1}{\gamma}}\right] - 220, \ 455^\circ = \varphi\left(\frac{p_*}{p_{A'}}\right). \quad (3)$$

As can be seen from Fig. 8, the pressure at $C(p_c)$ is given by

$$-2\theta_{A'} = \varphi\left(\frac{p_*}{p_c}\right) \quad (4)$$

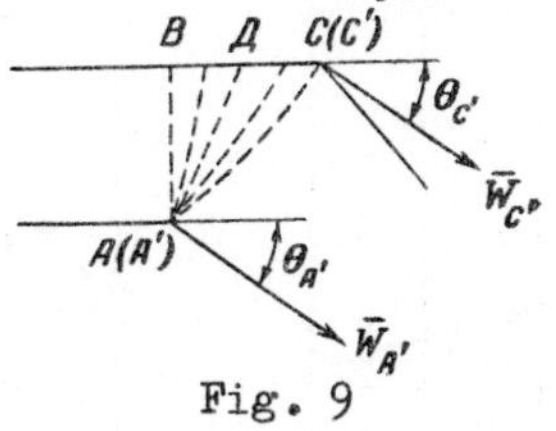

Fig. 9

Knowing p_C/p_* we can find M_C, the Mach number before the shock.

From this quantity and the pressure ratio before and after the shock we determine the angle of flow deflection behind the shock front and obtain a final expression for the dependence of the angle of deflection of the flow on the pressure ratios $p_{A'}/p_*$ and p_C/p_*.

$$\theta_{C'} = -\arctan\left|\frac{\sqrt{\dfrac{2\gamma}{\gamma-1}\,\dfrac{\left(\dfrac{p_*}{p_C}\right)^{\frac{\gamma-1}{2}} - \dfrac{2}{\gamma+1}}{\dfrac{p_{A'}}{p_*}\dfrac{p_*}{p_C} + \dfrac{\gamma-1}{\gamma+1}} - 1}}{\dfrac{\gamma+1}{\gamma(\gamma-1)}\,\dfrac{\left(\dfrac{p_*}{p_C}\right)^{\frac{\gamma-1}{2}} - \dfrac{2}{\gamma+1}}{\dfrac{p_{A'}}{p_*}\cdot\dfrac{p_*}{p_C} - 1} - 1}\right|$$

Solution of equations (3)-(5) gives the sought-for angle of the stagnation zone.

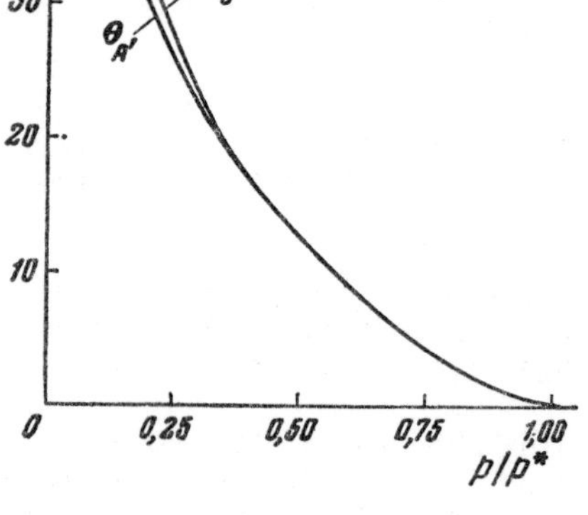

Fig. 10

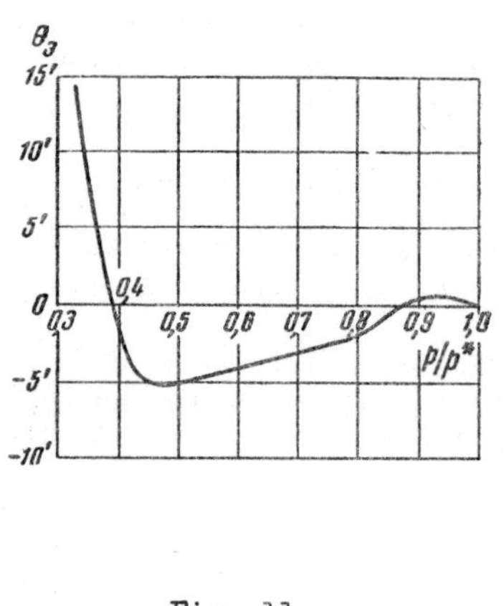

Fig. 11

The results of the calculations are in Figs. 10 and 11. Fig. 10 is a plot of the angle of flow deflection in isentropic expansion ($\theta_{A'}$) and with passage through the corresponding shock wave ($\theta_{C'}$) and Fig. 11 a plot on a large scale $p_{A'}/p_*$ of the angle of the stagnation zone, as a function of the ratio. It can be seen that between values of this ratio of 0.39 and 1 the plot of θ_{stag} against this ratio twice intersects the abscissa, and when the ratio is between 0.39 and 0.86, θ_{stag} is negative.

Generally speaking, the same qualitative result can be obtained by other means [1]. Hence, in the indicated range of $M_{A'}$ (and therefore of cut angle) continuous flow with critical expansion is strictly speaking impossible. However, the deviation from this condition is small, since the negative value of the angle of the stagnation zone does not exceed 0.1°

An analysis of the curves in Fig. 10 shows that no great error would be committed in taking θ_{stag} as about zero for $M_{A'} < 1.85$. Hence in the cases of critical expansion which are of practical interest, it can be taken that the surface of contact interruption starts from C in the flow of an ideal gas.

2. Supercritical Expansion

As has already been indicated in section 1, in supercritical expansion the "last" rarefaction line from A does not intersect BC, which we can state as $x_D > x_C$. As in the case of critical expansion there is no effect of the form of the streamline AM for this condition (Fig. 6) on the flow in the oblique-cut region.

For an analysis of supercritical expansion we select any definite condition of critical expansion ($p_{A'}/p_*$) and consequently α_{cut} (Fig. 7), and we start to lower $p_{A'}$. Since p_C and M_C (Fig. 8) will not change, and $p_{A'} = p_{C'}$ will decrease the intensity of the shock and the angle of flow rotation at it will both fall. Hence decrease of the pressure at the edge simultaneously increases the numerical value of $|\theta_{A'}|$ and decreases that of $|\theta_{C'}|$, in contrast to what happens in critical expansion. Obviously this is only possible if there is some initial stagnation zone angle. It can therefore be concluded that continuous flow is impossible, in supercritical expansion, between values of $p_{A'}/p_*$ of 0.39 and 0.86.

3. Subcritical Expansion

Here, as indicated above, the "last" characteristic from A will intersect the opposite wall of the channel at some distance from the latter's edge $(x_D<x_C)$.

The main difference of this from critical and supercritical expansions is the dependence of the flow parameters in the oblique-cut region on the form of the extreme streamlines in the jet.

The intensity and sign of the disturbance reflected from the interfaces will depend on the shape of the latter. In exceptional cases the perturbations may be completely unreflected. The shape of the boundaries will then resemble the wall of the supersonic part of an ideal Laval nozzle. If the curvature of the boundaries is greater or less than in the above case, reflected compressions or rarefactions, respectively, will arise.

As already indicated, the shape of the extreme streamlines should be such that with equality of pressure at all adjacent points the streamlines do not intersect (in exceptional cases there will be a gap between the streamlines).

Let us study from this viewpoint the possibility of the existence of an interface from which perturbation lines will not be reflected (below, for brevity, this case will be referred to as the ideal Laval nozzle case).

As can be seen from Fig. 6, the flow parameters in the region of the oblique cut NDC will be constant, and along the extreme streamline AM they will be fitted by the Prandtl-Meyer flow equation, as perturbations in the ADM zone are propagated only along one group of characteristics.

Owing to a shock at the interface between two adjacent streamlines (for clarity let us refer to the streamlines AM and CF) the retarding pressure will differ and $p_{0_P}=p_{0_Q}$. From the condition of stable existence of a streamline boundary, the static pressures at adjacent points will be equal, so that there will be a similar inequality of the Mach numbers, namely $M_P>M_Q$ (the line PQ is drawn parallel to AC).

Let us assume that at a certain point of the jet boundary the direction of flow and the static pressure of adjacent jets will be the same. Then since at corresponding points of the boundary $p_P = p_Q$ the necessary and sufficient condition for contact discontinuity is

$$\frac{d}{dp}(\theta_P-\theta_Q)=0. \tag{6}$$

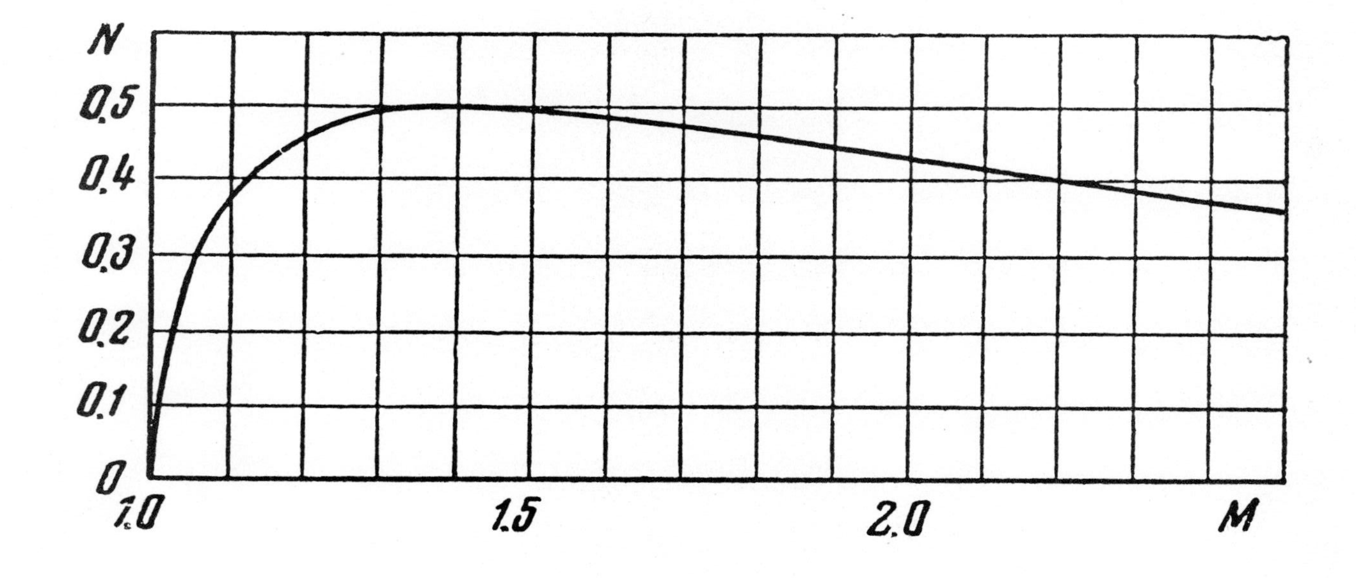

Fig. 12.

We know that for Prandtl-Meyer flow

$$\frac{d\theta}{dp} = \frac{\gamma}{p} \frac{\sqrt{M^2-1}}{M^2}. \tag{7}$$

From a comparison between (6) and (7) we can conclude that for contact discontinuity at the jet boundary in the case of an oblique cut, the discontinuity having the form of the ideal Laval nozzle, the Mach numbers of adjacent streamlines must be equal at corresponding points of the boundary, and this is impossible. Hence, strictly speaking, the boundary between adjacent jets cannot have the above-indicated form.

However an analysis of equation (7) shows that, other conditions being the same, the change in the angle of rotation with the pressure is directly proportional to some quantity $N(M)$ where

$$N = \frac{\sqrt{M^2-1}}{M^2} \tag{8}$$

and therefore the divergence between adjacent streamlines is:

$$\frac{d}{dp}(\theta_P - \theta_Q) = \frac{\gamma}{p}(N_P - N_Q), \tag{9}$$

i.e., proportional to the differences in the corresponding Ns.

Fig. 12 shows the dependence of N on M. It will be seen that this quantity varies most between M = 1.0 and = 1.2. But if $M_{A'}$ falls within these limits, the values of M_P and M_Q will be practically identical (calculations show that in this case $p_{0_Q}/p_{0_P} \approx 0.999$. For greater values of M the plot of N against M is extremely flat, so that $\frac{d}{dp}(\theta_P - \theta_Q)$ is small.

Although the discussion presented is not absolutely exact, it can be concluded with fair accuracy that in the cases of practical interest the lines of elementary perturbations of rarefaction in interaction with the boundaries of adjacent jets will not be reflected from them and the shape of the boundary will be close to that of the ideal Laval nozzle.

Physically this means that although in the interaction of an elementary rarefaction wave with a jet boundary there will be reflections their intensity and effect on the flow in the oblique-cut region will be small.

4. Analytical Method of Calculating Flow in an Oblique Cut of a Nozzle Apparatus

A great number of papers have to date appeared on the solution of problems concerning flat potential flow of ideal compressible fluids, but so far no really effective method applicable to different boundary conditions has been found. Recently two methods for solving the problem have been noted. In studies by the first method, attempts have been made at an approximate method of solving the accurate gas-dynamic equations. This applies, for instance, to the well-known characteristic method.

The other method involves attempts to change the differential equations for the process themselves, so that the least deviations from the experimentally observed relations between the parameters of a fluid in flow will make these equations solvable. Considerable success was achieved in this direction as long ago as 1902 by Chaplygin [5], who proposed to replace the Poisson adiabatic by an approximating linear relation between pressure and specific volume. There is a generalization of this method to any relation between pressure and density in a paper by Sedov [6].

Below we will use the method of calculation potential flow in an oblique cut, based on similar ideas.

It can be shown that the equations for potential motion of a compressible gas reduce to an equation in partial second differentials of the function ψ [6]:

$$\frac{\partial^2\psi}{\partial t^2}-\frac{\partial^2\psi}{\partial\theta^2}-\frac{1}{2}\left(\frac{d}{dt}\ln k_1\right)\frac{\partial\psi}{dt}=0, \qquad (10)$$

where

$$t=\int_{W_*}^{W}\frac{\sqrt{M^2-1}}{W}\,dw, \qquad (11)$$

W = numerical value of the gas velocity;
θ = angle of inclination of the velocity vector;
$k_1=k_1(t)$ is a known function for selected or specified function $p=p(\rho)$.

The asterisk subscript refers to critical parameters. For flow of gas from a nozzle, in the narrowest section of the latter the velocity will be sonic. Let us assume that the flow is fairly homogeneous, so that the transition line can be taken as straight.

Most of the investigated methods of solving problems about supersonic flow, including the characteristic and the Khristianovich analytical methods [7], the main features of which are used below, consider flows in which in the whole of the region studied, including the boundary region, the gas speed is supersonic. Thus to use them directly for the complete solution of our problem is impossible, and we find it of interest to study a problem where, as in our case, the gas velocity is accurately sonic in one part of the boundary of the region studied. To obtain such a solution we use the equations given above.

As shown in the work [8], in the case of an adiabatic relation between pressure and density, the connexion between k and t can be presented as a series:

$$\frac{1}{2}\frac{d}{dt}\ln k_1=\frac{1}{3t}+A_1t^{-\frac{1}{3}}+A_1t^{\frac{1}{3}}+\ldots+A_nt^{\frac{2n}{3}-1}+\ldots \qquad (12)$$

In accordance with equation (11), where $W=W_*$ $t=0$. Thus, it can be considered that for approximately sonic flows the main part in equation (12) will be played by the first term of the series, i.e.,

$$\frac{1}{2}\frac{d}{dt}\ln k_1\approx\frac{1}{3t}\,. \qquad (13)$$

We find the connexion between p and ρ which satisfies equation (13), and the constants obtained in integration of the equations are chosen in such a way that at the speed of sound the equations

$$[k_1(\rho_*)]_{approx.} = [k_1(\rho_*)]_{adiab.} \tag{14}$$

$$\left[\left(\frac{dk_1}{d\rho}\right)_*\right]_{approx.} = \left[\left(\frac{dk_1}{d\rho}\right)_*\right]_{adiab.} \tag{15}$$

are satisfied.

A graph illustrating the numerical calculation is shown in Fig. 13. As can be seen, in the range $1.0 \leqslant M \leqslant 1.1$ equation (10) can be replaced with completely sufficient accuracy by the following:

$$\frac{\partial^2\psi}{\partial t^2} - \frac{\partial^2\psi}{\partial\theta^2} + \frac{1}{3t}\frac{\partial\psi}{\partial t} = 0. \tag{16}$$

Physically it is clear that the solution to such an equation will not differ greatly from the true solution, since the assumed connexion between pressure and density differs little from the experimental connexion (in this case adiabatic).

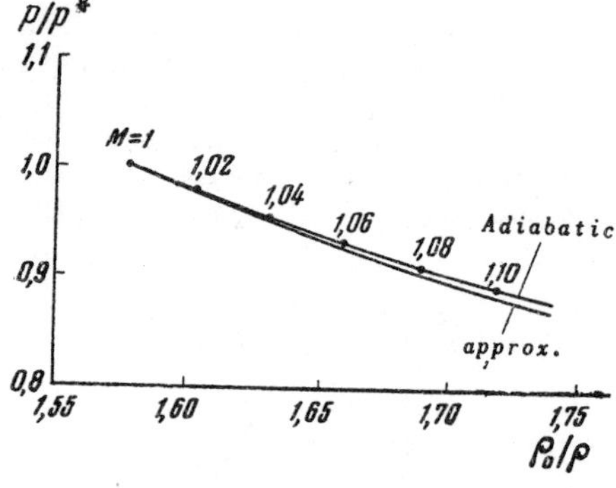

Fig. 13

A solution to equation (16) was obtained by Rudnev [9]:

$$\psi(\theta_1 t) = f(\mu) = C' \int (1-\mu^2)^{-\frac{5}{6}} d\mu + C_1', \tag{17}$$

where

$$\mu = \frac{\theta}{t}.$$

To investigate gas flows at high values of Mach numbers, it is convenient in our case to use Khristianovich's approximate method [7], which again amounts to replacement of the adiabatic connexion between pressure and density in the flow by some other, fairly well approximated adiabatic in a certain range of Mach numbers.

By introducing new variables defined by the equations:

$$\chi = f_1(\lambda);\ t = f_2(\lambda) \tag{18}$$

$$\begin{cases} \xi = \frac{1}{2}(t-\theta) \\ \eta = \frac{1}{2}(t+\theta) \end{cases} \tag{19}$$

where $\lambda = W/a_*$, and f_1 and f_2 are known functions of λ, Khristianovich showed that the relation between $\sqrt{\chi}$ and t, expressed parametrically by the equations (18), is approximated in the range

$1.06 < M < 2.2$ with a fair degree of accuracy by the parabola:

$$\sqrt{\chi} \approx 18.5\,(t + 0.185)^2. \tag{20}$$

It is also possible to find a similar parabolic relation for $M > 2.2$, but in our problem such flows are of no practical interest.

As a result, the equations of motion are reduced to the Darboux equation, which can be resolved in the form:

$$\psi(\xi;\, \eta) = k\,\frac{\Psi_1(\xi) + \Psi_2(\eta)}{\xi + \eta + C}, \tag{21}$$

where $\Psi_1(\xi)$ and $\Psi_2(\eta)$ are arbitrary functions of one argument, determinable from the boundary conditions.

Thus it is possible to solve by analysis the problem of the flow of an ideal gas from an oblique cut in the range of variation of Mach numbers which is of practical interest.

We will consider the flow of an ideal fluid from an oblique cut of a nozzle, the rate of flow at the inlet to which is exactly equal to the speed of sound, while the transition line is a segment of a straight line. In this case, on the basis of the data given in the previous paragraph, we will assume that the disturbance lines do not reflect from the boundary of adjacent jets (cf. Fig. 6).

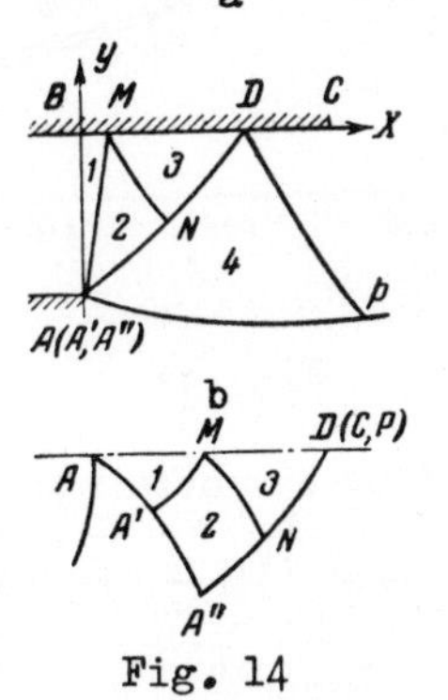

Fig. 14

We will divide the region studied into four zones, bounded by characteristics and extreme streamlines as shown in Fig. 14, where $M_{A'} = 1.07$ (the reason for this division will become clear later).

We will choose as origin of the co-ordinates the point B, and calculation of the streamlines will be carried out in such a way that the zero line ($\psi = 0$) coincides with the solid wall BC. Then, obviously, the flow function on the line AP will be proportional to the discharge of fluid $\psi = -Q$.

The numbering of the characteristics is such that at the point $A(B)$ of the plane of the hodograph (cf. Fig. 14b), the equation

$$\xi_A = \eta_A = 0. \tag{22}$$

is valid.

a) Resolution of the first region. The choice of the value $M_{A'} = 1.07$ is explained by the fact that in this case the maximum value of the Mach number in the first region is $M_M = 1.1$, and this means that over the whole isolated section the arguments put forward at the beginning of the present section are applicable.

On the basis of the above, the boundary conditions in the plane of the hodograph take the form:

$$\left.\begin{array}{ll}\psi = 0 & \text{where } \mu = 0 \\ \psi = -Q & \text{where } \mu = -1\end{array}\right\}. \tag{23}$$

By direct substitution it can be confirmed that both the basic equation (16) and the boundary conditions (23) will be satisfied by the expression:

$$\psi = Q \frac{\int\limits_0^\mu (1 - z^2)^{-\frac{5}{6}} dz}{\int\limits_0^1 (1 - z^2)^{-\frac{5}{6}} dz}. \tag{24}$$

If the flow conditions are such that $M_C \leqslant M_M$, then the total problem is limited to resolution of only the first and fourth regions. Knowing M_C, from equation (11) we determine t_C, and taking into account the fact that along the characteristic $A'C\ \xi = \frac{t_C}{2}$ the equation for the flow function along it is written as follows:

$$\psi_{A'C}(\eta) = \frac{Q}{C_1} \int\limits_0^{\frac{2\eta - t_C}{2\eta + t_C}} (1 - z^2)^{-\frac{5}{6}} dz, \tag{25}$$

where

$$C_1 = \int\limits_0^1 (1 - z^2)^{-\frac{5}{6}} dz = \frac{1}{2} \frac{\Gamma\left(\frac{1}{2}\right) \cdot \Gamma\left(\frac{1}{6}\right)}{\Gamma\left(\frac{2}{3}\right)} = 3.69.$$

However, in practice much greater interest is offered by the case of the flow when $M_C > M_M$. In this case the second and third regions must be included in the calculation, and calculation of the first is carried out up to the critical value of the characteristic $\xi = t_M/2$.

Equation (25) moreover will take the form

$$\psi_{A'M}(\eta) = \frac{Q}{C_1} \int\limits_0^{\frac{2\eta - t_M}{2\eta + t_M}} (1 - z^2)^{-\frac{5}{6}} dz. \tag{26}$$

To simplify the calculations, the function

$$I = \int\limits_0^z (1 - \eta^2)^{-\frac{5}{6}} d\eta. \tag{27}$$

is shown in Fig. 15.

b) Resolution of the second region. It has just been indicated that the need for this resolution arises in the most interesting case when $M_C > M_M$. As is clear in Fig. 14b, in the whole of the second region the Mach number $M > 1.07$, so that it is possible to use the corresponding Khristianovich relations with a satisfactory degree of accuracy.

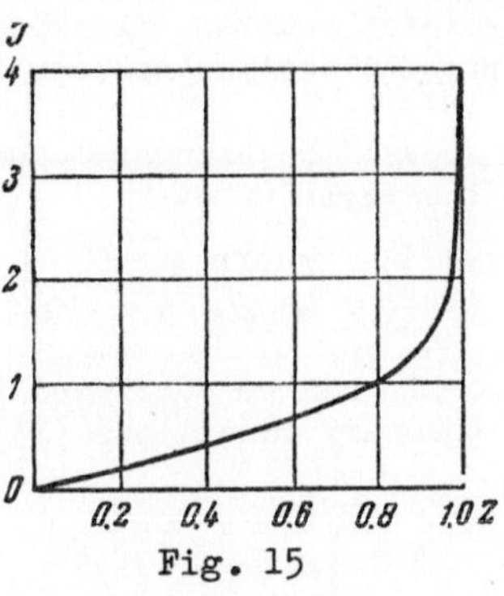

Fig. 15

From the physical point of view, the transition from equation (16) in the first region to the relation (21) in the second implies the assumption of a sudden change in the properties of the gas, expressed by the function $p(\rho)$, at the intersection of the characteristic AM by the flow. In actual fact of course this is impossible. However, taking into account that both functions $p(\rho)$ were fairly close to that observed in experiment (let us say to the adiabatic), it can be presumed that the error occurring with such an assumption will be fairly small.

Thus, resolution of the second region will be presented in the form of equation (21), taking into consideration that, in the case in which we are interested, $k = 1$. The unknown functions must be found with the aid of the following conditions at the boundary of the region:

$$\psi(\eta) = \psi_{A'M}(\eta) \quad \text{where} \quad \xi = \frac{t_M}{2}, \tag{28}$$

$$\psi(\xi) = -Q \quad \text{where} \quad \eta = 0, \tag{29}$$

where expression (28) is defined as shown in the first paragraph.

Equations (28) and (29), together with relation (21), enable us to write:

$$\psi(\xi;\eta) = -\frac{Q}{2C_1(\xi+\eta+C)}[C_1(2\xi - t_M) - (2\eta + t_M + 2C) \times \\ \times \int_0^{\frac{2\eta - t_M}{2\eta + t_M}} (1 - z^2)^{-\frac{5}{6}} dz. \tag{30}$$

From equation (19) it follows that, along the characteristic MN, $\eta = t_M/2$, and, consequently, the change in the stream function along it is defined by the equation:

$$\psi_{MN}(\xi) = -Q\frac{2\xi - t_M}{2\xi + t_M + 2C}. \tag{31}$$

c) Resolution of the third region. The need for a resolution for the third region arises in the same cases as for the second.

As is clear in Fig 14b, here also $M > 1.07$ throughout, which allows us to seek the solution in the form of relation (21), taking into consideration that $k = 1$.

To find the arbitrary functions, the following boundary conditions are used:

$$\psi(\xi) = \psi_{MN}(\xi) \quad \text{where} \quad \eta = t_M/2 \tag{32}$$

$$\psi = 0 \quad \text{where} \quad \eta = \xi, \tag{33}$$

where expression (32) is found from the previous paragraph, and expression (33) follows from joint consideration of equations (19).

On the basis of relations (31), (32) and (33) we write:

$$\psi(\xi; \eta) = Q\frac{\eta - \xi}{\eta + \xi + C}. \tag{34}$$

If in the case of subcritical expansion we specify $\xi_{A''D} = \xi_{max}$ (it is possible to determine its value, knowing the pressure at the edge), then the variation of the stream function along the corresponding characteristic of the first group can be found with the aid of the following equations:

in the range $0 \leqslant \eta \leqslant (t_M/2)$

$$\psi(\eta) = -\frac{Q}{2C_1(\xi_{max} + \eta + C)}[C_1(2\xi_{max} - t_M) - (2\eta + t_M + 2C)\int\limits_0^{\frac{2\eta - t_M}{2\eta + t_M}} (1 - z^2)^{-\frac{5}{6}} dz \tag{35}$$

in the range $(t_M/2) \leqslant \eta \leqslant \xi_{max}$

$$\psi(\eta) = Q\frac{\eta - \xi_{max}}{\eta + \xi_{max} + C}. \tag{36}$$

d) Resolution of the fourth region. The need for a resolution of this region arises in any flow conditions with subcritical expansion. Under other conditions it is fully satisfied by the results obtained in resolution of the preceding regions.

In fact, as is clear from the graph in Fig. 14a, in accordance with the assumptions made, in the fourth region disturbances are only propagated along one (the second) group of characteristics, which leads to representation of the whole region in the plane of the hodograph by one curve $A''D$ (the so-called Prandtl-Meyer type flow).

Thus it can be considered that in characteristic variables the flow in the fourth region is fully defined by equation (25) or the relations (35) and (36), depending on the flow conditions.

We will now move from the plane of the characteristic variables to the physical plane. We will consider how, using the data obtained in the previous paragraph, it is possible to determine the distribution of the flow parameters in the region of the oblique cut. We will begin the analysis from conditions of subcritical expansion ($x_D < x_C$), in which case the line AC which interests us is wholly located in the fourth region (cf. Fig. 16)

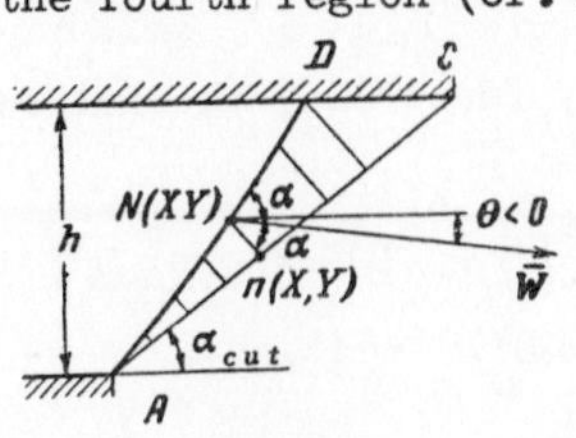

Fig. 16

We will indicate an arbitrary point of the extreme characteristic of the first group of the second and third or first regions ($\xi = \xi_{max}$) by the letter $N(X, Y)$, and the corresponding point of the line of the cut AC, lying on one characteristic of the second group with the point N, running in the fourth region, by the letter $n(x, y)$. Then, bearing in mind the symbols used in Fig. 16, the connexion between the co-ordinates of points N and n can be defined as follows:

$$X = \frac{y + x\tan(\alpha - \theta)}{\tan\alpha_{cut} - \tan(\theta - \alpha)}. \tag{37}$$

Taking into consideration that $\tan\alpha = (M^2 - 1)^{-\frac{1}{2}}$, equation (37) can be presented in the form:

$$X = \frac{(\sqrt{M^2 - 1} + \tan\theta)\, y + (1 - \tan\theta\sqrt{M^2 - 1})\, x}{\sqrt{M^2 - 1}\,(\tan\alpha_{cut} + \tan\theta) + \tan\alpha_{cut}\tan\theta - 1}, \tag{38}$$

where M and θ are parameters of the flow at the point N. If these parameters, and also the co-ordinates of the characteristic AD, are expressed as functions of any one variable, e.g., η, it will be possible to write:

$$x = f(\eta). \tag{39}$$

As is clear from Fig. 16, the critical value of the co-ordinate $x(x_{cr})$, up to which the flow parameters will vary, is defined by the relation:

$$x_{cr} = f(\xi_{max}). \tag{40}$$

When $x \gg x_{cr}$ the flow parameters remain constant.

Consequently, the mean value of any flow parameter (Π) along the plane of the cut can be defined by means of the equation:

$$\Pi_{mean} = \frac{1}{l\cot\alpha_{cut}}\left[\int_0^{\xi_{max}} \Pi(\eta)\frac{df}{d\eta}d\eta + \Pi_D(l\cot\alpha_{cut} - x_{cr})\right]. \tag{41}$$

Thus, for example, to discover the mean angle of deviation of the flow, we use the formula:

$$\theta_{mean} = \frac{1}{l\cot\alpha_{cut}}\int_0^{\xi_{max}} f(\eta)\,d\eta. \tag{42}$$

It should be noted that relations (41) and (42) give averaged values.

However, averaging with any other parameter (e.g., momentum) does not present any fundamental difficulties.

Thus, from equations (38) and (41) it follows that to solve the problem in question it is necessary to determine the position, in the region of the oblique cut, of the characteristic of the first group $\xi = \xi_{max}$ and the distribution along it of the flow parameters.

We will approach the analysis of this problem, beginning from the case where the characteristic $\xi = \xi_{max}$ lies in the first region.

Above it was shown that the flow conditions considered in the paragraph relate to extremely weak expansion in the region of the oblique cut. Moreover, the maximum angle of deviation of the flow (θ) does not exceed 0° 48', so that with sufficient accuracy it is possible to assume:

$$\sin\theta = \theta, \quad \cos\theta = 1.$$

In this case it is possible to obtain the following equation for the characteristic $\xi = \xi_{max}$ situated in the first region (in terms of the parameter t):

$$x = \frac{BQ\xi_{max}^{\frac{1}{6}}}{W}\left(\sqrt{b_1} + \frac{\rho_0}{\rho} t^{\frac{2}{3}}\right)(t - \xi_{max})^{\frac{1}{6}} \tag{43}$$

$$y = -\frac{Q}{C_1 W t}\left[\sqrt{b_1} t^{-\frac{2}{3}} \int_0^{t-2\xi_{max}} \left(1 - \frac{\theta^2}{t^2}\right)^{-\frac{5}{6}} \theta^2 d\theta - \right.$$
$$\left. - \frac{\rho_0}{\rho} \int_0^{t-2\xi_{max}} \left(1 - \frac{\theta^2}{t^2}\right)^{-\frac{5}{6}} d\theta. \tag{44}$$

For full expression of the co-ordinates of the characteristic in terms of the parameter t, it is necessary to expand the following functional relations:

$$\frac{1}{W} = f(t), \tag{45}$$

$$\rho_0/\rho = f_1(t), \tag{46}$$

which may be achieved with the aid of equations (11) and (13).

Then, using the work of Fal'kovich [10], we can find:

$$\frac{1}{W} = k_1 u(\varepsilon) + k_2 v(\varepsilon), \tag{47}$$

where u and v are the Airy functions tabulated by Fok [11], and ε is determined from the equation:

$$t = -\frac{2}{3}\varepsilon^{\frac{3}{2}}.$$

The integration constants k_1 and k_2 will be obtained from the condition of tangency of the adiabatic and the curve of the function $p(\rho)$ chosen by us at a critical point.

$$k_1 = \frac{1}{a_*}\left[\frac{v(0)}{\sqrt[3]{\gamma+1}} - v'(0)\right] = \frac{0{,}929}{a_*} \tag{48}$$

$$k_2 = \frac{1}{a_*}\left[u'(0) - \frac{u(0)}{\sqrt[3]{\gamma+1}}\right] = -\frac{0{,}017}{a_*}. \tag{49}$$

Expanding the functional relation (46), we find:

$$\frac{\rho_0}{\rho} = \sqrt{b_1} \sqrt[3]{\frac{2}{3} \frac{k_1 u'(\varepsilon) + k_2 v'(\varepsilon)}{k_1 u(\varepsilon) + k_2 v(\varepsilon)}} . \quad (50)$$

We will now consider the more interesting case of subcritical flow, characterized by the relation $x_D > x_M$ (cf. Fig. 14). It was shown above that, to determine the position and distribution of the parameters of the flow along the "extreme" characteristic, it will be necessary in this case to include the second and third regions, whereas the first must be resolved for the critical value $\xi = \xi_M$.

It can be shown [1] that in Khristianovich's approximate method the adiabatic relation $k_1(t)$ (12) is replaced by another, viz.:

$$\sqrt{k_1} = A(t+C)^2. \quad (51)$$

By means of transformations similar to those performed in equations (45), (46), in this case we obtain:

$$\frac{1}{W} = \frac{1}{t+C}[k_3 \sin(t+C) + k_4 \cos(t+C), \quad (52)$$

$$\begin{aligned} \frac{\rho_0}{\rho}\frac{1}{W} = A\{[k_3 \sin(t+C) + k_4 \cos(t+C)] - \\ -(t+C)[k_3 \cos(t+C) - k_4 \sin(t+C)]. \end{aligned} \quad (53)$$

A fairly good approximation of the adiabatic by the new relation $p(\rho)$ resulting from equation (51), in the range of Mach numbers indicated above, is obtained when the corresponding curves touch at the point $M = 1.47$ ($t = 0.2$). In this case the integration constants assume the following values:

$$k_3 = \frac{0{,}553}{a_*}; \quad k_4 = \frac{0{,}082}{a_*} . \quad (54)$$

Taking into consideration the relation (51), and introducing, to shorten the formula, the symbols

$$\begin{aligned} \omega_1 = \operatorname{arc\,tan}\frac{k_3}{k_4} \\ N_1 = \sqrt{k_3^2 + k_4^2} \end{aligned} \quad (55)$$

we obtain the following expressions for the relation of the physical plane to the plane of the characteristic variables:

$$\begin{aligned}
\frac{\partial x}{\partial \xi} &= -AN_1[(t+C)\sin(t+C-\theta+\omega_1) + \sin\theta \sin(t+C+\omega_1)]\frac{\partial \psi}{\partial \xi} \\
\frac{\partial x}{\partial \eta} &= AN_1[(t+C)\sin(t+C+\theta+\omega_1) - \sin\theta \sin(t+C+\omega_1)]\frac{\partial \psi}{\partial \eta} \\
\frac{\partial y}{\partial \xi} &= -AN_1[(t+C)\cos(t+C-\theta+\omega_1) - \cos\theta \sin(t+C+\omega_1)]\frac{\partial \psi}{\partial \xi} \\
\frac{\partial y}{\partial \eta} &= -AN_1[(t+C)\cos(t+C+\theta+\omega_1) - \cos\theta \sin(t+C+\omega_1)\frac{\partial \psi}{\partial \eta}
\end{aligned} \quad (56)$$

On the basis of the above, we obtain the following parametric expression for the characteristic of the first group in the second region (the parameter η):

$$X = \frac{AN_1Q}{C_1}\int_0^{\eta} [(\eta + \xi_{max} + C)\sin(2\eta + C + \omega_1) -$$
$$- \sin(\eta - \xi_{max})\cdot\sin(\eta + \xi_{max} + C + \omega_1)]\{(\xi_{max} - \xi_M)[C_1 +$$
$$+ \int_0^{\frac{\eta-\xi_M}{\eta+\xi_M}} (1 - z^2)^{-\frac{5}{6}} dz\Big] + (\eta + \xi_{max} + C)(\eta + \xi_M +$$
$$+ C)\sqrt[6]{\frac{\xi_M}{16\,\eta^5(\eta + \xi_M)^2}}\Big\}\frac{d\eta}{(\eta + \xi_{max} + C)^2} \tag{57a}$$

$$Y = -\frac{AN_1Q}{C_1}\int_0^{\eta} [(\eta + \xi_{max} + C)\cos(2\eta + C + \omega_1) -$$
$$- \cos(\eta - \xi_{max})\sin(\eta + \xi_{max} + C + \omega_1)]\Big\{(\xi_{max} - \xi_M)\Big[C_1 +$$
$$+ \int_0^{\frac{\eta-\xi_M}{\eta+\xi_M}} (1 - z^2)^{-\frac{5}{6}} dz\Big] + (\eta + \xi_{max} + C)(\eta + \xi_M +$$
$$+ C)\sqrt[6]{\frac{\xi_M}{16\,\eta^5(\eta + \xi_M)^2}}\Big\}\frac{d\eta}{(\eta + \xi_{max} + C)^2} - \frac{Q}{\rho_* W_*}. \tag{57b}$$

From all the above it is clear that for the third region the same arguments are applicable in principle as for the second. The parametric expression for the equation of the characteristic $\xi = \xi_{max}$ in the physical plane takes the form:

$$x = AN_1Q(2\xi_{max} + C)\int_{\xi_M}^{\eta} [(\eta + \xi_{max} + C)\sin(2\eta + C + \omega_1) -$$
$$- \sin(\eta - \xi_{max})\sin(\eta + \xi_{max} + C + \omega_1)]\frac{d\eta}{(\eta + \xi_{max} + C)^2} + X_N \tag{58a}$$

$$y = -AN_1Q(2\xi_{max} + C)\int_{\xi_M}^{\eta} [(\eta + \xi_{max} + C)\cos(2\eta + C + \omega_1) -$$
$$- \cos(\eta - \xi_{max})\sin(\eta + \xi_{max} + C + \omega_1)]\frac{d\eta}{(\eta + \xi_{max} + C)^2} + Y_N, \tag{58b}$$

where X_N and Y_N are the co-ordinates of the point N (cf. Fig. 14), determined with the aid of the equations (57) where $\eta = \xi_M$.

Similar arguments may also be used for the case of critical and supercritical expansion (for details see the work [1]).

Thus, the problem set in this paper of analytical resolution of the process of potential flow of an ideal gas from a flat oblique-cut cascade consisting of straight, infinitely thin plates can be considered as solved. We should not, of course, forget the series of assumptions introduced into the calculations, of which that relating to the form of the extreme streamline, ensuring the absence or extremely low intensity of the reflections of the elementary disturbances occurring on it, should be considered the most important.

The calculations shown, and also some experimental data [4], allow us to confirm that the evaluation of the flow parameters in an oblique cut, obtained with the aid of the equations given above, agrees fairly well with experimental results.

Obviously, a number of simplifications of this method are possible, facilitating its use in actual engineering calculations. Thus, for example, in a wide range of flow conditions it is possible to calculate the flow in the first region once for all, etc.

It should be noted that in the present work we examined in detail the most complex case of a tapering nozzle, which made it necessary to investigate the zone around the speed of sound. Calculation of the Laval oblique-cut nozzles, which can be carried out in principle by the same methods, will be simpler.

REFERENCES

1. V.P. MOTULEVICH, Expansion of a gas in an oblique cut of the nozzle apparatus of a turbine (K voprosu o rasshirenii gaza v kosom sreze soplovogo apparata turbiny), Dissertatsiya, Energ. Inst. Akad. Nauk SSSR.
2. V.S. PUSHKIN et al. Scientific report (Nauchnyi otchet), Lab. fiz. gor., Energ. Inst. Akad. Nauk SSSR (1951).
3. N.E. KOCHIN, I.A. KIBEL', N.V. ROZE, Theoretical Fluid Mechanics (Teoreticheskaya gidromekhanika), 2 (1948).
4. Investigation of blade equipment of the upper level of a double-level stage of an SVK-158 turbine (Issledovaniye lopatochnykh apparatov verkhnego yarusa dvukh'yarusnoi stupeni turbiny SVK-158), Otchet Mosk. Energ. Inst. (1953).
5. S.A. CHAPLYGIN, On Gas Jets (O gazovykh struyakh) (1949).
6. L.I. SEDOV, Plane Problems of Hydrodynamics and Aerodynamics (Ploskiye zadachi gidrodinamiki i aerodinamiki) (1950).
7. S.A. KHRISTIANOVICH, Approximate integration of the equations of a supersonic gas flow, Prikl. mat. mekh., 11, No. 2 (1947).
8. M.P. MIKHAILOVA, The flow of a gas from a container, sb. Teoreticheskaya gidromekhanika, No. 9 (1952).
9. Yu.V. RUDNEV, The flow of a gas jet into a vacuum, ibid.
10. S.V. FAL'KOVICH. On one classs of Laval nozzles, Prikl. mat. mekh., 11, No. 2 (1947).
11. V.A. Fok, Tables of Airy functions (Tablitsy funktsii Eiri) (1946).

V.P. Motulevich

Unsymmetrical Supersonic Gas Flow around Edges of Finite Thickness

I. Experimental Study of the Problem

From an analysis of the results of experiments, obtained in the works [1], [2], it becomes clear that the resolution of the problem of expansion of a gas flow in an oblique cut of the nozzle apparatus of a turbine is closely bound up with the clarification of the main features in the process of the flow of a real gas around the edges of blades with finite thickness. The reason for this is the fact that the distribution of the rates of flow of a fluid in respect of size and direction, and also the hydraulic losses, depend on the location of compression shocks in the flow.

The actual configuration of the front of the pressure discontinuity is determined by the conditions for the occurrence of the shock, which result from the characteristic features of the flow process around blade edges. Moreover, as is shown by experiment, the system of shocks forming in a real gas differs considerably from that which might be expected in examination of the flow of an ideal fluid. Thus, for example, in Fig. 1 it is very clear that with a total supersonic drop of $\delta_k = 0.244$ (the letter δ denotes the ratio of the pressure in the chamber to the pressure in front of the nozzle) there are, from the end of a fairly thin blade (0.5 mm) forming the oblique cut, not one [1] but two shocks leaving - on both sides of the blade.

A qualitatively similar pattern is also given by symmetrical flow (Fig. 2). This indicates that the formation of tail shocks, both in the case of the flow of a gas from a cascade of blades forming an oblique cut and in other cases of supersonic flow of a real gas around bodies, is provoked by some general causes.

The most obvious physical explanation for this fact may be considered the formation behind the edge of a zone of reduced pressure, the interaction of which with the surrounding supersonic flow also leads to the formation of the compression shocks observed in experiment.

The occurrence of a zone of reduced pressure behind the edges of bodies around which a fluid is flowing has been observed experimentally by many investigators. As examples of works in which this problem has been studied in greater or lesser detail in respect of turbine cascades, we can cite the works of the Soviet scientists Zhiritskii and Kontsevich [3], Markov [4], Sennichenko [5] and others.

It should be noted that analysis of supersonic flow around edges has a direct connexion with the problem of the resistance of bullets and artillery shells, both motorless and with their own motors. This is why, up to the present, the greatest number of theoretical and experimental studies in this field have been devoted to determination of the base pressure of rotating bodies.

In the non-Soviet literature, some information about experimental studies carried out in connexion with this problem can be found in the articles of Chapman and Perkins [6], Bogdonov [7], Kurtsveg [8], Wick [9] and others.

In the first part of the present paper are presented the results of an experiment conducted with the object of obtaining some additional information in connexion with the problem of the base vacuum, with respect to the expansion of a gas in conditions of unsymmetrical flow.

All the experiments were carried out on the gas-dynamics test bed of the Laboratory of Combustion Physics of the Energy Institute of the Academy of Sciences of the U.S.S.R. (ENIN), with the aid of the universal nozzle, detailed description of which can be found in [1].

The blades investigated had an identical shape in plan, shown in Fig. 3, and differed from each other in thickness, shape of edge and material (the only exception was the blade with a thickness $h = 0.5$ mm, which in plan was a rectangle with dimensions of 51 × 12 mm).

The thickness of the blades varied as follows: $h = 0.5$; 1.2; 2.0 and 3.0 mm. The manufacturing materials were: for blades with $h = 0.5$ mm, steel, for blades with $h = 1.2$ and 2.0 mm, bronze, and for blades with $h = 3$ mm, Plexiglas (polymethacrylic resin). Irrespectively of material, the side walls of the blades in contact with the gas flow were carefully ground.

To clarify the effect on the flow process of the shape of the trailing edge, we investigated blades with a thickness of $h = 3$ mm, the ends of which had different profiles: rectangular, oval and triangular.

During the experiments, apart from visual examination and photographing of the flow by means of the Toepler device, we measured a series of pressure values, viz. : pressure in front of the nozzle and in the pressure chamber, static and ram pressure in the vortex track, and static pressure of the flow directly in front of the

Knife from
the left

$\delta = 0.244$

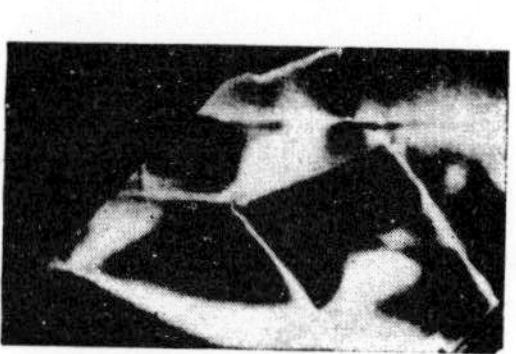
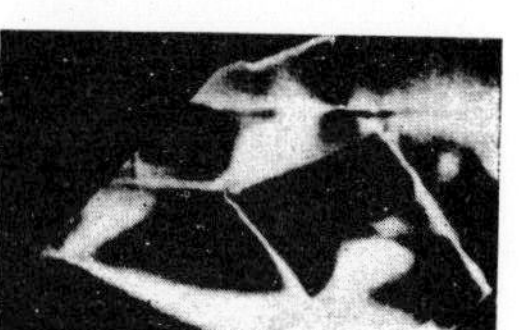

Knife from
above

Fig. 1

Knife from
the left

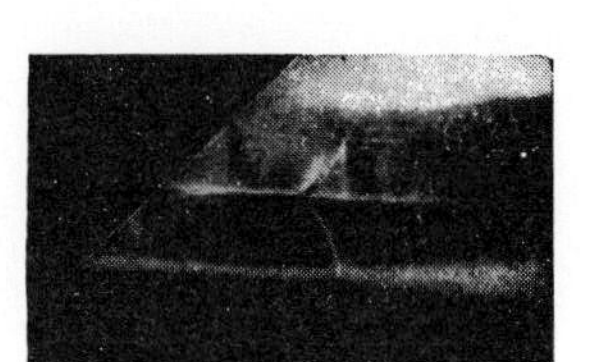

Knife from
above

Fig. 2

flow around the thick edge.

The static pressure measuring probe employed was a carefully polished thin steel tube (D = 0.8 mm), tapered at the front and with side openings (d = 0.25 mm) at a distance of 8 mm from the point. The accuracy of the manufacture of the probe was checked under a microscope.

In order to have the opportunity of measuring the static pressure on the axis of the vortex track, beginning from the surface of the edge, a hole was drilled normal to the latter, the size of which was enough to take the needle up to the meeting of the axis of the side opening and the edge surface. When measuring pressures at points distant from the blade, the needle was gradually withdrawn from the body of the latter. The distance of the side opening from the edge was recorded by means of a co-ordinatograph, and, as a check, at the same time as the dial reading, a photograph was taken at one position,which was subsequently analysed under a microscope.

To check the effect on the instrument readings of the interaction of the boundary layer of the needle with the flow in the vortex track, in the blade with the thickness h = 3 mm we made a through hole (Fig. 3), by means of which the base pressure value was directly determined. The variation between the results of these measurements and the measurements with the needle, the axis of the side opening of which coincided with the surface of the edge, did not exceed 0.5 per cent.

In investigating the base pressure values behind the blades with a thickness h = 1.2 and 2.0 mm, in which it was impossible to make long through holes for technological reasons, we used a probe with an end opening. For this, in the body of the blade on the side of the end face of the edge, we drilled a small hole with a diameter slightly greater than the outside diameter of the probe. Into this opening the open end of the needle was placed to a depth of 1.5 - 2 mm.

To judge the effect of the interaction of the external shock wave with the vortex track, which may occur during expansion in the oblique cut of the nozzle, we used a wedge firmly fixed in the holder of the co-ordinatograph, which made it possible to eliminate the vibrations of the wedge in the flow, which were observed when carrying out exploratory experiments.

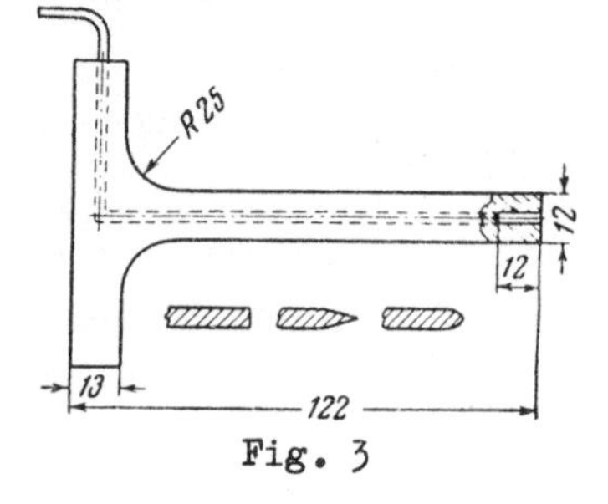

Fig. 3

All experiments without exception were accompanied by visual examination of the flow, and the most characteristic types of flow were recorded on film. Moreover, for greater clarity of the flow pattern created by the development of regions both of longitudinal and transverse density gradients, photographs were taken with the Foucault blade in the vertical and horizontal positions.

The main problem of the present experiments was the qualitative determination of the effect on the flow process around obtuse edges in general, and on the value of the base pressure in particular, of such parameters as the throttling pressure - proportional, other conditions being equal, to the Reynolds number - the thickness and shape of the edge of the blade, and also the position of the latter in the cascade (symmetrical and unsymmetrical flow).

The arrangement of the blades in the channel is shown diagrammatically in Fig. 4 (a), (b), (c).

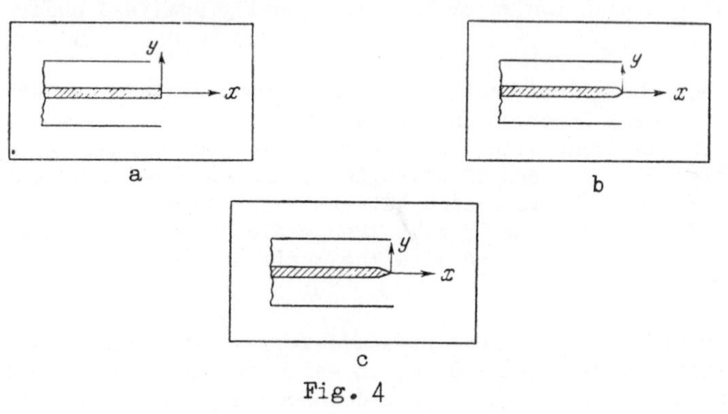

Fig. 4

Fig. 5 gives the results of measurement of the static pressure on the symmetry axis of the vortex track (p_{tr}/p_0), produced by a blade (h = 3 mm) with a straight edge at different throttling pressures (p_0) and different ratios of the pressure in the chamber to the pressure at the input to the nozzle $(\frac{p_k}{p_0})$.

Figs. 6 and 7 give results of similar measurements for an edge with an oval and triangular shape.

Fig. 8 shows photographs of typical flow processes around edges with an oval shape.

To clarify the effect on the flow process around edges of different boundary conditions (solid wall instead of free surface), we conducted a series of experiments on the measurement of the static pressure in the vortex track of a blade arranged in the depth of the channel. The results of the measurements with different throttling pressures and different values of $\frac{p_k}{p_0}$ are shown in Fig. 9. The most typical corresponding photographs of the flow process are given in Fig. 10 (p_0 = 0.985 atm).

To determine how the edge thickness affects the value of the base pressure, a series of experiments was carried out with blades having an edge of a rectangular shape. The thickness of the edge was chosen as h = 1.2; 2.0 and 3 mm. The results of the test for h = 3 mm are given in Fig. 11, in which the axis of ordinates given the ratio of the pressure directly behind the edge to the pressure in front of the inlet to the nozzle (p_b/p_0) .

To clarify the effect on the base pressure of unsymmetrical flow, which, as is known, occurs in an oblique cut of the nozzle apparatus of a turbine, a series of experiments was carried out with blades of different thickness, and the angle of cut of the nozzle was fixed

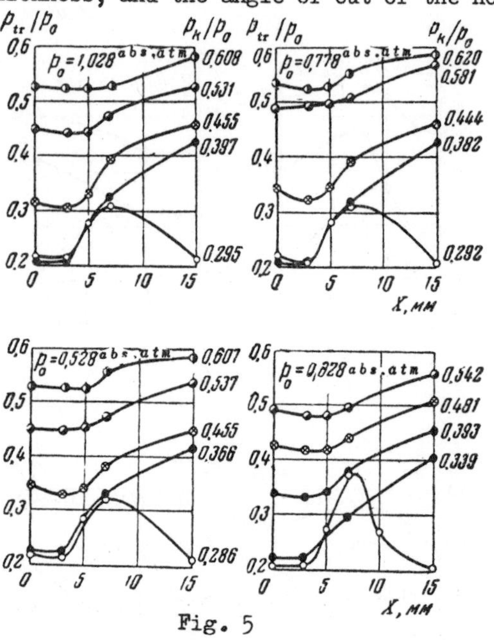

Fig. 5

at about 26°. Typical results of the experiments are shown in Fig. 12. As was to be expected, the Mach number in front of the edge on that side of the blade on which the rarefaction wave does not fall retains values corresponding to symmetrical flow, and on the other it varies as a function of the ratio of the pressure in the chamber to the pressure in front of the nozzle (see Fig. 12).

Finally to obtain a qualitative idea of the interaction of a shock wave with the vortex track, we carried out experiments during which, by means of fixed displacement of the wedge, causing the development of a compression shock, and by measurement of the base pressure at the blade with a through opening (h = 3 mm), it was established from what moment and to what degree the base pressure varied. The most characteristic of the photographs are shown in Fig. 13. This illustration also shows diagrammatically the variation of the base pressure. In these experiments the pressure before the nozzle was approximately 1 atm.

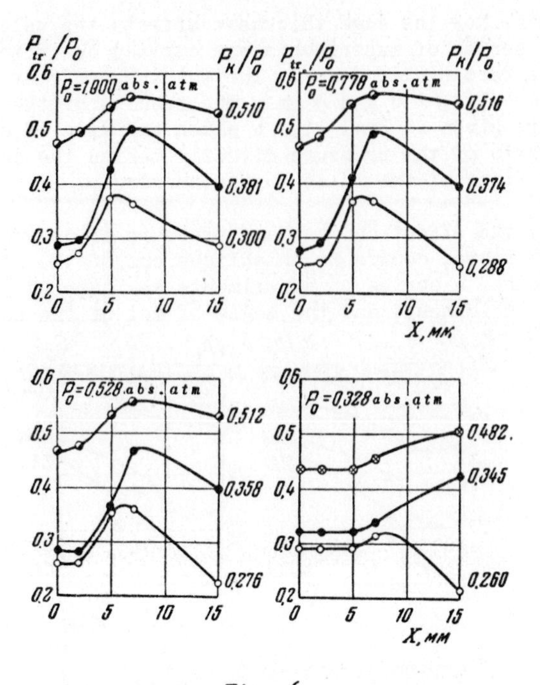
P_{tr}/P_0
P_K/P_0
P_0=1.000 abs. atm
P_0=0.778 abs. atm
P_0=0.528 abs. atm
P_0=0.328 abs. atm
0.510
0.381
0.300
0.516
0.374
0.288
0.512
0.358
0.276
0.482.
0.345
0.260
X, мм

Fig. 6

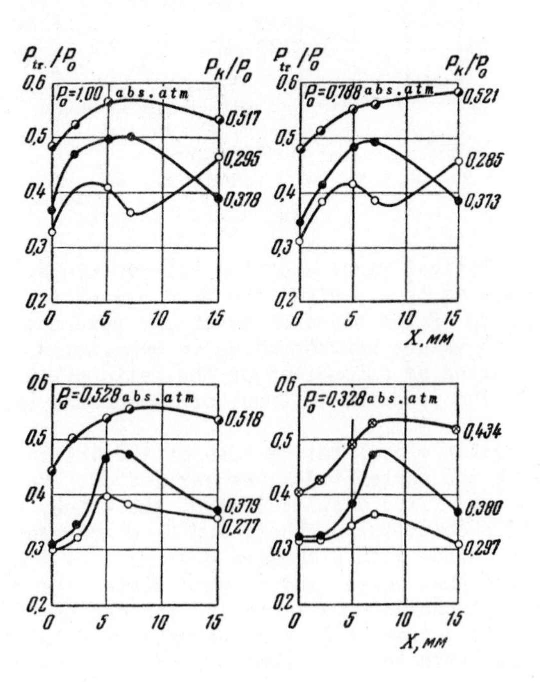
P_{tr}/P_0
P_K/P_0
P_0=1.00 abs. atm
P_0=0.788 abs. atm
P_0=0.528 abs. atm
P_0=0.328 abs. atm
0.517
0.295
0.378
0.521
0.285
0.373
0.518
0.379
0.277
0.434
0.380
0.297
X, мм

Fig. 7

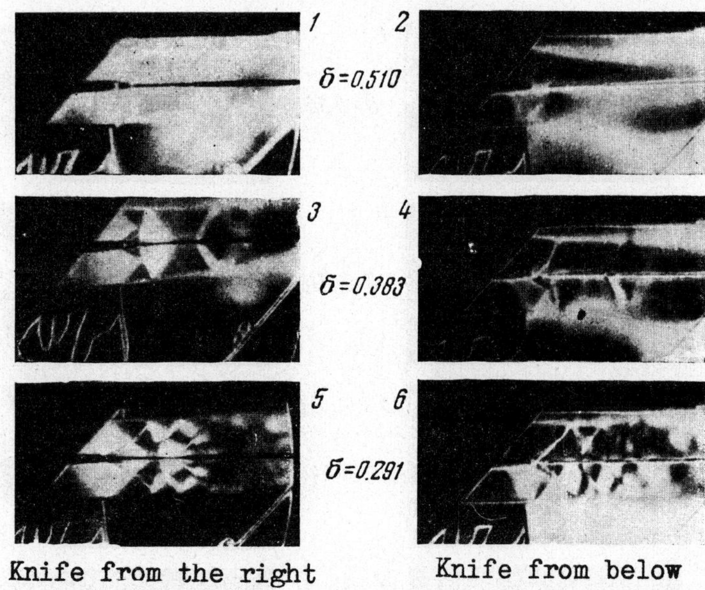

Knife from the right Knife from below

Fig. 8

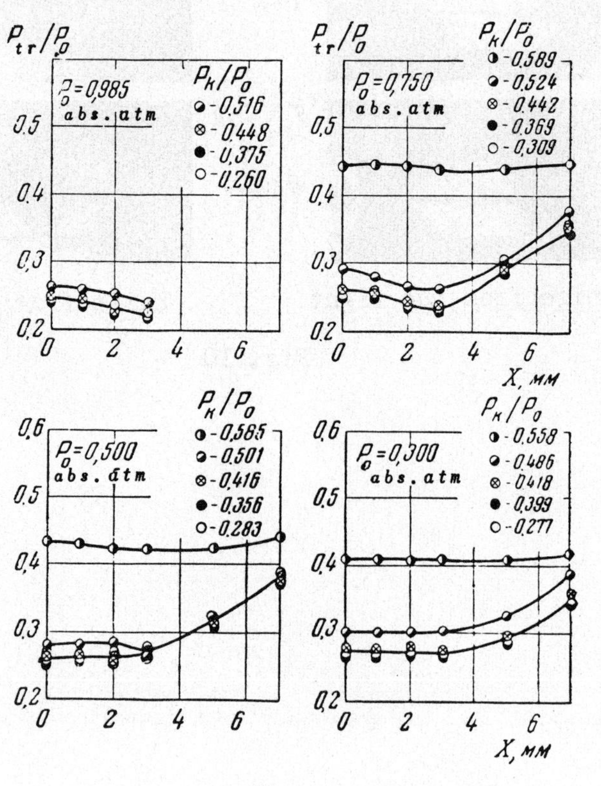

Fig. 9

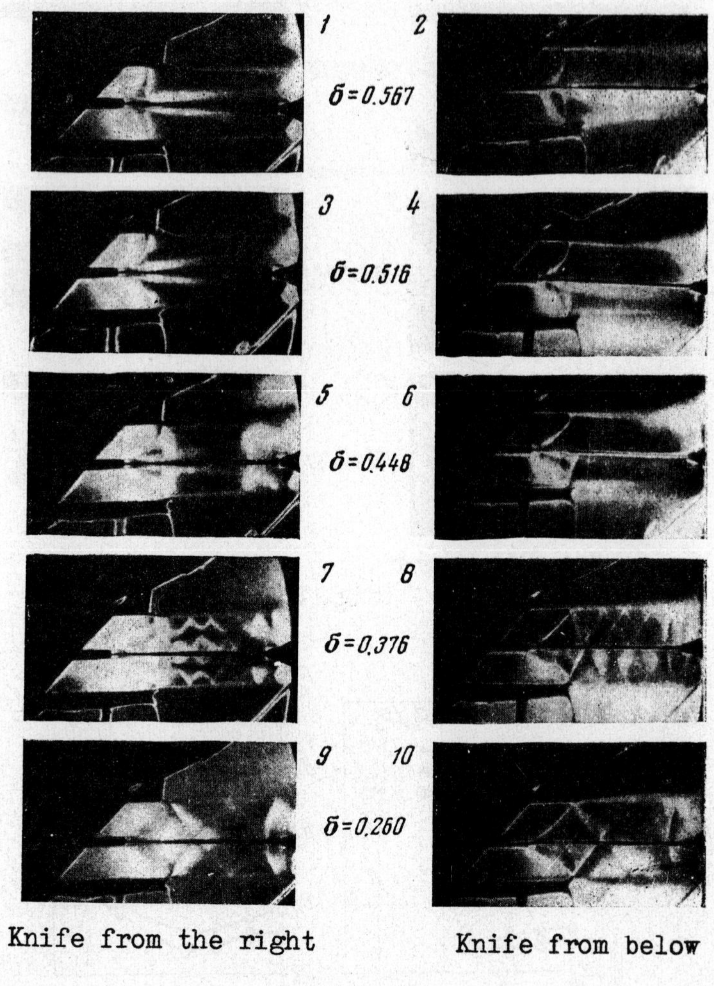

Knife from the right Knife from below

Fig. 10

We will proceed to an analysis of the experimental data.

As is clear from Fig. 5, the character of the curves of variation of the static pressure along the track at various values of $\frac{p_k}{p_0}$ is approximately the same. At the very edge within the limits of approximately 4 mm the pressure varies little. At first it drops slightly and then it increases with increasing intensity. At subsonic and close to supersonic pressure variations between the inlet to the nozzle and the pressure chamber, with increasing distance from the edge, the pressure in the vortex track tends evenly towards the pressure of the surrounding medium.

As the total pressure difference increases, the slope of the rise of the latter in the vortex track increases, and as a result it may exceed the pressure of the surrounding medium.

The recorded slope of the curves is explained, in the main, by the interaction of the process of flow around a thick edge with the wedge-shaped rarefaction waves occurring at the ends of the blades forming the outside walls of the channel.

The initial reduction in pressure is caused both by the existence of a vortex behind the edge, and also by the influence of the above-mentioned rarefaction waves. With the gradual movement away from the edge, a mixing process begins to play an ever greater part, causing an increase in pressure. The latter is accompanied by the appearance of a shock wave in the flow.

In the case of fairly large pressure differences, the intensity of the rarefaction wave leaving the edges of the extreme blades is so great that it not only offsets the influence of the mixing process but also leads to a reduction in the pressure in the track to values close to the base pressure. The pressure variations observed experimentally during further displacement of the needle along the axis of the track with $x > 15$ mm is explained by the interaction of the compression and rarefaction waves developing with the free surface of the jet. The above arguments are confirmed by photographs.

A generally identical pattern can be observed in an experiment with the oval and triangular edges; the reading of the distance along the x-axis here, as in the first case, is made from the extreme right part of the edge (see Figs. 6,7). The pressure rise from the extremity of the edge ($x = 0$) is caused, in the main, by the shift of the reference point to the right with respect to the breakaway point of the boundary layer of the blade (as can be seen in the photographs in Fig. 8, this point lies higher in the flow).

The beginning of the pressure reduction at lower values of x than in the case of the rectangular edge is explained, on the one hand, by the same cause, and on the other, by the influence of the rarefaction waves reflected from the solid surfaces of the outer blades and forming at the convex surface of the blade with an oval edge, and at the apex of the obtuse angle of the blade with a triangular

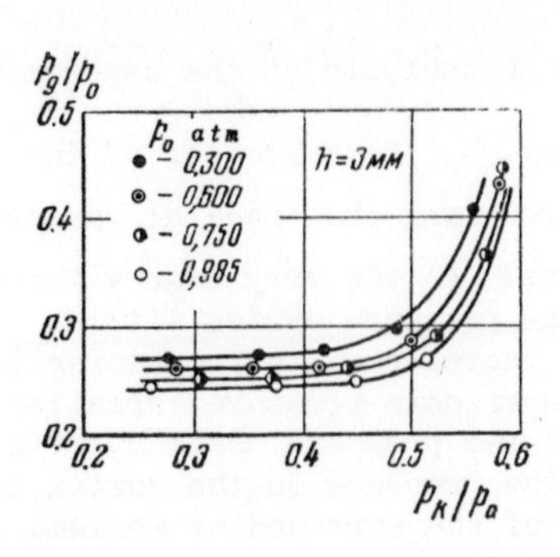

Fig. 11

edge. All this is clearly visible on the photographs of the process (Fig. 8).

It should be noted that the pressure distribution at points of the vortex track fairly distant from the edge ($x > 6$-7 mm), both in the present and in subsequent experiments with other boundary conditions, did not interest us and was investigated only very roughly.

It is possible to judge the effect of the shape of the edge on the nature of the flow from the diagram given in Fig. 14. As can be seen, in a fairly wide range of throttling pressures, at considerable supersonic pressure variations, the relative base pressure (p_b/p_0) increases in the transition from the rectangular to the oval and triangular edge.

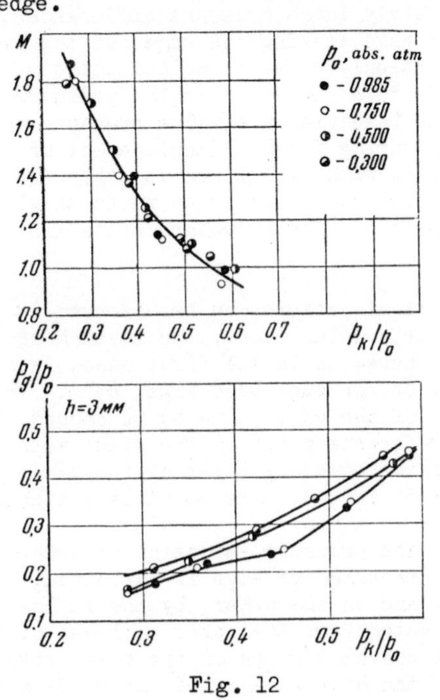

Fig. 12

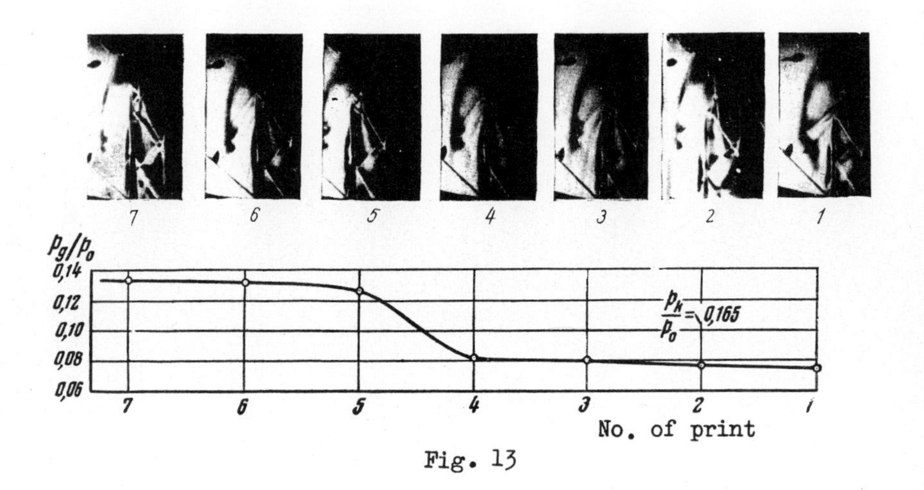

Fig. 13

A similar mechanism in the variation of static pressure in the vortex track of a blade with a rectangular edge is also observed in experiments with slightly altered boundary conditions. In this case the influence of the surrounding medium, as was to be expected, is substantially restricted: the parameters of the vortex track, varying suddenly in the case of subsonic pressure differentials, in the transition to supersonic values of the latter quickly become stable, and at a further reduction in $\frac{p_k}{p_0}$ they show practically no change.

For a clearer explanation of the effect of the Reynolds number and edge thickness, Fig. 15 shows the relative base pressure as a function of the brake pressure for blades of different thickness, in the range where the base pressure is independent of $\frac{p_k}{p_0}$. As can be seen, as p_0 increases in the given conditions, the relative base pressure falls slightly. An increase in the thickness of the edge tends to have the same effect on it. This can be explained by the increase in the turbulence of the vortex track as the Reynolds number increases. An increase in h has the same effect.

The results of experiments with unsymmetrical flow around the blades, shown in Fig. 12, were slightly different from those given in Fig. 11. Consequently, in conditions similar to those existing in an oblique cut of the nozzle apparatus of a gas turbine, the base pressure drops more or less steadily with a decrease in $\frac{p_k}{p_0}$. This occurs for two reasons: in the first place, because in front of the actual edge on that side of the blade on which the rarefaction wave falls, as $\frac{p_k}{p_0}$ decreases the rate of flow increases, and in the second place, in connexion with the fact that, owing to the total taper of the flow which increases as $\frac{p_k}{p_0}$ decreases, the reduction in the pressure in the vortex track continues down to lower values than in the case of symmetrical flow.

As can be seen in Fig. 13, at a fairly large distance from the edge the rate of flow in the track is supersonic (the wave front intersects the line of the track). As was to be expected, in such a case the existence of the wave has no effect on the value of the base pressure. The variation in the slope of the section of the wave passing through the track indicates a reduction in the rate of flow in the latter in proportion to the proximity to the edge. Finally, beginning from some point (as is clear from the photographs, it is lower in the flow, compared to the base of the tail shock), the flow becomes subsonic - the wave falling on the track does not intersect it. As was to be expected, it is approximately from this moment that the base pressure begins to rise. When the falls on the part of the track in the immediate vicinity of the edge, there is a tendency towards breakaway of the boundary layer from the wall of the blade.

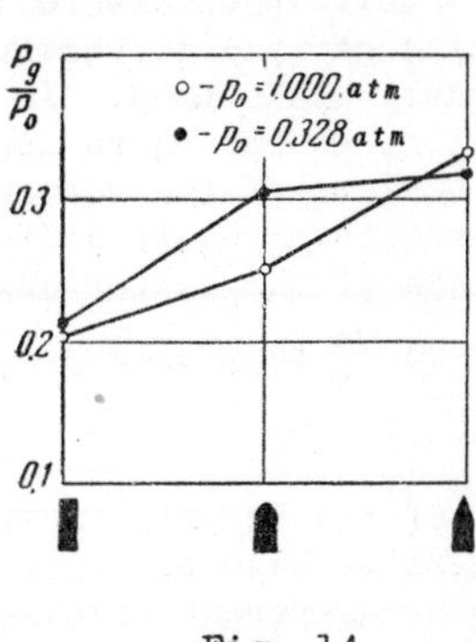

Fig. 14

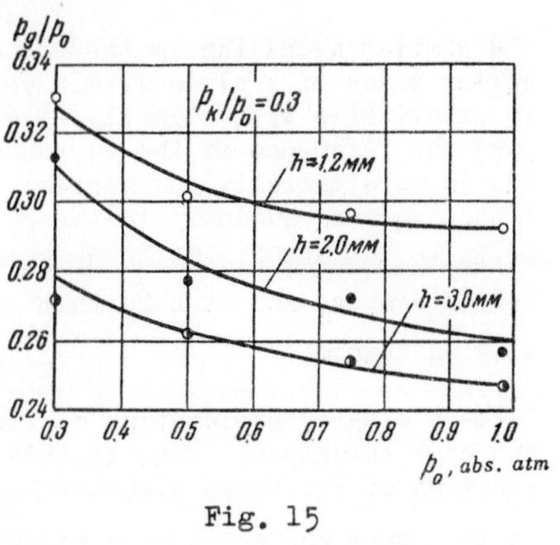

Fig. 15

On the basis of the experiments carried out, the following conclusions may be drawn.

1. In the direct vicinity of the edge, the pressure does not change very intensively, which allows us to take it as constant in rough calculations.

2. The thickness of the edge exerts an influence on the magnitude of the base pressure: other conditions being equal, an increase in the former causes a drop in base pressure.

3. The Reynolds number of the outer flow affects the magnitude of the base pressure. In the conditions of our experiments, the relative base pressure drops as the former increases.

4. The base pressure also depends on the shape of the edge. As the latter becomes sharper, the pressure tends to increase, as a rule.

5. In the case of flow around the thick edge of a blade in conditions of an oblique cut, a reduction in the total back-pressure leads to a steady drop in the base pressure.

6. Intersection of the vortex track by a shock wave leads to an increase in the base pressure only in those cases when the zone of intersection is above the section of the vortex track where the rate of flow is equal to the speed of sound. If the rise in base pressure occurring here is large enough, there is a tendency towards premature breakaway of the boundary layer of the blade.

II. Analysis of the Phenomena Associated with the Unsymmetrical Sonic (or Supersonic) Flow of a Real Gas Around Obtuse Edges

To investigate the main features of a sonic (or supersonic) flow of gas around the edges of blades of finite thickness, we will first examine the simpler case of symmetrical sonic (or supersonic) flow around a rectangular edge. As shown in the diagram (Fig. 16), the streamlines do not bend round the continuously sharp tip of the edge, but are deflected, forming behind it a certain "stagnant" zone, in which the forward speeds of the gas are small in size, and in direction vary up to the direction directly opposite the movement of the flow.

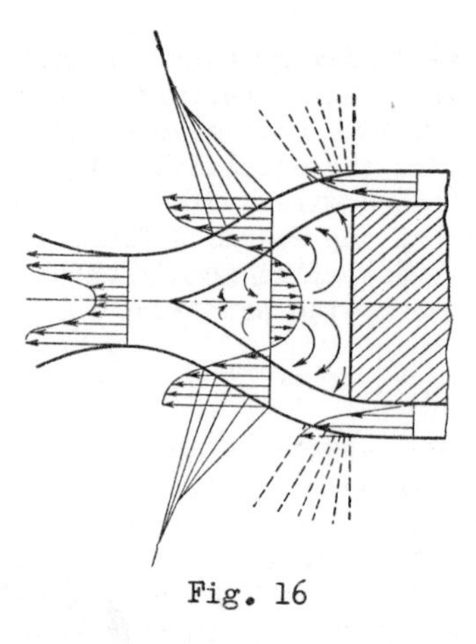

Fig. 16

The stagnant zone is a place of intense vortex formation. Between it and the main flow there is a continuous exchange of gas. The existence of a fairly stable counterflow in the central part of the zone indicates that the transfer of fluid from the zone to the outside flow largely takes place in the forward part and from the outside flow to the stagnant region in the rear part of the latter. Thus, in the direct vicinity of the edge there occurs a continuous movement of material in the direction of the main flow, the result of which is that conditions are created similar to the conditions of the flow of a jet into a flooded space. We will make use of this fact in the following theoretical analysis of the phenomenon.

The correctness of the quoted model of the process is confirmed to a certain extent by a series of experimental data, including those given above.

Thus, for example, the observed nature of the flow of the gas in the stagnant region explains the fact, noted in experiments, of a certain drop in pressure in the immediate vicinity of the edge when moving from the end of the latter down the gas.

As a result of the mixing between the main flow and the vortex zone, there must be a reduction in the amount of movement in the direction coinciding with the direction of the flow. From all the above it follows that the mixing process is inseparably bound up with the formation of the vortex boundary, which forms in the space behind the edge and continuously drifts downstream. In view of the fact that the total kinetic energy of the gas molecules remains constant (we are considering adiabatic flow), then, even without the transition of the energy of the progressive movement of the moles of the material into heat energy, the kinetic energy of progressive movement drops through the development of vortices. Parallel with this, the amount of movement along the flow also decreases; consequently, the pressure in the same direction must increase. The transition of some of the energy into heat energy only intensifies this process.

For simplicity in the following we will examine the symmetrical flow around a plane body of an infinitely wide sonic (or supersonic) homogeneous gas flow. In this case we can assert with a sufficient degree of accuracy that in the streamline of an outer, almost isentropic flow there will be a well-defined connexion between the magnitude and direction of the speed, defined by an epicycloid in the hodograph plane (the so-called Prandtl-Meyer flow). As we know, this connexion is defined by the equation:

$$\pm\theta = \arccos\frac{1}{M} - \sqrt{\frac{\gamma+1}{\gamma-1}}\arctan\left(\sqrt{M^2-1}\sqrt{\frac{\gamma+1}{\gamma-1}}\right) + \text{const.}$$

In fact, because of the infinite width of the flow and the absence of original disturbances in it, the disturbances developed when flowing around the edge are only propagated along the characteristics of one group (we are considering the region of the flow bounded by the axis of symmetry of the body), which is also a sign of the flow of the type indicated. In this case we ignore the disturbances along the characteristics of another group, which develop in the interaction between the disturbances along the characteristics of the first group and the shock wave developing in the flow.

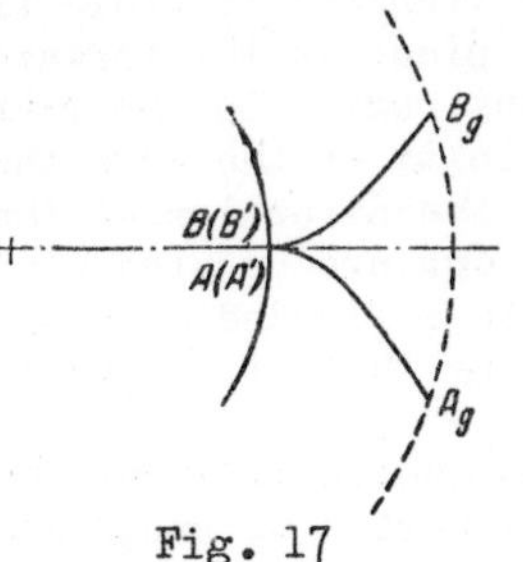

Fig. 17

The possibility of intersection of the front of a compression shock with the boundary of the stagnant zone is excluded, because, as is shown by experiment, the velocity in the latter is known to be subsonic and, consequently, there can be no terminal discontinuity of the flow parameters, either in the vortex region behind the edge or at its boundary (the pressure gradient across the dissipative layer is taken as almost zero). The pressure shock occurring in the main flow close to the stagnant zone turns into a more or less intensive bunch of elementary compression lines, within the limits of which the above well-defined relation between the amount and direction of the velocity is preserved. Since, with symmetrical flow, the velocity direction at the conclusion of the process of flow around the edge must coincide with the direction of an undisturbed flow, then the pressure must also rise to the same value.

Thus, the experimentally observed fact of the formation of tail shocks behind obtuse edges of bodies, around which there is a sonic (or supersonic) flow of gas, has a simple explanation.

In the hodograph plane, the variation of the parameters of flow streams close to a vortex cut takes the form shown in Fig. 17, where the letters A, B denote the parameters before expansion, A_g, B_g those after expansion, A', B' the parameters after the subsequent compression of the gas. As is clear from the diagram, $u_A = u_B = u_A = u_{B'}$, and consequently,

$$p_A = p_B = p_A = p_{B'}.$$

If we trace the boundary between the "almost isentropic" flow, where the influence of viscosity can be ignored, and the dissipative vortex layer where it plays a decisive part (it should be stressed that such a division is extremely arbitrary, since the flow parameters in a direction perpendicular to the vortex track gradually change), then the following general arguments may be expressed: the pressure differential maintained by the vortex track, and with it the difference between the pressure in the undisturbed part of the main flow and the base pressure, will increase with the rise in the velocity of the main flow, in the intensity of the mixing between it and the dissipative layer.

It should be noted that the quantity of matter participating in the mixing depends to a great extent on the degree of turbulence in the vortex track. Thus, for example, if we introduce the mixing coefficient k, defined by the equation:

$$k = \frac{1}{\rho_e u_e} \frac{dm}{dx},$$

where dm/dx is the derivative of the mass flow in the vortex layer in the direction of motion of the main flow, then, from the data in Krokko and Liz [10] $k_{turb} = (5-10) k_{lam}$. This is why the base pressure in the case of a turbulent vortex track is much lower compared with a laminar one. In the case of a supersonic flow of gas from a cascade forming an oblique cut, behind the edge there also develops a certain stagnant zone with reduced pressure, the interaction of which with the surrounding flow leads to the formation of a pair of tail shocks. However, in contrast to the symmetrical process, where the pressure behind the edge is always less than the pressure in the flow in the direct vicinity in front of it, in the case of flow from an oblique cut we can distinguish three varieties of the process, differing from each other in the ratio of the base pressure to the pressure in front of the edge on that side of the blade where the gas is most expanded.

The static pressure in the so-called stagnant zone in the general case is a variable quantity, and the tail shocks are the result of interaction of elementary compression waves. However, for rough calculations giving a qualitatively correct picture of the process, it can be assumed that in the stagnant zone the pressure is approximately constant and equal to some, say, base pressure. Some experimental data confirming such an assumption are given above. Defining it by some means or other and knowing the flow parameters at points A and B, we immediately find the primary elements of the shock, whereupon further synthesis of it becomes simpler. More details of this are given in [1].

Thus, on the basis of all the above, it can be stated that behind the thick edge of bodies placed in a gas flow the so-called vortex track is formed, the pressure in which in the direct vicinity of the edge is, as a rule, low. The process of vortex formation is extremely complex. It is clear that intensive molar mixing plays an important part in it. Thus there are reasons for assuming that an attempt to solve the problem with the aid of traditional equations of hydrodynamics (e.g., the Navier-Stokes equations) will not be successful. It seems more correct to use the integral methods of calculation applied in the theory of the boundary layer; it will be necessary to take some coefficients directly from experiment.

The short review given in [1] shows that this problem is still far from being solved.

Described below is an attempt at a theoretical analysis of the phenomena, which is a generalization of the method developed by Krokko and Liz [10], for the case of unsymmetrical flow around edges of finite thickness with expansion in the oblique cut of the nozzle apparatus of a turbine. Great attention was paid to the determination of the base pressure, but concrete conclusions may also be drawn from the arguments about the distribution of the flow parameters along the vortex track. This latter fact may make it possible to determine more exactly the configuration of the compression shocks which develop.

The suggested method for calculating the process can by no means be considered as completely final. Obviously, it only reflects qualitatively the main factors affecting the phenomenon in question. To obtain **quantitative** agreement between theory and experiment, further investigations, both experimental and theoretical, are necessary.

In what follows we will consider the case of an obtuse edge of rectangular shape, since it lends itself most easily to mathematical analysis. The proposed method, however, is also applicable in the general case to edges of other configurations.

The main assumptions relating to all stages of the arguments are the following:

1. The static pressure at any point of the cross-section of the vortex track parallel to the face of the edge is constant and equal to the corresponding pressure of the almost isentropic flow at the boundary of the dissipative zone.

2. We are only considering adiabatic flows, when there is no heat exchange and the impact temperature at any point of the flow is the same.

Other assumptions will be discussed as they are introduced into the calculation.

Thus, we will examine sonic (or supersonic) flows of a real gas around a blade with a rectangular rear edge of finite thickness, and we will consider that the parameters of the boundary layer in front of the actual edge are fully known to us. For simplicity we will assume that the blade in question has semi-infinite gas flows with identical throttle pressure but different values of λ numbers flowing around it on both sides.

The latter fact makes it possible to use the familiar relation between direction of flow and pressure (and, consequently, other parameters) which is characteristic of the Prandtl-Meyer flow. This relation can be defined by the following differential equation:

$$\frac{dp}{p} = \pm \frac{\gamma M^2}{\sqrt{M^2-1}} d\theta. \quad (1)$$

In oblique cut conditions, such an assumption is not strictly true, since in that case the disturbances are propagated along the characteristics of both groups. However, in the zone in which we are interested, directly abutting on the rear edge, the phenomena associated with the flow around the latter will apparently exert a greater influence on the flow than other disturbances. If we also take into account the approximate nature of other assumptions, then, obviously, to simplify the calculations without greatly re-

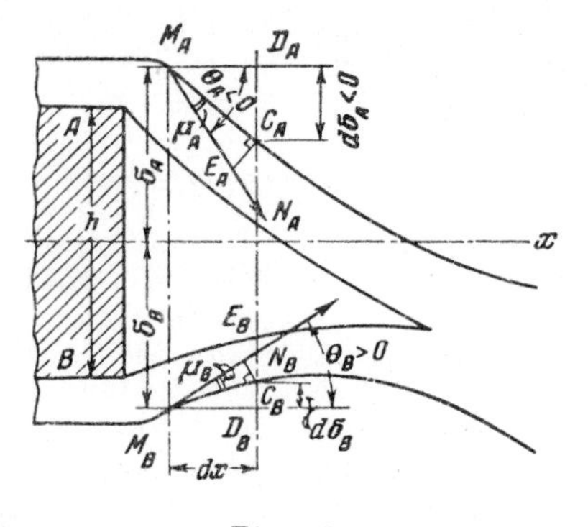

Fig. 18

ducing the accuracy, it will be possible to use the relation (1). However, in those cases when the error which results from such an assumption is too great, we can without any difficulty whatsoever use other and more exact methods of calculation, for example the characteristic method, and the irreversible processes taking place in the development of impact waves can even be taken into account.

A calculation diagram for the phenomenon in question is shown in Fig. 18. All arguments given can be applied directly to continuous flow around blades.

The whole flow is divided into two regions - a dissipative and an almost isentropic region - and the upper and lower boundaries of these regions in the zone of the vortex track are at distances of δ_A and δ_B respectively from the axis of symmetry of the blade $x - x$.

We will assume that the angle of inclination of the velocity vectors to the axis x is not large.

We will draw two sections parallel to the surface of the edge, at a distance of dx from each other, and we will write for the isolated part of the vortex track the momentum equation in the direction of the x-axis:

$$dI_x = u_e(\cos\theta_A\, dm_A + \cos\theta_B\, dm_B) - (\delta_A + \delta_B)\, dp, \qquad (2)$$

where dm_A and dm_B are quantities of mass of matter moving from the outer flow to the dissipative layer through the upper and lower boundaries of the latter. In deriving this equation, we allowed for constant pressure in the cross-sections of the vortex track and equal throttling pressures in the upper and lower parts of the almost isentropic flow.

We will introduce the so-called mixing coefficient k, which describes the intensity of the movement of matter from the outer flow to the dissipative layer

$$\frac{dm_k}{dx} = k\rho_{ek}u_{ek} \qquad (3)$$

The quantity k varies along the track in the general case, but, as a first approximation based on the data in [10] for turbulent vortex tracks, we will assume k = const.

Taking this into account, the momentum equation (2) takes the form:

$$\frac{dI_x}{dx} = u_e\frac{dm_A}{dx}(\cos\theta_A + \cos\theta_B) - (\delta_A + \delta_B)\frac{dp}{dx} \qquad (4)$$

We will derive the discharge equation, taking into account that an increase in the discharge in the dissipative layer corresponds to intersection of the boundary of the latter with the velocity vector of the outer flow. In this case, the angle between them μ is small enough to assume that $\sin\mu \approx \mu$.

$$\frac{dm_A}{dx} = \frac{dm_B}{dx} = \rho_{eA}u_{eA}\frac{\operatorname{arc\,tan}\frac{d\delta_A}{dx} - \theta_A}{\cos\theta_A} = \rho_{eB}u_{eB}\frac{\operatorname{arc\,tan}\frac{d\delta_B}{dx} + \theta_B}{\cos\theta_B}. \qquad (5)$$

With a view to simplifying the consequent calculations, it is convenient to use the following formulae for averaging the velocity, density and temperature in the vortex track:

$$u_1 = \frac{I_x}{m} \qquad (6)$$

$$\rho_1 = \frac{m}{u_1\delta} \qquad (7)$$

$$T_1 = \frac{pu_1\delta}{Rm}, \qquad (8)$$

where $\delta = \delta_A + \delta_B$, and m is the total mass flow of gas in the vortex track.

On the example of [10], using the mean values of the flow parameters, we introduce two new theoretical quantities:

$$\varkappa = \frac{u_1}{u_e} \tag{9}$$

$$F = \gamma \sqrt{\frac{2}{\gamma+1} \frac{p\lambda\delta}{\varkappa m a_0}} - A. \tag{10}$$

In [10] it is shown that by using a method similar to that of Dorodnitsyn it is possible to find for each type of flow of an incompressible fluid (and consequently for the corresponding flows of a compressible gas) a definite function $F(\varkappa)$. Moreover it is not difficult to find the following relations between F and $\varkappa$ on the one hand and the values of the thickness of the boundary layer in the corresponding flow of an incompressible fluid on the other:

$$F = \frac{\delta_i^* + \delta_i^{**}}{\delta_i - \delta_i^* - \delta_i^{**}}. \tag{11}$$

$$\varkappa = \frac{\delta_i - \delta_i^* - \delta_i^{**}}{\delta_i - \delta_i^*}. \tag{12}$$

The presence of the single function $F(\varkappa)$ is theoretically only confirmed for laminar flows of a definite type, not including broken boundary layers. Moreover, the form of the curve depends to a considerable extent on how the boundary of the dissipative layer is defined. Thus, for example, Fig. 19, taken from [10]. shows the functions $F(\varkappa)$ for laminar flows of different types [11], [12] for two ratios of the velocity at the boundary of the dissipative layer and the velocity of an undisturbed flow: $u(\delta)/u_e = 0.95$ and $u(\delta)/u_e = 0.99$.

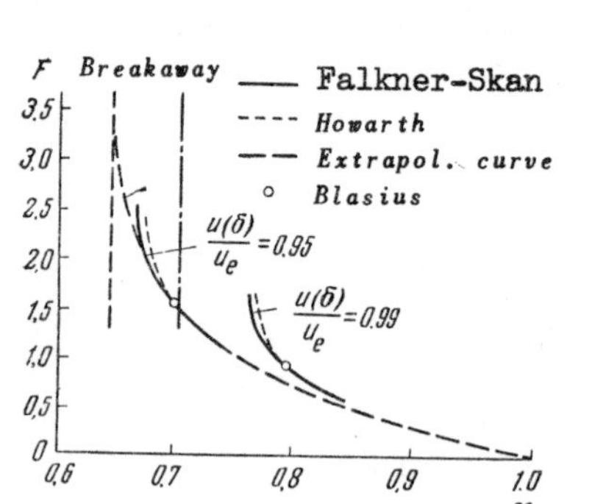

Fig. 19

However, it should be noted that the curves corresponding to the laminar flows of different types pass fairly close to one another, and qualitatively the nature of the slope in all of them is one and the same: as $\varkappa$ decreases, F at first rises steadily, until with $\varkappa$ corresponding to the point of the break in the boundary layer, the curve of the function $F(\varkappa)$ becomes practically a vertical line, indicating great variations in F with small increases in $\varkappa$.

Thus, apparently, the family of curves of $F(\varkappa)$ corresponding to the different laminar flows can be replaced with a satisfactory degree of accuracy by one universal function, plotted even on the basis of the curve relating to the flows $u_{i_e}=c\xi^s$. In this case the curve must pass through a point corresponding to the zero longitudinal gradient (the so-called Blasius solution for a plane plate), and on the left become a vertical at values of $\varkappa$ characteristic of a free half-jet.

As for that part of the curve relating to the vortex track behind a body, from physical considerations it is clear that at a large distance behind the edge, because of the equalization of the flow, $\delta^* \to 0$ and $\delta^{**} \to 0$ and, in accordance with equations (11) and (12), $\varkappa \to 1$ and $F \to 0$. Thus, the curve in question of $F(\varkappa)$ can be smoothly continued to the right up to the point $\varkappa = 1, F = 0$ (in Fig. 19, in order not to encumber the diagram, this plot was only made for the curve $u(\delta)/u_e = 0.95$).

It should be noted that in examining turbulent jets, the result of the lack of data on the influence of compressibility is that it is not yet possible to carry out any theoretical discussion justifying the use of a universal curve of $F(\varkappa)$. It is necessary, therefore, to use an analogy which must be found in the general nature of the slope of this curve for laminar and turbulent flows. Obviously, in the latter case the curve must also pass through the point with the zero longitudinal pressure gradient; to the left of it when approaching the point of the break ($\varkappa \approx \varkappa_j$) it must practically become a vertical, and to the right, in a region corresponding to a sufficient distance from the disturbing effect of the body located in the flow, it tends towards the point $\varkappa = 1$, $F = 0$. The above qualitative arguments are confirmed by some experimental data obtained in [13] and shown in Fig. 20 which is taken from [10].

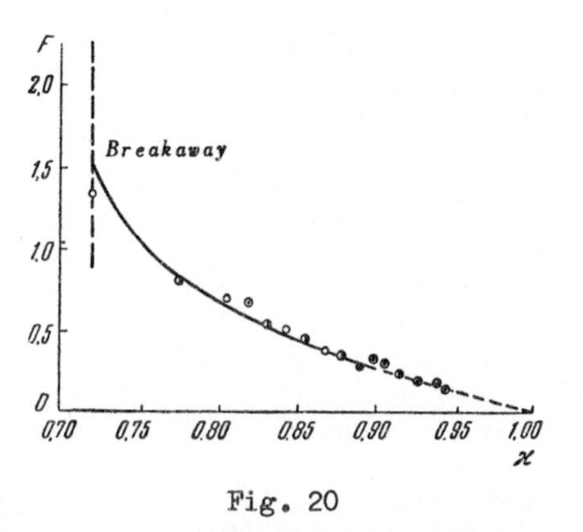

Fig. 20

Thus, on the basis of the above, by using some theoretical and experimental data, it is possible to plot two universal curves of the function $F(\varkappa)$ corresponding to the laminar and turbulent dissipative layers. These curves, being approximate, largely preserve the nature of the actual flow.

Using the assumptions made, we come to the derivation of the function $F(\lambda_e)$ in the vortex track.

Using equations of impulses and discharge, we find two relations with the unknowns $d\varkappa/d\ln m$ and $d\lambda_e/d\ln m$:

$$\left(F+A+\varkappa\frac{dF}{d\varkappa}\right)\frac{d\varkappa}{d\ln m}-\varkappa\left[(F+A)\left(\frac{1}{\lambda_e}-\frac{2\gamma}{\gamma+1}\frac{\lambda_e}{A}\right)+\frac{2(\gamma-1)}{\gamma+1}\lambda_e\right]\frac{d\lambda_e}{d\ln m}=$$

$$=\frac{A}{2k}\left[\tan(k\cos\theta_A+\theta_A)+\tan(k\cos\theta_B-\theta_B)\right]-\varkappa(F+A) \tag{13}$$

$$\lambda_e\frac{d\varkappa}{d\ln m}-\frac{\varkappa F}{A}\frac{d\lambda_e}{d\ln m}=\lambda_e\left(\frac{\cos\theta_A+\cos\theta_B}{2}-\varkappa\right) \tag{14}$$

Expressions (13) and (14) can be considered as a system of equations defining $d\varkappa/d\ln m$ and $d\lambda_e/d\ln m$. This system can be reduced to a non-linear differential equation giving the sought-for relation between F and λ_e. After simple transformations this relation takes the following form:

$$\frac{dF}{d\lambda_e}=\frac{dF}{d\varkappa}\frac{\frac{d\varkappa}{d\ln m}}{\frac{d\lambda_e}{d\ln m}}=\frac{f_1(\lambda_e;F)}{f_2(\lambda_e;F)} \tag{15}$$

where

$$f_1(\lambda_e;F)=\frac{\varkappa}{A\lambda_e}\Big\{A(\lambda_e^2-1)(\cos\theta_A+\cos\theta_B-$$
$$-2\varkappa)+F\Big\{\frac{2\gamma}{\gamma+1}\lambda_e^2(\cos\theta_A+\cos\theta_B-2\varkappa)-2F\varkappa+$$
$$+A\left[\frac{\tan(k\cos\theta_A+\theta_A)+\tan(k\cos\theta_B-\theta_B)}{k}-(\cos\theta_A+\cos\theta_B)\right]\Big\}\Big\} \tag{16}$$

$$f_2(\lambda_e;F)=\Big\{\frac{A}{k}\left[\tan(k\cos\theta_A+\theta_A)+\tan(k\cos\theta_B-\theta_B)\right]-$$
$$-(F+A)(\cos\theta_A+\cos\theta_B)\Big\}\frac{d\varkappa}{dF}-\varkappa(\cos\theta_A+\cos\theta_B-2\varkappa) \tag{17}$$

Since in our case k = const, $\theta(\lambda_e)$ is the known relation characteristic of the Prandtl-Meyer flow, and $F(\varkappa)$ is given by the corresponding curve (Fig. 20), all the data necessary for resolution of equation (15) are present.

In that case, if the angles formed by the velocity vectors and the boundary of the dissipative layer with the x axis are small enough for the approximate equations $\cos\theta\approx 1$, $\tan(k\cos\theta+\theta)\approx k+\theta$ to be satisfied, equation (15) is somewhat simplified and takes the form:

$$\frac{dF}{d\lambda_e}=\frac{\varkappa}{A\lambda_e}\frac{1}{\left(A\frac{\theta_A-\theta_B}{2k}-F\right)\frac{d\varkappa}{dF}-\varkappa(1-\varkappa)}\cdot$$
$$\cdot\left\{A(\lambda_e^2-1)(1-\varkappa)+F\left[\frac{2\gamma}{\gamma+1}\lambda_e^2(1-\varkappa)-F(\varkappa)+A\left(\frac{\theta_A-\theta_B}{2k}\right)\right]\right\} \tag{18}$$

Let us analyse the expression obtained.

In the first place, in view of the fact that $\theta_A = \varphi(\lambda_e; \lambda_A)$, and

$\theta_B = \varphi(\lambda_e; \lambda_B)$, then also $F = \varphi_1(\lambda_e; \lambda_A; \lambda_B)$,

where the letters λ_A and λ_B denote the dimensionless velocities of an almost isentropic undisturbed flow on both sides of the blade. Consequently, for each pair of values of λ_A and λ_B equation (15) defines some single series of curves which are not dependent on such parameters as the thickness of the boundary layer before break-away from the edge and the thickness of the edge itself.

In the second place, the relation (15) introducing a first-order differential equation gives the resolution in the form of a series of curves in the $F - \varkappa$ plane. On the basis of some further physical considerations, we must select that one which corresponds to the actual process.

In [10] it is shown that of the whole series only the critical curve along which $dF/d\lambda_e > 0$ throughout has any physical sense.

Thus, from the multiplicity of curves satisfying equation (15) we select a single one, along which the numerator and the denominator of expression (15) revert to zero simultaneously at some critical point $(\lambda_{e_{cr}}; F_{cr})$. To find its co-ordinates it is sufficient to resolve the system of equations:

$$f_1(\lambda_{e_{cr}}; F_{cr}; \lambda_A; \lambda_B) = 0 \qquad (19)$$

$$f_2(\lambda_{e\,cr}; F_{cr}\lambda_A; \lambda_B) = 0 \qquad (20)$$

As is clear from the above equations, the parameters of the critical point are fully defined by the quantities of the dimensionless velocities of an undisturbed flow on both sides of the blade. In the cases of practical interest, the values θ_{cr} are small enough for us to proceed from the approximate relation (18) when determining the co-ordinates of the critical point. In this case equations (19) and (20) will take the form:

$$A_{cr}(\lambda^2_{e_{cr}} - 1)(1 - \varkappa_{cr}) + F_{cr}\left[\frac{2\gamma}{\gamma+1}\lambda^2_{e_{cr}}(1 - \varkappa_{cr}) - F_{cr}\varkappa_{cr} - A_{cr}\frac{2\nu_{cr} - \bar{\nu}_A - \bar{\nu}_B}{2k}\right] = 0 \qquad (19a)$$

$$\left(A_{cr}\frac{2\nu_{cr} - \bar{\nu}_A - \bar{\nu}_B}{2k} + F_{cr}\right)\left(\frac{d\varkappa}{dF}\right)_{cr} + \varkappa_{cr}(1 - \varkappa_{cr}) = 0 \qquad (19b)$$

The system of equations obtained must be resolved by graphical analysis.

At the critical point the numerator and the denominator of equations(15) revert to zero, and therefore in the calculation it is convenient, in the vicinity of zero, to set the approximate relation $F(\lambda)$ - linear or parabolic depending on the required degree of accuracy.

Defining $\left(\frac{dF}{d\lambda_e}\right)_{cr}$ and $\left(\frac{d^2F}{d\lambda_e^2}\right)_{cr}$ (more details about this are given in [1]), we use the expansion in the Taylor series by degrees $(\lambda - \lambda_{cr})$ until it becomes possible to use directly the basic equation (15) with a sufficient degree of accuracy. Further calculation is carried out by the usual numerical methods.

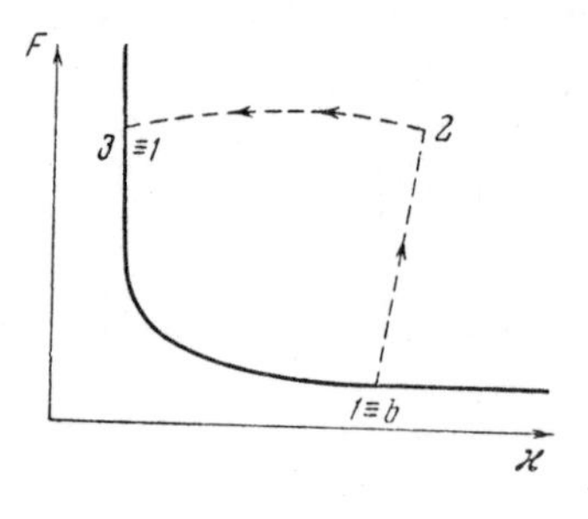

Fig. 21

Plotting the relation $F(\lambda_e)$ by the method given above, to find the flow parameters at the edge itself it is necessary to introduce some condition describing the process of transition of the boundary layer from the surface of the body into the vortex track. In Fig. 21, taken from [10], this process is shown diagrammatically in the plane of $F - \varkappa$ by the broken line 1 - 2 - 3. The part 1 - 2 corresponds to flow around a sharp edge, when $\varkappa$ increases slightly through the equalizing effect of rarefaction and F increases sharply because of the inclusion of the stagnant zone in the dissipative layer. The other arm of the curve (2 - 3) corresponds to the stagnant zone in the immediate vicinity of the edge, where the quantity $\varkappa$ drops sharply to values characteristic of a free jet and F undergoes inconsiderable changes associated with the presence of a counter-flow in the stagnant zone. Here the quantity F at first rises slightly and then drops.

In view of the complexity of this phenomenon, at present it is difficult to describe it with sufficient accuracy. For this it is necessary to carry out a series of special experimental and theoretical investigations, all the more important since, in the problem of expansion in an oblique cut now being examined, the ratio of the thickness of the boundary layer before the break to the thickness of the edge may attain considerable values.

In view of the lack of data on the phenomenon in question, and also taking into account the approximate nature of the whole theoretical analysis given here, we will replace the smooth transition along the curve 1 - 2 - 3 by a jump from the point 1 to the point 3, which physically corresponds to the assumption of the introduction of the conditions characteristic of a free jet fairly close to the edge of the body. In this case, within the limits of the transition section we will ignore the transfer of matter from the almost isentropic flow to the dissipative layer. Equation (10) for the vortex track in the immediate vicinity of the edge may then be written thus:

$$F_d = \frac{A_d}{\varkappa_d} \frac{1}{\left(1 - \frac{\delta^*}{\delta}\right)_d} - A_d \tag{21}$$

Using the diagram (Fig. 22), we find the following expression for F_d:

$$F_d = \frac{A_d}{\varkappa_d}\left\{\varphi_d\left[\frac{h}{\delta_{b_A}} - \mu_1(\tan\theta_{d_A} - \tan\theta_{d_B})\right] + \right.$$
$$\left. + \frac{\left(1-\frac{\delta^*}{\delta}\right)_{b_A}}{\left(1-\frac{\delta^*}{\delta}\right)_j}\left(\frac{\varphi_{b_A}}{\cos\theta_{d_A}} + \frac{\varphi_{b_B}}{\cos\theta_{d_B}}\frac{\delta_{b_B}}{\delta_{b_A}}\right)\right\} \cdot \tag{22}$$
$$\left[\varphi_{b_A}\left(1-\frac{\delta^*}{\delta}\right)_{b_A} + \varphi_{b_B}\frac{\delta_{b_B}}{\delta_{b_A}}\left(1-\frac{\delta^*}{\delta}\right)_{b_B}\right]^{-1} - A_d \cdot$$

At fairly small values of θ_d and μ_1, expression (22) is slightly simplified:

$$F_d = A_d\left\{\frac{1}{\varkappa_d}\frac{\frac{\varphi_d h}{\delta_{b_A}} - \frac{\left(1-\frac{\delta^*}{\delta}\right)_{b_A}}{\left(1-\frac{\delta^*}{\delta}\right)_j}\left(\varphi_{b_A} + \varphi\frac{\delta_{b_B}}{\delta_{b_A}}\right)}{\varphi_{b_A}\left(1-\frac{\delta^*}{\delta}\right)_{b_A} + \varphi_{b_B}\frac{\delta_{b_B}}{\delta_{b_A}}\left(1-\frac{\delta^*}{\delta}\right)_{b_B}} - 1\right\} \tag{23}$$

The quantities $(1-\delta^*/\delta)_{b_A}$ and $(1-\delta^*/\delta)_{b_B}$ are assumed as known, as are all the parameters of the boundary layer before the break.

Thus, for given quantities of λ_A and λ_B (and, consequently, φ_{b_A} and φ_{b_B}), equation (22) gives a single relation $F_d(\lambda_{e_d})$. Obviously, the values of F and λ_e simultaneously satisfying equations (15) and (22) will also correspond to the flow parameters in the direct vicinity of the edge behind it.

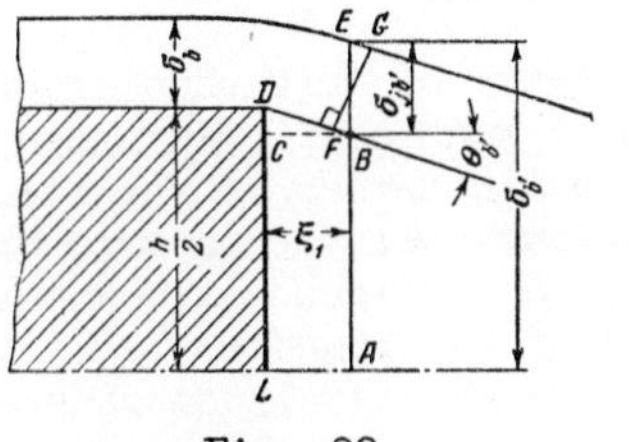

Fig. 22

Analysis of equation (22) shows that, other conditions being equal, F_d depends on the ratio of the thickness of the edge to the thickness of the boundary layer before the break. Such a dependence is confirmed by the experimental studies of a number of foreign investigators [14].

Since the slope of the curve $F(\lambda_e)$ plotted from equation (15) does not depend on the relative thickness of the edge (h/δ_b), the relation (22) shows that as the ratio h/δ_b rises F_d rises, λ_{e_d} also increases, and consequently the base pressure must decrease. Precisely this effect of the thickness of the edge was observed in our experiments.

In view of the fact that the relation $F(\varkappa)$ is given as a graph, equation (22) must be resolved by graphical analysis. To simplify the calculation, Fig. 23 shows the relation of the product $F\varkappa$ to $\varkappa$. The values of the parameters in which we are interested may be simply found at the point of intersection of this curve with a straight line defined by the following equation [to simplify the equation we used the approximate relation (23)]:

$$F_d\varkappa_d = -A_d\varkappa_d + A_d\frac{\varphi_d\frac{h}{\delta_{b_A}} + \frac{\left(1-\frac{\delta^*}{\delta}\right)_{b_A}}{\left(1-\frac{\delta^*}{\delta}\right)_j}\left(\varphi_{b_A} + \varphi_{b_B}\frac{\delta_{b_B}}{\delta_{b_A}}\right)}{\varphi_{b_A}\left(1-\frac{\delta^*}{\delta}\right)_{b_A} + \varphi_{b_B}\frac{\delta_{b_B}}{\delta_{b_A}}\left(1-\frac{\delta^*}{\delta}\right)_{b_B}} \qquad (24)$$

The relation $F(\lambda_e)$ found makes it possible to determine not only the base pressure, but also the distribution of the flow parameters along the track. In fact, taking logarithms and differentiating equation (10) will give:

$$\frac{d\lambda_e}{dx} = \frac{2k\varkappa\left(\frac{F}{A}+1\right) - [\tan(k\cos\theta_A+\theta_A) + \tan(k\cos\theta_B-\theta_B)]}{\delta\left[\frac{1}{\lambda_e} - \frac{2\gamma}{\gamma+1}\frac{\lambda_e}{A} + \frac{2(\gamma-1)}{\gamma+1}\frac{\lambda_e}{F+A} - \left(\varkappa\frac{d\varkappa}{dF} + \frac{1}{F+A}\right)\frac{dF}{d\lambda_e}\right]} \qquad (25)$$

In this equation only δ is an unknown quantity, but it is easily found (see [1]):

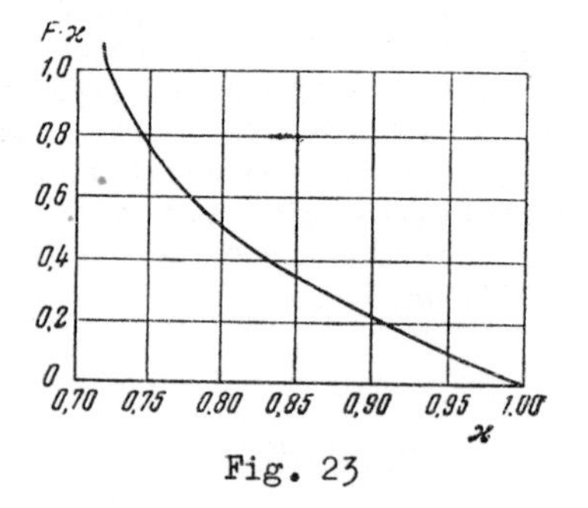

Fig. 23

$$\delta = h + \mu_1\delta_{b_A}(\delta_{b_A}(\tan\theta_{\lambda_A} - \tan\theta_{dB}) + \delta_{b_A}\frac{\varphi_{b_A}}{\varphi_d}\frac{\left(1-\frac{\delta^*}{\delta}\right)_{b_A}}{\left(1-\frac{\delta^*}{\delta}\right)_j}\left(\frac{1}{\cos\theta_{dA}} + \right.$$

$$\left. + \frac{\varphi_{b_B}}{\varphi_{b_A}}\frac{\delta_{b_B}}{\delta_{b_A}}\frac{1}{\cos\theta_{dB}}\right) + \int_{\mu_1\delta_{b_A}}^{x}[\tan(k\cos\theta_A+\theta_A) + \tan(k\cos\theta_B-\theta_B)]\,dx \qquad (26)$$

At fairly low values θ and μ_1, equations (25) and (26) can be simplified:

$$\frac{d\lambda_e}{dx}=\frac{2k\varkappa\left(1+\frac{F}{A}\right)-\left[2(k-\nu)+\bar{\nu}_A+\bar{\nu}_B\right]}{\delta\left[\frac{1}{\lambda_e}-\frac{2\gamma}{\gamma+1}\frac{\lambda_e}{A}+\frac{2(\gamma-1)\lambda_e}{(\gamma+1)(F+A)}-\left(\varkappa\frac{dx}{dF}+\frac{1}{F+A}\right)\frac{dF}{d\lambda_e}\right]}$$

$$\delta=h+\delta_{b_A}\frac{\varphi_{b_A}}{\varphi_{д}}\frac{\left(1-\frac{\delta^*}{\delta}\right)_{b_A}}{\left(1-\frac{\delta^*}{\delta}\right)_j}\left(1+\frac{\varphi_{b_B}}{\varphi_{b_A}}\frac{\delta_{b_B}}{\delta_{b_A}}\right)+x\left(2k+\bar{\nu}_A+\bar{\nu}_B\right)-2\int_0^x\nu\,dx \quad (26a)$$

Integrating equation (25) by some means or other, we will know the distribution of λ_e along the x axis, and consequently also all the other flow and vortex track parameters.

Analysing the suggested method of calculation as a whole, we should stress that despite the approximate nature of the solution the use of this method for calculating the processes associated with symmetrical flow [10] gave very good qualitative agreement with the results of experimental studies [6], [7], [15].

This indicates that the adopted calculating diagram correctly reflects the main physical factors defining the phenomenon.

Again we will note that the method given in this study for calculating the flow around edges with regard to the expansion of a gas in oblique cut conditions should only be considered as the first approximation to the theoretical resolution of this problem. Considerable theoretical and especially experimental investigations are still necessary in this field, which may introduce substantial additions and greater accuracy to the proposed method. It would seem that the main problems due for resolution in the next stage of the investigations in this field are: experimental determination of the relation of k to the various flow parameters; further theoretical and experimental studies devoted to the mechanism of the process of vortex formation directly behind the edge; and justification of the validity of the use of the universal relation $F(\varkappa)$ for flows of different types.

REFERENCES

1. V.P. MOTULEVICH, Expansion of a gas in an oblique cut of the nozzle apparatus of a turbine (K voprosu o rasshirenii gaza v kosom sreze soplovogo apparata turbiny) Dissertatsiya, Energ. Inst. Akad. Nauk SSSR (1953).
2. Scientific Report (Nauchnyi otchet), Lab. fiz. gor., Energ. Inst. Akad. Nauk SSSR (1951).
3. G.S. ZHIRITSKII, Yu. F. KONTSEVICH, Direction of flow at outlet from lattice of turbine blades (Napravleniye potoka na vykhode iz reshetki turbinnykh lopatok), Kotloturbostroenie, No. 3, 1951.

4. N.M. MARKOV, Calculation of the Aerodynamic Characteristics of a Plane Cascade of Sections of Axial Turbo-machines (Raschet aerodinamicheskikh kharakteristik ploskoi reshetki profilei osevykh turbomashin), Mashgiz (1952).
5. M.D. SENNICHENKO, Pressure distribution in turbine reaction channels (O raspredelenii davleniya v turbinnykh reaktivnykh kanalakh), Kotloturbostroenie, No. 2, 1949.
6. D.R. CHAPMAN, F.A. PERKINS, N.A.C.A. Report, 1036 (1951).
7. S.M. BOGDONOFF, J. aer. sciences, No. 3, 1952.
8. Kh. KURTSVEG, Relation between boundary layer and base vacuum (Svyaz'mezhdu pogranichnym sloyem i donnym vakuumom), Mekhanika, No. 4, 1952.
9. R. WICK, J. aer. sciences, No. 10, 1953.
10. L. KROKKO, L.LIZ, Theory of mixture for determination of interaction of dissipating and near-isentropic currents (Teoriya mesheniya dlya opredeleniya vzaimodeistviya dissipativnogo i pochti izoentropicheskogo potokov), Voprosy raketnoi tekhniki, No. 2, 1953.
11. L. HOWARTH, On the solution of the laminar boundary layer equations, Proc. Royal Soc., 164 A (1938).
12. V.M. FALKNER, S.W. SKAN, Some approximate solution of the boundary layer equations, British A.R.C., No. 1314 (1930).
13. G.B. SHUBANER, B.S. KLEBANOFF, Investigation of separation of the turbulent boundary layer NACA TN, No. 2133 (1950).
14. D.R. CHAPMAN, N.A.C.A. Report No. 1051 (1951).
15. D.R. CHAPMAN, W.R. WIMBROW, R.H. KESTER, NACA TN, No. 2611 (1952).

T.V. Bazhenova, R.I. Soloukhin,

Pressure Field Occurring in Water during an Electrical Discharge

In order to investigate the possibility of using an underwater spark discharge as a pressure source in water, it is necessary to know the law of motion of the liquid and of distribution in time and space of the pressures occurring during the discharge.

The present work contains the results of an investigation into the movement of a gaseous sphere forming during a discharge, and the pressure field occurring in this case.

1. Movement of a Gas Bubble Developing During an Underwater Discharge

Fig. 1 shows a shadow photograph of an underwater spark discharge. The photograph was made through a slot by projection on to a rotating drum, as a result of which, on the photograph, the time axis is in the direction of the axis of abscissae, and the radius of the expanding gas sphere is along the axis of ordinates. The discharger was placed at the inspection hole of the tank in such a way that the electrodes were covered by the screen of the inspection hole and only a slot, perpendicular to the direction of rotation of the film, was illuminated. The narrow slot was illuminated from the opposite side by a constant light source.

The gas sphere developing during the electrical discharge was clearly visible, because the gas, having a different refraction index, deflected the rays of light from the source to the side, and the area occupied by the gas sphere was obtained on the photograph in the form of a dark spot. The photograph represents a continuous series of successive images of the slot of the inspection hole, past which the gas sphere was moving. The photograph was taken under the following conditions: voltage at the capacitors $V = 15$ kV, capacity of the capacitors $C = 30\,\mu F$, distance between the electrodes in the water $d = 10$mm. The voltage was fed to the electrodes of the underwater discharger through an air gap 15 mm long with keep-alive electrodes. The water was taken from town water mains.

From the time scan of the discharge (Fig. 1) it is clear that the gas bubble occurs in the water before the moment when there is the main energy release, accompanied by a bright spark ($t = 0$).

In fact, for a period of 0.004 sec before the main discharge, at the moment of breakdown of the air gap, on the photograph there appears a shadow of the gas bubble, gradually increasing at a low rate up to the radius $R_0 = 1.8$ cm. During this period, apparently, there is evaporation of a small volume of water when heated by the relatively weak electric current flowing initially between the electrodes of the discharge device, since in our experiments the high capacity ensured an adequate charging current for this. Then there follows the bright flash of the spark discharge in the water vapours, greatly increasing the temperature and pressure of the gas in the bubble. After the flash the gas sphere begins to expand rapidly and, at the moment $t = 0.005$ sec after the main discharge, reaches its maximum radius $R_{max} = 6.3$ cm (in Fig. 1 the boundary of the bubble at $R_{max} = 6.3$ cm touches the shadow of the crossbeam of the discharge device).

During a period of 0.007 sec the gas sphere begins to contract under the pressure of the surrounding water, at first slowly and then more rapidly. The highest speed is achieved at the moment $t = 0.009$ sec. At this time, it is possible on the photograph to see compression waves proceeding into the liquid from the surface of the bubble in the form of dark strips. The compression waves occurring in water during the movement of a gas sphere are clearly visible on the photographs made by the Toepler method (Fig. 2). On these photographs it is clear that intensive compression waves only appear for approximately 0.002 sec after the main discharge. At the moment of contraction of the bubble, a large wave emerges, which is then reflected from the bottom of the tank. After compression, the bubble attains a radius of 3.2 cm (1.8 times greater than the initial measurement) and continues to contract slowly, partially breaking into layers. Subsequently the bubble continues to pulsate about the radius of $R = 3$ cm, periodically emitting compression waves into the surrounding medium for a period of the order of 0.03 sec, and gradually breaks up.

2. Calculation of the Initial Pressure of the Discharge According to the Law of Expansion of a Gas Bubble

In hydrodynamics, the resolution of the problem of the expansion of a gas sphere in water with a momentary energy release is familiar [1]. The solution obtained by Lamb [2] while neglecting the pressure in the surrounding medium compared to the pressure inside the sphere was generalized by O. Vlasov [3] for the case when the pressure in the surrounding space is not negligible compared with the pressure inside the sphere. Using these solutions it is possible to calculate theoretically the law of expansion of a gas sphere in an infinite liquid if the initial radius of the sphere and the initial pressure in it are given.

Integration of the equations of motion of an incompressible fluid with allowance for the conditions at the boundary of the gas sphere gives the following expression for the rate of movement of the boundary of a gas sphere:

$$\frac{dR}{dt} = \sqrt{\frac{2p_1}{3\rho}\left\{3\left(1-\frac{R_0}{R}\right)\frac{R_0^3}{R^3} - \frac{p_H}{p_1}\left(1-\frac{R_0^3}{R^3}\right)\right\}}. \quad (1)$$

Here R_0 is the initial radius of the sphere, R is the current radius, p_1 is the initial pressure in the sphere, p_H is the pressure of the liquid at that depth H at which the sphere is immersed, ρ is the density of the water.

In integrating we assumed that the expansion of the water vapours proceeds roughly according to an adiabatic law with an index γ = 1.33, i.e., without allowing for dissociation or condensation of the water.

The law of movement of a gas bubble can be obtained by graphical integration of the relation:

$$t = \frac{1}{\sqrt{\frac{2p_1}{3\rho}}} \int_{R_0}^{R_{max}} \frac{1}{\sqrt{3\left(\frac{R_0}{R}\right)^3\left(1-\frac{R_0}{R}\right) - \frac{p_H}{p_1}\left[1-\left(\frac{R_0}{R}\right)^3\right]}} dR. \quad (2)$$

From the given law of movement of the bubble $R(t)$ with the aid of the relation (2) it is possible to calculate the initial pressure p_1.

The photographs of the movement of the boundary of the gas bubble (Figs. 1 and 2) make it possible to plot the graph of the function $R(t)$. Such a graph is shown in Fig. 3(a). The part of the curve which corresponds to the section illuminated by the discharge near $t = 0$ was interpolated from adjacent values of R. The data of several experiments in similar conditions show good recurrence.

From the graph in Fig. 3 it is possible to determine the radius of the bubble R and the values of the rate of expansion of the bubble $\frac{dR}{dt} = u_R$ for any moment t. This makes it possible to calculate the initial value of the pressure p_1 when $R = R_0$ with the aid of the formula (10) [2]. However, such a calculation is only correct in the case when the actual expansion of the bubble obeys the theoretical law.

We will determine p_1 from the data for $R = R_{max}$. At this point $\frac{dR}{dt} = 0$ and from the relation (10) we find easily:

$$p_1 = \frac{p_H\left[1 \cdot \left(\frac{R_0}{R_{max}}\right)^3\right]}{3\left(\frac{R_0}{R_{max}}\right)^3\left(1-\frac{R_0}{R_{max}}\right)}. \quad (3)$$

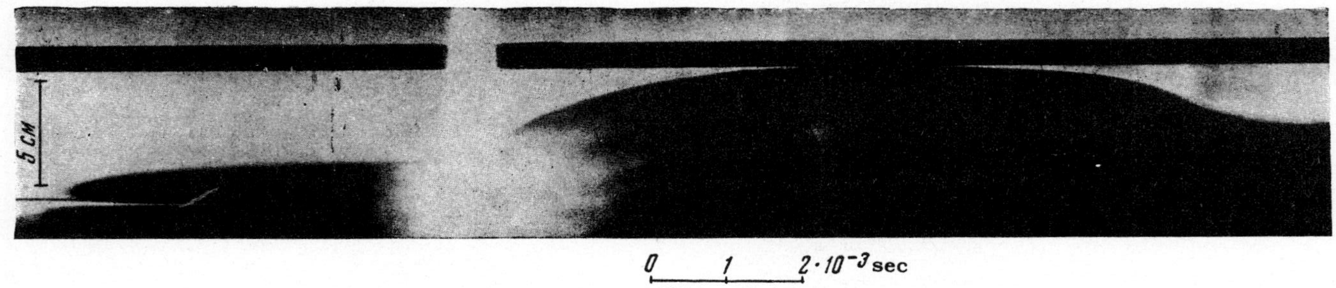

5 CM

0 1 $2 \cdot 10^{-3}$ sec

Fig. 1
Time scan of the process of formation and expansion of a gas bubble occurring during an electrical discharge in water

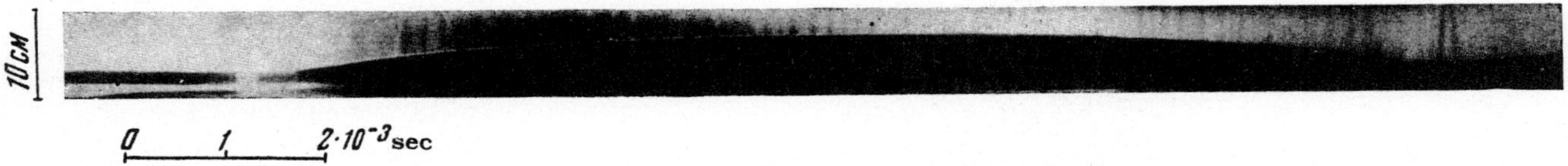

10 CM

0 1 $2 \cdot 10^{-3}$ sec

Fig. 2
Compression waves emanating from the boundary of a gas bubble expanding in water

The experimental data of the experiment, shown in Fig. 1, give the following values which are needed for calculating p_1: $R_0 = 1.8$ cm, $R_{max} = 6.3$ cm, $p_H = 1.1 \times 10^6$ bar. Substituting these data into formula (3) we find the value of the initial pressure occurring in the gas sphere during a discharge as 23 kg/cm^2.

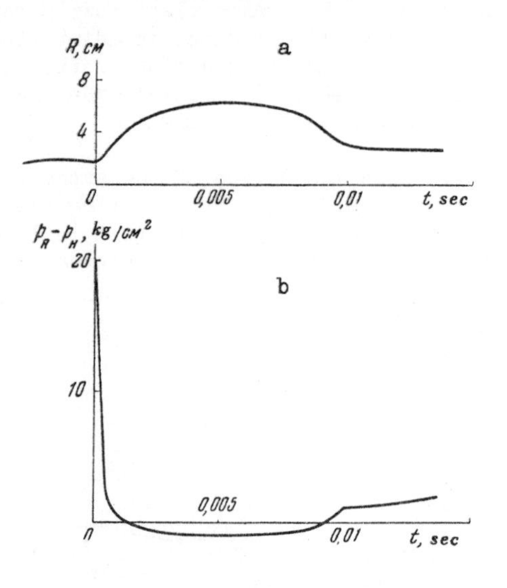

Fig. 3
Curves of the expansion of the gas bubble and of the pressure in the bubble

The pressure p_1 can also be calculated from known values of R and $\frac{dR}{dt}$ at any moment t.

In fact, from formula (2) we have

$$p_1 = \frac{\frac{\rho u_R^2}{2} + \frac{p_H}{3}\left[1 - \left(\frac{R_0}{R}\right)^3\right]}{\left(\frac{R_0}{R}\right)^3\left(1 - \frac{R_0}{R}\right)}. \tag{3a}$$

Substituting the data taken from the graph in Fig. 3 (a) into formula (3a), we find for p_1 a value of 23 kg/cm^2, i.e., the same value as was obtained from the data for R_{max}.

We will check whether the experimental law of the expansion of a gas bubble conforms with the theoretical relation (2). For this we calculate, by means of graphical integration, the values of t for a series of values of R where $p_1 = 23$ kg/cm^2 and compare with the experimental data.

Calculation shows that the law of expansion and contraction of a gas sphere, which was found experimentally, is practically no different from that found theoretically.

3. Variation of the Pressure Inside a Gas Bubble and in the Surrounding Medium as a Function of Time

The pressure developing in a gas bubble during a discharge immediately begins to change because the bubble is expanding. The process of expansion of the bubble takes place fairly rapidly (0.005 sec), and therefore it can be considered as adiabatic. Using the adiabatic equation and the law of expansion of the bubble known from experiment, it is possible to calculate the law of variation in time of the pressure inside the bubble.

Figs. 3 (a) and (b) show the curves of the expansion of the bubble and the pressure inside it. By comparing these curves it can be seen that during the first moments (1×10^{-3} sec) the bubble expands under the action of the increased internal pressure.

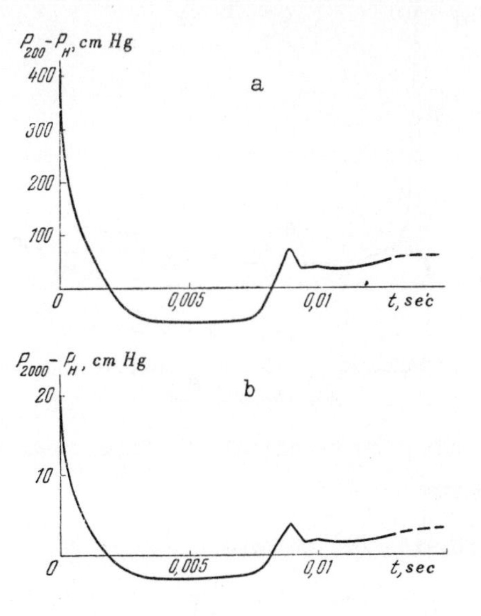

Fig. 4
Curves of the pressure in the water at distances of 1 and 20 m from the expanding gas bubble

In this case the pressure in the bubble drops rapidly and becomes equal to the pressure of the surrounding medium p_H. The greatest rate of expansion of the bubble on this section is attained not at the initial moment when the bubble has to overcome the inertia of the water, but at the moment $t = 0.75 \times 10^{-3}$ sec, when the surrounding layers of water have come into motion, although the pressure drop at this time is not yet very great.

After the pressure inside the bubble becomes equal to the pressure of the surrounding medium, the expansion of the bubble does not stop but continues because of inertia. Hereupon the pressure in the bubble becomes lower than the pressure in the surrounding medium and fairly great rarefaction occurs ($p_R - p_H$ = -0.94 atm).

After the gas bubble attains its maximum radius R_{max} its movement ceases, and within 6×10^{-3} sec it begins to contract slowly under the pressure of the surrounding liquid. The pressure in the bubble gradually rises. At the moment when the adjacent layers of water attain a considerable velocity towards the centre of the bubble, the bubble begins to contract very rapidly. The pressure in the bubble at this time is again already equal to the pressure of the surrounding medium, but contraction continues because of inertia. The pressure in the bubble rises rapidly to 1.2 atm, and then continues to rise slowly.

Integration of the equations of the hydrodynamics of an incompressible liquid in the spherical co-ordinates from R to ∞, with allowance for the conditions at the boundary of the gas sphere, gives the following expression for the pressure p at any point of space r at any moment of time t:

$$\frac{p - p_H}{\rho} = \frac{R}{r}\left(\left[\frac{p_1 \frac{R_0^4}{R^4} - p_H}{\rho} + \frac{1}{2}\left(\frac{dR}{dt}\right)^2\left(1 - \frac{R^3}{r^3}\right)\right]. \qquad (4)$$

Analysis of this formula shows that at great distances from the sphere ($\frac{R^3}{r^3} \ll 1$) the pressure in the liquid differs from the pressure inside the sphere by the term $\frac{1}{2}\left(\frac{dR}{dt}\right)^2$, expressing the energy of movement of the boundary of the bubble, and the factor $\frac{1}{r}$, describing the decrease in pressure with distance.

The pressure field in the surrounding medium can be calculated from the known law of motion of the bubble.

Theoretical curves of the variation of pressure with time for $r = 1$ m and $r = 20$ m are shown in the graphs in Fig. 4.

The relation of pressure to distance can be expressed by the formula:

$$\frac{p - p_H}{p_R - p_H} = \frac{r}{R_0}. \qquad (4a)$$

This law is correct for all cases of the pressure curve where the rate of movement of the boundary of the gas bubble is small, or on the condition that $\frac{R^3}{r^3} \sim 1$.

4. Experimental Determination of the Pressure Field Occurring in Water During a Discharge

In order to check the correctness of the calculations of the pressure curves given in section 1, the pressures occurring during a discharge were measured.

To measure the rapidly changing pressures we used a piezo-electric pressure gauge with a d.c. voltage amplifier.

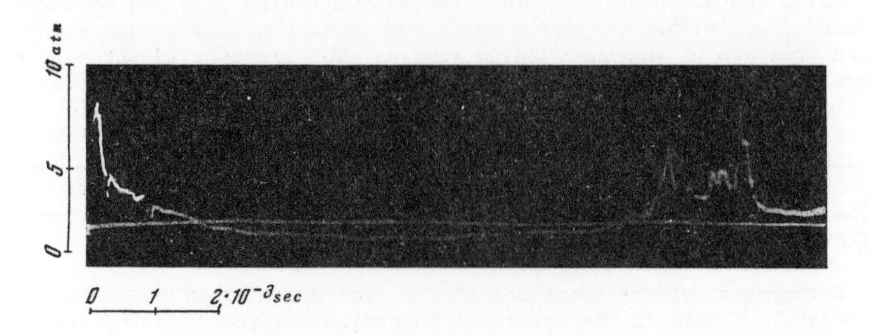

Fig. 5
Oscillogram of the pressure in the water at a distance of 6 cm from the discharge device

Fig. 5 shows an oscillogram of the pressure occurring in the water during an electrical discharge. The time is along the abscissa, and the deflection of the oscillograph beam, corresponding to variation of pressure, along the ordinate. The bright flash of the main discharge illuminates the oscillograph screen with the scale. At this moment the beam of the oscillograph rises suddenly and then begins to drop in accordance with the variation of the pressure in the given point in space. Within 0.03 sec the oscillograph beam returns to the initial position, which corresponds to equalization of the pressure in the given point of the medium.

In Figs. 6 (a), (b) the small circles on the theoretical curves show the experimentally determined pressures at corresponding moments of time. Theory shows good agreement with experiment over the whole curve, with the exception of those sections where there is an increase in the pressure of the liquid through the great rate of contraction of the gas bubble. The experimental data show at these times a higher increase in pressure than that prophesied by theory.

The agreement between experiment and theoretical data indicates that for calculation of the pressure field occurring during an electrical discharge under water, with a high charging current, it is possible to use the formula (4). The initial radius of the gas sphere and the initial pressure in it can be determined from the law of expansion of the gas sphere.

An experimental check on the pressure curves calculated for distances of $r = 1$ m, $r = 2$ m and $r = 20$ m proved difficult in laboratory conditions in view of the limited dimensions of the tank.

An investigation was carried out into the drop in the first pressure peak with distance. The results are shown on the graph (Fig.7). The points lie satisfactorily on the theoretical curve plotted according to formula (4 a). (In this series of experiments the initial pressure in the bubble was 40 atm).

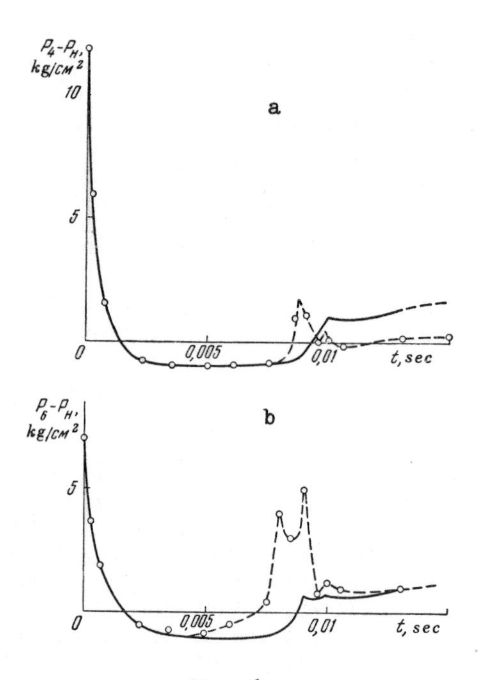

Fig. 6, a, b
Comparison of theoretical pressure curves with the experimental ones

The results shown were obtained with no allowance for the influence of the boundaries of the water tank. It was possible to achieve this experimentally in a small tank on account of the fact that the distance from the source to the measuring point was much less than to the boundaries of the water, and the reflected signals arrived at the measuring point much weaker than the main signal.

An allowance for the reflections from the free surface and from the bottom of the water tank indicates that the form of the initial impulse is distorted. The resultant disturbance at some point in the medium is a succession of positive and negative impulses, and the pressure integral in time is practically equal to zero (Fig. 8). The impulses follow each other at intervals of a few milliseconds with ever-decreasing amplitude. The reflecting action of the boundaries concentrates the energy of the impulse between the bottom and the free surface of the tank, so that the actual duration of the disturbance is approximately 10 times greater than the duration of the main impulse. The duration of the positive part of the first impulse is reduced by reflection.

These results of calculations were confirmed quantitatively by experiments carried out in more spacious tanks.

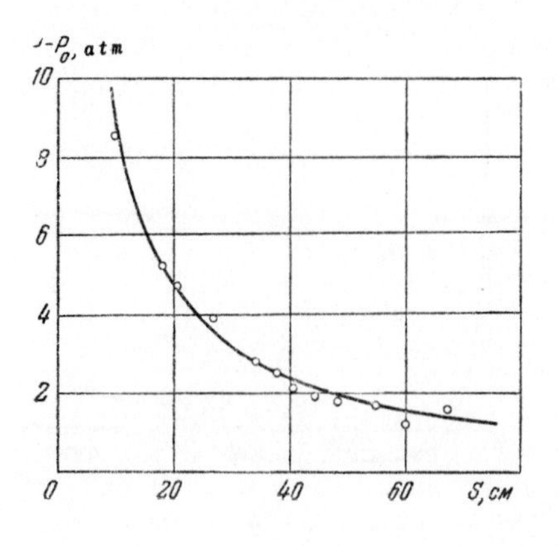

Fig. 7
Maximum pressure in the water as a function of the distance from the discharge device

An increase in the pressure developing inside the gas sphere can be achieved by varying the parameters of the electrical circuit causing the discharge. It was established that the pressure in the bubble is in direct proportion to the energy released between the electrodes. Within the limits of consumed energy of 1 to 3 kJ the relation between the energy consumed for the discharge E_p and the energy released between the electrodes E_3 is expressed by the following empirical formula: $E_3 = 0.1\ E_p^{0,9}$. An increase in the discharge energy is achieved in the main by an increase in the voltage. An increase in the capacity very soon ceases to affect the energy of the initial impulse, and only helps to increase the duration of the discharge. An increase in the inductance and ohmic resistance helps to reduce the amount of energy released in the discharge. For each set of operating conditions there is an optimum value for the distance between the electrodes. In the experiments described it was 10 mm.

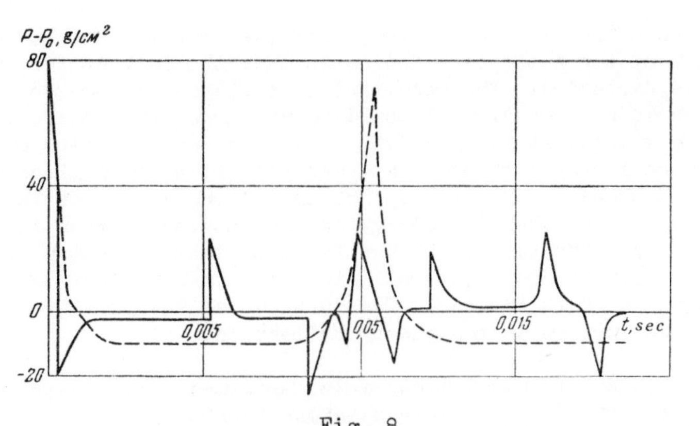

Fig. 8
Curves of the resultant pressures against time, in the presence of reflecting surfaces

Conclusions

1. During an electrical discharge under water, the energy of the discharge is released in a finite volume of water vapour, the dimensions of which are determined by the distance between the electrodes.

2. The pressure field developing in a liquid during an underwater discharge can be calculated by means of hydrodynamic laws; it consists of a positive peak and a negative region. Experiments showed agreement with theoretical calculation.

3. From theory and experiment it follows that the rate of decrease in pressure with distance drops as the initial radius R_0 increases, and the duration of the positive part of the impulse increases as R_0 increases and as p_1 decreases.

REFERENCES

1. R. KOUL, Podvodnye vzryvy (Underwater explosions) (Translation into Russian), Izd. inostr. lit. (1950).
2. G. LAMB, Hydrodynamics (Gidrodinamika), Gostekhizdat (1947).
3. O. VLASOV, Fundamentals of explosion dynamics (Osnovy dinamiki vzryva), Moscow (1945).

R.I. Soloukhin

Shock Waves Forming during an Electrical Discharge in Water

1. Introduction

This work is devoted to a photographic investigation of the formation of a shock wave during an electrical discharge in water (one-dimensional case). It borders upon numerous investigations into underwater explosions [1]. However, in the case of explosions of explosive materials under water it is a question of already-developed shock waves of great intensity. These waves are the result of the passage into the liquid of a powerful detonation wave passing through the explosive materials.

In the case of an electrical discharge with a fairly high discharge current, the reason for the development of the wave is largely the accelerated movement of the wall of the gas bubble to which the energy of the discharge is imparted. In these conditions it is possible to study the initial stage of the development of the shock discontinuity.

The development of disturbances of finite amplitude in water is very difficult because of its low compressibility. However, water as a gas-dynamic medium has a number of interesting features. To create shock waves in a liquid which move with a velocity greatly in excess of the speed of sound, very high pressures are required compared with the pressure in shock waves in a gas. Thus in water, for example, for a shock wave the velocity of which is twice the speed of sound the pressure behind the wavefront is 18,000 atm. In contrast, for wave velocity in air to be twice the speed of sound the pressure behind the wavefront must only be 4.5 atm.

During the propagation in any medium of a compression wave of finite amplitude, the medium is involved in movement in the direction of propagation with a velocity u, and the speed of sound increases to the quantity $c > c_0$, whereupon the sum $u + c$ is always greater than the rate of propagation of the disturbance D. The ratio

Fig. 1
Waves during discharge in air

Fig. 2
Scan of discharge in water in small chamber

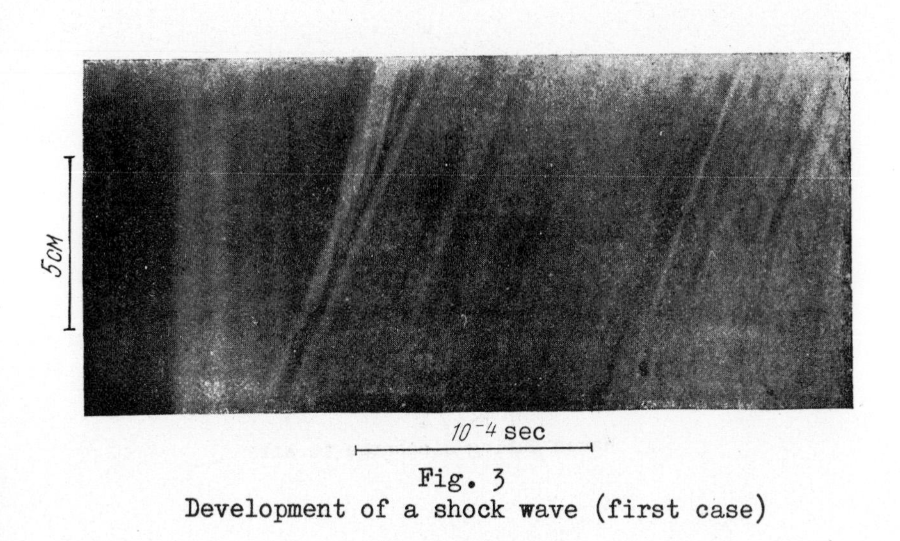

Fig. 3
Development of a shock wave (first case)

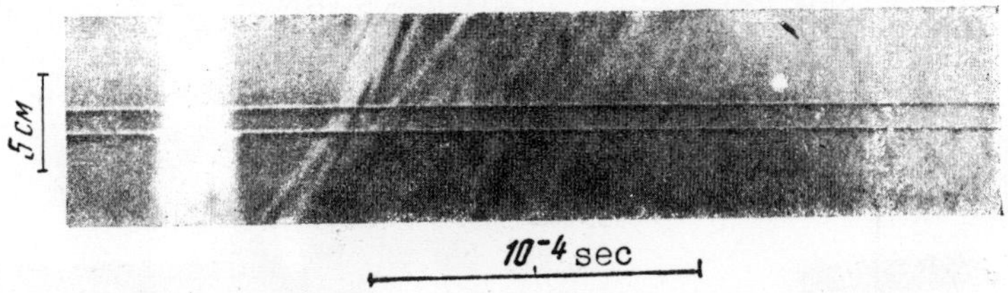

5CM

10^-4 sec

Fig. 4
Development of a shock wave (second case)

$$r = \frac{u + c}{D}$$

is the important characteristic of the medium. It describes the rate of formation of the discontinuity from the elementary disturbances. For an ideal gas with $\gamma = 1.4$ (for example, for air) r rises rapidly with the intensity of the wave to a value of 1.28, then remaining almost unchanged. In water $r = 1.28$ at $\Delta p = 5{,}000$ atm. At $\Delta p = 50{,}000$ atm, $r = 1.58$.

Thus, in that range of pressures when waves develop with velocities greatly in excess of the speed of sound in water, the waves can build up more rapidly than in gas. It is of great interest that in water the speed of sound behind a shock wave is always greater than the rate of propagation of the wave:

$$c > D,$$

i.e., in a liquid it is impossible to create a supersonic flow behind a shock wave, whereas in gas this is achieved even for comparatively weak shock waves (where $M \gg 2.1$ for air).

2. Photographing a Discharge

To photograph the propagation of the disturbances developing during a discharge, we used the Toepler apparatus type IAB-451. In the field of vision of the device we placed an explosion chamber with water. One of the chambers was a cylindrical channel with a diameter of 60 mm and a length of up to 600 mm, with eye holes, the other chamber (a small one) was a parallelepiped with dimensions of 25 × 35 × 120 mm, which we looked right through.

Across a spark gap of 2-8 mm we discharged a bank of capacitors, the capacity of which varied from 0.25 to 3 μF at a voltage of 10 to 30 kV. The discharge circuit passed through the contacts of the shutter which allows light into the optical device for the period of exposure. The time recording was carried out with the aid of a rotating drum with a film. The linear speed of the film varied from 10 to 50 m/sec. The density disturbances were recorded in the form of lines with a tangent of the angle of inclination proportional to their rate of movement.

3. The Process Developing During a Discharge

Fig. 1 shows a photograph of the disturbances obtained on the described apparatus in air. Elementary compression waves overtaking each other can be seen. The flow pattern of a discharge in water has a number of special features. Fig. 2 shows a typical photograph of the process in a small chamber, in which the spark gap is placed in the field of vision (lower part of the photograph). After a voltage is applied to the spark gap, there is a period of slow discharge through the water (about 10^{-3} sec). Between the electrodes there forms a gas bubble of about 1 cm in size. In the bubble thus forming there is also a sudden flashover (light spot on the photograph). The rapidly expanding gas bubble becomes a source of compression waves, going from bottom to top on the photograph. The bubble pulsates two or three times. At the moment of maximum contraction of the bubble in the pulsations, abrupt disturbances develop which are clearly visible on the photograph. The wave velocity in the photograph presented, within the limits of measuring accuracy, does not exceed the speed of sound in water.

4. Development of the Shock Wave

The nature of the discharge may vary in accordance with the electrical parameters of the discharge circuit and the size of the spark gap. In the general case the discharge takes place in the form of damped oscillations with a frequency of approximately 10^5 c/s. For each discharge intensity peak there is a corresponding bright band on the scan of the process.

Figs. 3 and 4 show photographs of the development of the shock wave in the large chamber. The spark gap and the gas bubble were outside the field of vision. In Fig. 3 it is possible to see the gradual rise in the velocity of the shock wave as it develops. The discharge in this case, as can be seen from the series of light vertical strips in the exposure, took place comparatively slowly. In Fig. 4 all the energy of the discharge was released during the first two peaks, which also caused a fairly sudden break-off in the velocity of the shock wave.

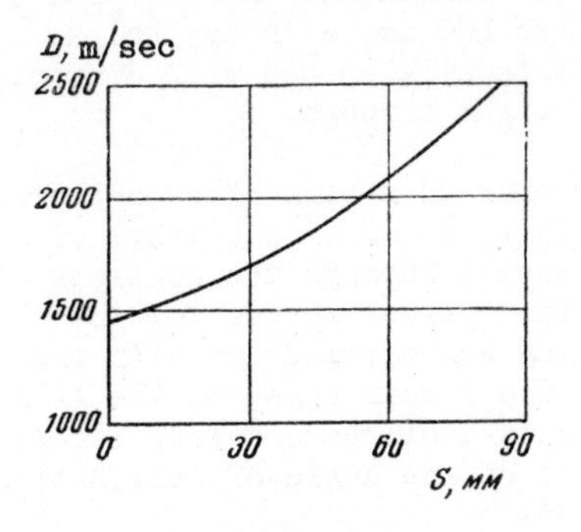

Fig. 5
Variation in velocity of shock wave with distance from spark

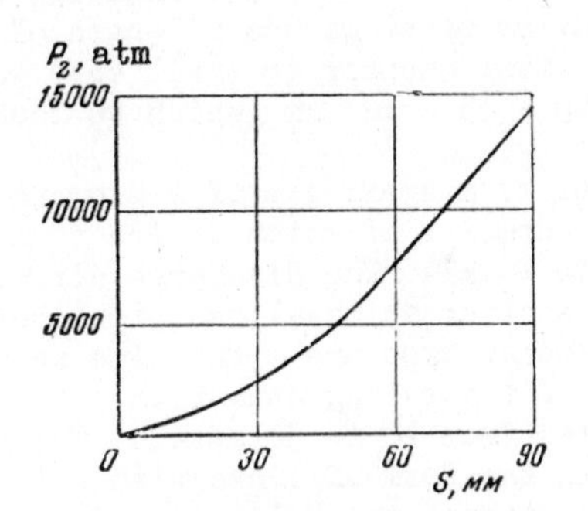

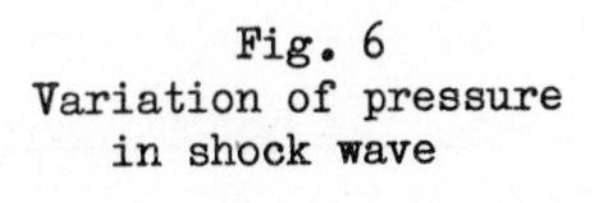

Fig. 6
Variation of pressure in shock wave

The graphs (Figs. 5 and 6) show the variation of the velocity and calculated pressure in the crest of the wave shown in Fig. 3, in relation to the distance covered by the wave. In calculating the pressure we used the data about under-water explosions [1].

5. Conclusions

This work contains a qualitative analysis of the phenomena accompanying an electrical discharge in water. A number of characteristics of liquid as a gas-dynamic medium are noted. It is shown that a rapidly expanding gas bubble can, in the one-dimensional case, lead to the development of a shock wave from the elementary disturbances.

REFERENCE

1. R. KOUL, Under-water explosions (Podvodnye vzryvy), Izd. inostran. lit. (1950).

T.V. Bazhenova

Development of Shock Waves in Water as a Result of Combination of Elementary Compression Waves

The shock waves occurring in water during an under-water explosion are usually caused by the passage of a detonation wave from the reaction products of the explosive material into the water. However, there may be cases when the result of the under-water explosion is, not a detonation wave in a gas bubble which develops, but possibly a shock wave developing in the water at some distance from the source of the explosion. This shock wave is the result of the addition of the elementary compression waves passing into the water from the boundary of the expanding gas bubble.

Setting a fixed distance at which the shock wave must develop, it is possible to calculate the law of expansion of the gas bubble necessary for this, and the law of energy release into the bubble which is necessary for the creation of such a bubble. In the present work the problem is solved for a one-dimensional case.

1. Necessary Law of Expansion of a Gas Bubble for Development of Shock Wave at a Given Distance

The equations for the motion of a compressible fluid for the one-dimensional case in Euler co-ordinates take the form:

$$\left.\begin{aligned} &\frac{\partial u}{\partial t} + u\frac{\partial u}{\partial x} + \frac{1}{\rho}\frac{\partial p}{\partial x} = 0 \\ &\frac{\partial \ln \rho}{\partial t} + u\frac{\partial \ln \rho}{\partial x} + \frac{\partial u}{\partial x} = 0 \end{aligned}\right\} \tag{1}$$

Here u denotes the velocity of the particles of the fluid, the other symbols being as usual. To such equations it is necessary to add the empirical equation of state for water [1].

$$p = B\left[\left(\frac{\rho}{\rho_0}\right)^n - 1\right]. \tag{2}$$

This equation is correct for pressures up to 25,000 atm at temperatures from 20 to 60°C. In these conditions the constant values are the following:

B = 3047 kg/cm ; n = 7.15 ± 4%.

The existence of a connexion between pressure and density (2) makes it possible to calculate the speed of sound $a^2 = \frac{\partial p}{\partial \rho}$ and to integrate equations (1). After integration we obtain the familiar Riemann solutions, coinciding with the equations of the characteristics of system (1). The integration constants are determined from the boundary conditions, the first of which is obtained from an investigation of the movement of the boundary of the bubble compressing the water: where $u = 0$ the speed of sound is that corresponding to an undisturbed medium. As a result we obtain the first characteristic equation:

$$u = \frac{2}{n-1}(a - a_0). \tag{3}$$

In the second characteristic equation there is an unknown function of the speed $F(u)$:

$$x = \left(\frac{n+1}{2} u + a\right) t + F(u). \tag{4}$$

The function $F(u)$ is determined from the condition that at the given point of occurrence of the shock wave, all the characteristics must intersect. This condition, together with (4), makes it possible to calculate the path of the boundary of the gas bubble

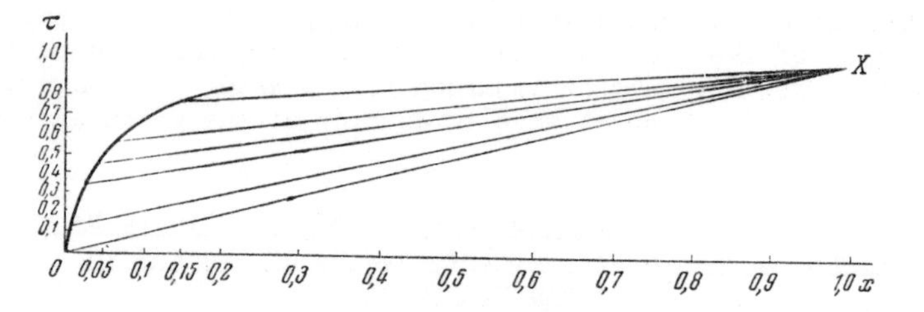

Fig. 1
Trajectory of the boundary of a gas sphere and intersection of the characteristics

$x(t)$ as a function of the given values of the time T or the place X of the development of the shock wave. This problem was first solved for a piston compressing a gas by Hugoniot [2]. A short solution to the problem on the basis of the Riemann characteristics is given in [3]. We use this solution

$$x = X + \frac{2}{n-1} a_0 (T - t) - \frac{n+1}{n-1} a_0 T^{\frac{n-1}{n+1}} (T - t)^{\frac{2}{n+1}} \tag{5}$$

In order to determine the trajectory of the boundary of the bubble in the general case, irrespectively of the numerical value of the quantity X , we turn to dimensionless co-ordinates:

$$\tau = \frac{a_0 t}{X}; \quad \bar{x} = \frac{x}{X}; \quad w = \frac{u}{a_0}. \tag{6}$$

After substitution and transformation we can represent the path of the boundary layer of the bubble (5) in the following form:

$$\bar{x} = \frac{n+1}{n-1}\left\{1-(1-\tau)^{\frac{2}{n+1}}\right\} - \frac{2}{n-1}\tau. \qquad (7)$$

The velocity of the boundary layer is defined from this relation:

$$w = \frac{2}{n-1}(1-\tau)^{\frac{n-1}{n+1}} - \frac{2}{n-1} \qquad (8)$$

The trajectory of the boundary of a gas bubble in dimensionless co-ordinates is shown in Fig. 1. This diagram shows the characteristics of the equations of motion of a fluid which correspond to boundary conditions (7) and (8). The first of the characteristics records the movement of the interface of the quiescent fluid and the first disturbance. Its slope is equal to the speed of sound in an undisturbed medium and in dimensionless co-ordinates is equal to 1. At the point X $(x=1)$ at the moment of time $T = \frac{X}{a_0}$ $(\tau = 1)$ all the remaining characteristics intersect, which proceed from the subsequent points of the trajectory of the bubble. This is in agreement with the fact that the rate of movement of each subsequent disturbance is greater than that of the preceding one, and all overtake each other at the point X. Fixing the necessary value of X, it is possible to calculate what must be the co-ordinate $x = X\bar{x}$ of the boundary of the bubble for each moment of time $t = \frac{\tau x}{a_0}$.

With the aid of the characteristics it is possible to calculate the variation of the state of the medium in time, and to work out what amount of energy must be imparted to the water at each moment of time in order for a shock wave to develop at the given distance.

2. Calculation of Energy to be Imparted to a Liquid by an Expanding Gas Bubble for Development of Shock Wave at a Given Point

To calculate the change in the energy of water during the propagation in it of an elastic wave, it is necessary to know the sum of the kinetic energy and heat content of the water for each moment of time

$$E = K + I. \qquad (9)$$

Here it is necessary to take into account that at different moments of time different masses of water are participating in the movement. These data can be obtained by a graphical method by examining the representation of the movement in the plane x, τ (Fig. 1).

To determine the kinetic energy K it is necessary to know for each moment the volume, density and velocity of the water.

The velocity of the water u is determined from the condition that along the characteristics the velocity remains constant and equal to the velocity of the boundary layer. Variation of the velocity with time occurs in the transition from one characteristic to another, since the characteristic is the boundary dividing two regions of the water with different rates of motion. Variation of the velocity of the water in transition through the characteristic is linked with the variation of the state of the water $\left(a^2 = \frac{\partial p}{\partial \rho} \right)$ by the relation (3)

Using this relation and knowing the initial state of the medium, it is possible to calculate the values of u and a for all points of the liquid at all moments of time.

From the known value $\frac{\partial p}{\partial \rho} = a_0^2 \left(\frac{\rho}{\rho_0} \right)^{n-1}$ it is possible to calculate the value ρ, and with ρ known the value of the pressure p can be obtained for each moment of time with the aid of the equation of state.

The specific enthalpy

$$i = \frac{p}{\rho} + c_p \cdot T$$

can be calculated if we know the pressure, density and temperature of the water. The relation of the temperature to the pressure in water is such that with a pressure drop $\Delta p = 5{,}000$ atm in the shock wave the temperature change is only 15° and the quantity c_p is equal to $3.9 \times 6 \times 24 \times 10^4$.

In our case, therefore, with fairly small pressure differentials, it is possible in calculating i to ignore the term $c_p\, dT$.

Using the characteristics obtained for the state of the water for different moments of time and determining graphically the volume of liquid participating in the movement, we can calculate what energy must be imparted to the water at any moment of time t_i:

$$E_i = m_i (k + i),$$

where k is the kinetic energy of a unit of mass.

Fig. 2 shows the graph of energy in joules as a function of the time in seconds for the case when the shock wave must form at a distance $X = 60$ cm from the gas bubble in a tube with a cross-section of 28.3 mm² .

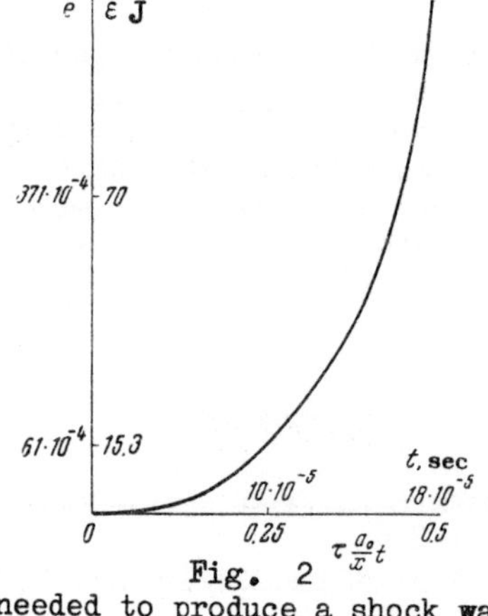

Fig. 2
Release of energy needed to produce a shock wave at a given point, as a function of the time

This case corresponds to the development of a shock wave in water as a result of the addition of elementary compression waves during an electrical discharge, as experimentally studied in the Energy Institute of the Academy of Sciences by R. Soloukhin [4].

From the theoretical calculation, for a discharge period lasting approximately 10^{-4} sec the energy transmitted to the liquid by the expanding gas bubble must equal 16 J.

In Soloukhin's experiments, the energy stored at the capacitors was 300 J. Half of the energy is lost in the air spark gap, and the energy is released in four successive sparks, in the first of which, as was shown by oscillographic measurements, 50 per cent of the energy of the discharge is released. Thus, no more than 75 J are used for the expansion of the gas bubble.

If it is taken into account that the role of a piston compressing the water in one direction is only played by half the gas sphere, and that the development of the shock wave occurs at the expense of the energy released with an increase only in the first half of a period, then the amount of the remaining energy of 18.5 J corresponds in amount to that calculated theoretically.

Thus, the above calculation and a comparison of it with experiment show that in water there may occur at a given distance a shock wave developing through combination of elementary compression waves. To control the process of the formation of the shock wave it is necessary to be able to regulate in time the release of energy in the gas bubble.

For example, in the case of an electrical discharge, the law of the release of energy in the spark gap $E(t)$ depends on the parameters of the electrical circuit and can be regulated by varying these parameters, especially by varying the self-inductance.

The calculation was carried out for a plane problem. To solve the spherically-symmetrical problem, it is possible to use a method of successive approximations [5].

It can be shown that, with an identical law of energy release in the gas bubble, in the case of spherical propagation of disturbances the shock wave develops at a greater distance than in the case of plane propagation, since in this case there is a greater dispersion of energy. Hence, to develop a spherical shock wave at a given distance an even faster rise in energy release with time is needed than in the plane case.

REFERENCES

1. R. KOUL, Underwater Explosions (Podvodnye vzryvy), Izd. inostran. lit. (1950).
2. HUGONIOT, Journ. de l'école polytechnique, No. 57 (1887), No. 58 (1889).

3. K.P. STANYUKOVICH, Theory of Non-Steady-State Movements of Gas (Teoriya neustanovivshikhsya dvizhenii gaza), Izd. byuro novoi tekhniki (1948).
4. R.I. SOLOUKHIN, Shock waves forming during an electrical discharge in water, Page 154 above.
5. M.Ya. KAABAK, Thesis, Energ. Inst., Mosk. gos. univ. (1954).

G.D. Salamandra and O.A. Tsukhanova

Formation of Shock Discontinuity before a Flame Front

The combustion of gases, despite its apparent simplicity, is such a complex process that many phenomena accompanying it have been insufficiently studied. Amongst such phenomena is the formation of a shock discontinuity before the front of a flame.

Study of this process, apart from theoretical interest, is also of great practical interest, since the presence of a shock discontinuity before the front of a flame is a necessary condition of the transition of slow combustion into detonation. Depending on the acceleration rate of the flame, the shock wave and consequently the transition to detonation occur further from or nearer to the start of the combustion chamber. In a first approximation it is possible to attempt to reduce the problem of the movement of the gas before the flame front to the problem of the movement of a gas before a piston accelerating according to the same law, according to which the flame is in fact propagated. The problem of the movement of a gas enclosed in an infinite cylinder bounded at one end by an accelerating piston was first solved by Hugoniot [1] at the end of the nineteenth century.

In solving this problem Hugoniot proceeded from the equation of motion of an ideal gas, obtained from the laws of conservation in the form:

$$\frac{\partial^2 u}{\partial t^2} = \varphi\left(\frac{\partial u}{\partial x}\right)\frac{\partial^2 u}{\partial x^2}, \qquad (1)$$

where

$$\varphi\left(\frac{\partial u}{\partial x}\right) = a^2\left(1 + \frac{\partial u}{\partial x}\right)^{-\gamma-1} \qquad (2)$$

Here u is the movement of the point with the co-ordinate x at the moment t ; $\gamma = \frac{c_p}{c_v}$; a is the speed of sound in the fresh mixture. In front of the piston accelerating along the tube there are disturbances, at the meeting point of which there forms a break in continuity - a shock wave. According to Hugoniot, two elementary disturbances, produced by the piston at moments of time close to one another, meet at a distance

$$X = \frac{2a^2\left(1 + \frac{\gamma - 1}{2a} v\right)^{\frac{2\gamma}{\gamma - 1}}}{(\gamma + 1)\frac{\partial v}{\partial t}} \quad (3)$$

where t is the excitation time of the given disturbance in the gas;
v is the rate of movement of the piston at the moment t.

Hugoniot showed that all the elementary disturbances will meet at one point only in the case of a fixed law of movement of the piston, viz. : if the velocity of the piston varies in time according to:

$$v = \frac{2a}{\gamma - 1}\left(1 - \frac{at}{X}\right)^{-\frac{\gamma - 1}{\gamma + 1}} - \frac{2a}{\gamma - 1}. \quad (4)$$

In the general case, the disturbances caused by the movement of the piston will meet not in one section of the tube but over some distance.

It should be noted that by reducing the problem of the movement of a gas before a flame front to the problem of the movement of a gas in front of a piston, we are imparting to the flame the properties of a solid wall compressing the gas in front of it.

The interval of time in which the elementary disturbance sent by the flame becomes a shock wave is determined by the nature of the variation of the velocity of the flame in the combustion process. The almost complete absence of experimental studies devoted to the examination of the process of formation of a shock discontinuity before a flame front complicates the answer to the question whether it is legitimate to reduce the complex problem of the movement of a gas before a flame front to the simpler, and already solved, problem of the movement of a gas in front of a piston.

It should be noted that in most studies examining combustion with waste products or the transition of slow combustion into detonation, use was made, to record the process, of direct photography, using the natural luminosity of the burning mixture.

A shock wave before a flame front is not accompanied by formation of luminosity of its own, and for all the details of this process to be followed, therefore, it should be recorded by the optical method, which allows us to follow the processes taking place in the burning mixture. As object of investigation hydrogen-oxygen mixtures are an expedient choice, since the process of combustion of these mixtures takes place so rapidly that the shock discontinuity forms at a comparatively short distance from the beginning of the combustion chamber.

In order to be able to follow all the phases of the process of formation of the shock wave, it is necessary for the recording of the process by the scan method to be supplemented by a high-speed cinematographic process. The best-known type of high-speed photograph is the "spark photograph", in which the photographed object is illuminated by a series of electrical sparks, which occur during the discharge of a capacitor to the illuminating spark-gap.

Distinctive features of spark apparatus are the simplicity of the sparking circuits, the ease with which the light sparks in the illuminating spark-gap can be synchronized with the process being investigated, and the possibility of varying the frequency of the photographs within wide limits. A spark discharge lasting 10^{-6} sec provides for a fairly short exposure time, making it possible to obtain clear photographs even in the case of very fast-moving processes. Since the rate of propagation of the elementary disturbances which evolve into the shock wave does not exceed 1,000 m/sec, to solve the problem set by us it is desirable to use a spark apparatus giving a picture frequency of 50,000-70,000 frames per sec with a total of about 100 frames in the general case.

1. Experimental Apparatus

The experimental apparatus for studying the process of formation of the shock discontinuity before a flame front consisted of the optical part which made visible the disturbances developing in the gas during the combustion of the mixture, the electrical part which provided for a series of fairly intensive electrical sparks of brief duration, and the photographic part which recorded the process. In order to make visible the disturbances developing in the gas, we used the reflex-meniscus equipment type IAB-451.

In photographing by the scan method, we used as a light source a PZh-26 lamp, and in the case of the high-speed spark photograph a discharge device was put in place of the lamp. In this case the light source was a series of illuminating sparks. The number of the sparks in the series and their frequency were determined by the parameters of the electrical circuit.

The electrical circuit of the spark apparatus is shown in Fig. 1. The supply equipment, consisting of a high-voltage transformer T_p, raising the voltage to 27 kV, and a diode K_p is disconnected before the exposure. Thus the source of electrical energy is the

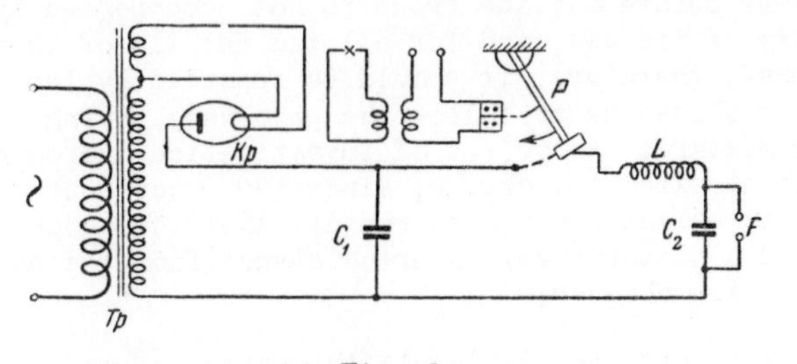

Fig. 1
Electrical circuit of the spark apparatus

capacitor C_1 with a capacity of 1 μF. When the switch P is closed the capacitor C_1 is discharged, charging the capacitor C_2 with a capacity of 0.125 μF. Each time the voltage at the capacitor C_2 reaches a value sufficient to break down the illuminating spark-gap, a spark jumps in the discharge device F. With an inductance of $L = 2$ henrys, we obtained 150-200 spark flashes following each other with a frequency of about 50,000 per second. Kozachenko, working with an apparatus of a similar type, varied the frequency from 5000 to 100,000 frames per second while varying the inductance from 10 to 0.5 henrys. The circuit which we have described for the spark apparatus is easy to operate. There is some difficulty, it is true, in preparing a selection of inductances calculated for a fairly high voltage. It was for this reason that the inductance in the circuit was later replaced by a resistance. If the resistance is made fairly high, and the capacitance C_2 low, then the capacitor C_2 will discharge over the illuminating spark-gap much more promptly than through the resistance. This ensures satisfactory attenuation of the illuminating spark. By changing the size of the resistance, it is possible to vary the exposure frequency within wide limits. With a voltage on the capacitor C_1 of 27 kV, the capacitances $C_1 = 2.75$ μF and $C_2 = 0.125$ μF, a breakdown voltage for the illuminating spark-gap of ≈ 15 kV and a resistance of 1200 ohms, the frequency of the sparks reached 50,000 per second with a total number of about 200 sparks. Synchronization of the detonation with the series of illuminating sparks was achieved by means of a special pendulum switch.

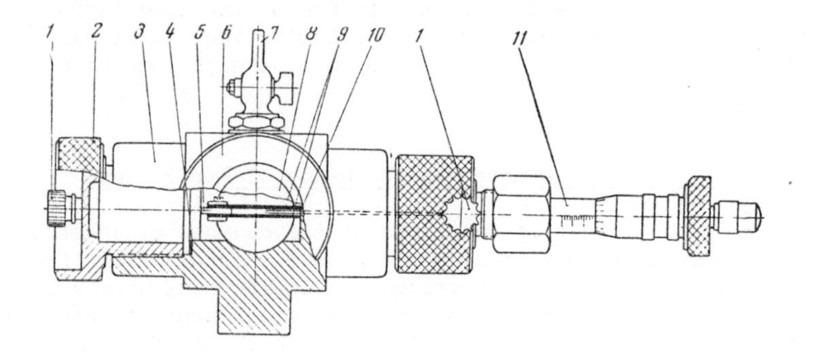

Fig. 2
The "linear light source" discharge device

To obtain bright illuminating sparks we prepared a special discharge device - a so-called "linear light source" - which is shown in Fig. 2. The electrodes of the discharge device are a bronze plate 5 held on two sides by fibrous plates 9, and a tungsten rod 10, moved by means of a micrometer screw 11. In the front part of the discharge device a hole is drilled, covered by a plexiglas plate 8, through which the light falls on to the slit of the optical apparatus. The cock 7 is used for evacuating the air from the discharge device and filling it with hydrogen. In spite of the very low luminescence with a discharge in a hydrogen atmosphere, hydrogen was chosen for filling the discharge device since it ensures the possibility of photographing at high frequency. The detonation process was recorded on film with a sensitivity of 250 GOST*, arranged on the outer surface of a uniformly rotating drum, driven by a synchronous motor. In order to determine the rate of movement of the film, an intermittent light source was photographed outside the image field, simultaneously with the photograph of the process, so that it left a row of dashes on the film. Knowing the frequency of the light sparks and measuring the distance between the time marks, it was possible to determine the rate of movement of the film. In our case the film was moving at a speed of 45 m/sec. As the intermittent light source for marking the time we used a MN-7 neon lamp, connected to the circuit of a frequency changer which raised the frequency from 50 to 500 c/s. So that the time marks would not be superimposed on one another we placed in a special tube in front of the neon lamp a shutter which was open for one revolution.

We used a "Zonnar" tele-lens with an aperture ratio of 1 : 4 and a focal length of 13.5 cm. It has already been mentioned above that the process was photographed by two methods: by the scan method and by the spark cinematograph method. In the first case we used a constant light source. So that the images were not superimposed on the path of the light rays, we fitted a roller-blind shutter which closed after each revolution. The unusual design of the shutter made it possible to synchronize the process with the operation of the shutter. In the case of the spark photograph the need for the shutter disappears. So that the frames would not be superimposed, the capacitance of the capacitor C_1 was so selected that the whole series of illuminating sparks was completed within one revolution of the drum of the photographic recorder.

2. Explosion Chamber and Sequence of Experiments

To clarify the effect of the shape of the chamber cross-section on the process of formation of a shock wave before a flame front, we compared the course of the process in chambers of circular and rectangular cross-section. The cross-sectional area of both chambers was kept the same. The chambers, in which the fuel mixture burned, consisted of several sections joined by flanges.

By fitting a different number of sections it was possible to vary the length of the explosion chamber from 280 to 608 mm. Blank flanges closed off the chamber at the ends. In one of the blank flanges we fitted a spark plug which ignited the mixture, and at the other a valve through which the air was pumped out and the chamber filled with the explosive mixture. The process was photographed through side windows drilled in one of the chamber sections.

The windows were closed off with plane-parallel plates of optical glass. The plates were fastened to the body of the chamber by

*All-Union State Specification. GOST emulsion speed is the same as the "Weston" emulsion speed used as a criterion in this country.

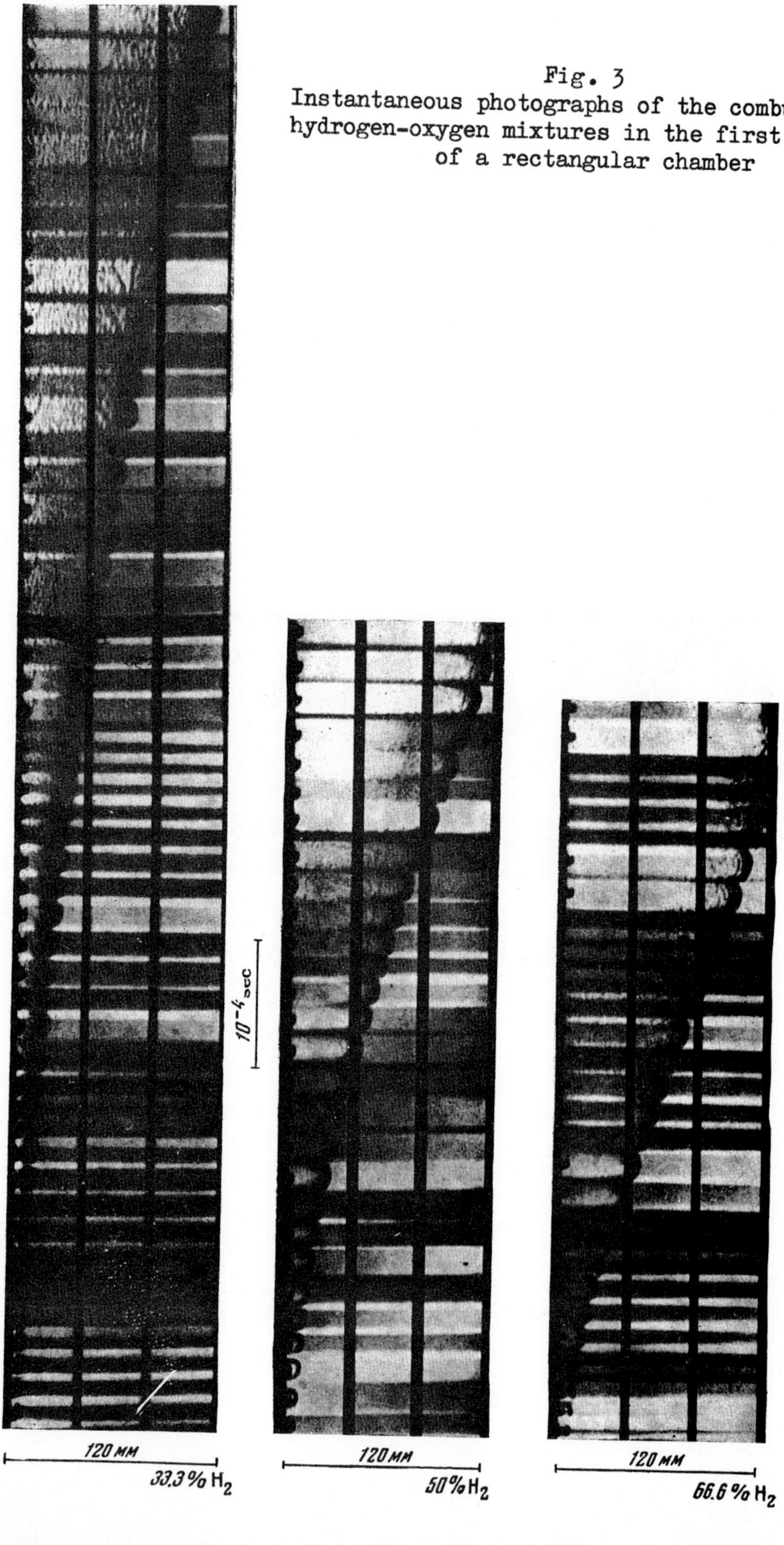

10^-4 sec

120 MM
33.3 % H_2

120 MM
50 % H_2

120 MM
66.6 % H_2

Fig. 3
Instantaneous photographs of the combustion of hydrogen-oxygen mixtures in the first section of a rectangular chamber

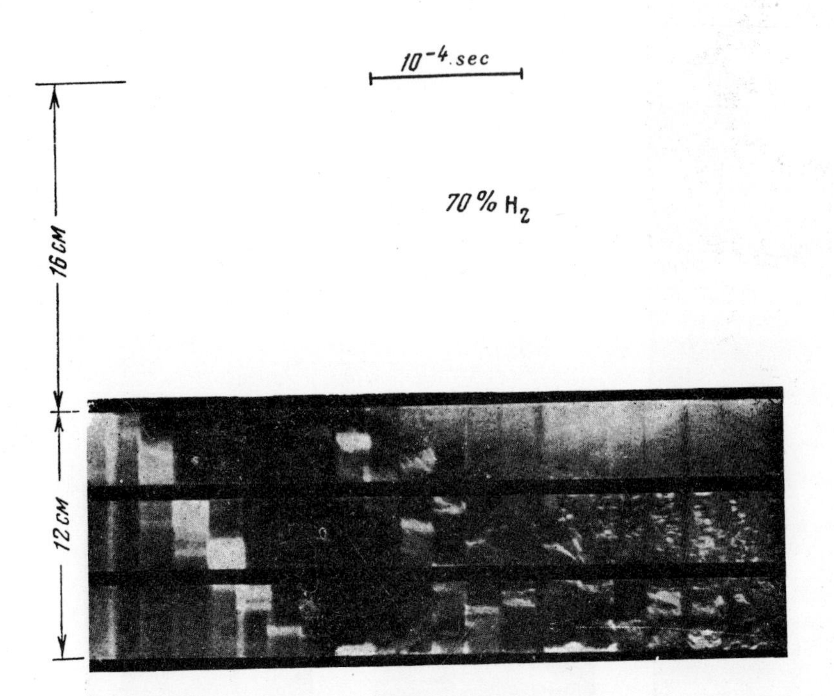

Fig. 4
Formation of a shock discontinuity before a flame front

means of covers with slots. The cross-pieces on the covers were used as scale marks. The fuel mixture was prepared by volume and stored in a gas tank without being dried before filling the chamber. We studied the combustion of hydrogen-oxygen mixtures containing 25% H_2, 33.3% H_2, 50% H_2, 66.6% H_2 and 70% H_2.

After filling the chamber with the explosive mixture we connected the electrical apparatus. The bank of capacitors was charged up to 27 kV, and then we switched on the motor of the photo-recorder and set in motion the pawl which held the pendulum of the synchronizing equipment in the horizontal position. By falling, the latter closed the high-voltage circuit of the spark apparatus. Simultaneously, the shaft of the pendulum broke the circuit of the primary winding of the transformer, causing a spark which ignited the mixture. On the uniformly rotating film of the photo-recorder, about 200 different phases of the process were recorded.

The first series of experiments was carried out in chambers of a length great enough to allow the shock wave to form in the fresh gas before the disturbances produced by the front of the flame reached the end of the chamber.

The second series of experiments was carried out in a short chamber. In this case the shock wave forms as a result of the accumulation of disturbances reflected from the end of the chamber.

3. Description of the Experimental Material and Analysis of Results

a) Formation of a shock wave before a flame front. Fig. 3 shows series of instantaneous photographs of the combustion of hydrogen-oxygen mixtures in the first section of a chamber with a rectangular cross-section of 19 × 37 mm.

As the photographs show, the flame is propagated from left to right, and the film moves in the vertical direction. The scale marks at a distance of 38 mm from each other are recorded on the photographs in the form of two black strips parallel to the time axis. The photograph was taken on the so-called "grey" background.

As can be seen from the photographs, the front of the flame, having at first a hemispherical shape, gradually elongates, becoming meniscus-shaped. As the flame is propagated, the flame front recorded on the photographs becomes somewhat thicker, which indicates the development of the surface of the flame front while its meniscus-like shape is retained.

Before the flame front there run disturbances, clearly visible in the series of photographs in Fig. 4, which depict the development of the process of combustion of a hydrogen-oxygen mixture containing 70% H_2 in the second section of a chamber 480 mm long. The distance from the ignition to the beginning of the section through which we are looking is 160 mm. The developing shock wave has the form of a gradually contracting bright band finally becoming a thin line, indicating the development of a shock discontinuity. The latter forms at about 25 cm from the spark plug which ignites the mixture. In a mixture containing 50% H_2, the shock discontinuity forms at a distance of 29-30 cm, and in a mixture with an even greater oxygen content the elementary disturbances produced by the flame develop into a shock wave at a distance of 57-58 cm from the plug. If the front of the flame running along the tube can be compared to a piston, compressing the gas in front of it, then to determine the distance from the ignition to the point of formation of the shock discontinuity the existing solution of Hugoniot can be used.

To evaluate the quantity X in formula (3) for the case of propagation of a flame in a tube we need to know the velocity and acceleration of the flame, the γ of the mixture and the rate of propagation of sound in the fresh mixture. The speed of sound is calculated from the formula

$$a = \sqrt{9{,}81\,\gamma R_{mix} T}.$$

Here T is the absolute temperature of the mixture

$$R_{cm} = \frac{R_{O_2} \cdot R_{H_2}}{\alpha R_{O_2} + \beta R_{H_2}};$$

$$R_{O_2} = 26{,}5 \text{ m/degree}$$
$$R_{H_2} = 420 \text{ m/degree}$$

α is the proportion of hydrogen in the mixture;
β is the proportion of oxygen in the mixture.

For the hydrogen-oxygen mixtures in which we are interested, the speed of sound at 20°C has the following values:

H_2, % in mixture	a, m/sec
70	567
66,6	535
50	448
33,3	394

It is easy to find the velocity and acceleration of the flame at any moment of time from experiment. In the first moments after ignition of the mixture, the velocity of the flame remains constant after a certain increase, and then gradually drops, decreasing suddenly at the moment when the flame hits the walls of the chamber. Then there follows a new increase in the rate of propagation of the flame. In the chamber of rectangular cross-section, in view of the fact that the front of the flame first touches the top and bottom and then the side walls of the chamber, it is not possible to fix the reduction in the rate of propagation of the flame caused by the increase in heat emission when the flame meets the walls. At later moments the rate of propagation of the flame, in chambers whether with a circular or with a rectangular section, increases as the flame moves through the tube. If we ignore the stage of propagation of the flame from ignition to the meeting with the walls, the function of the path covered by the flame in the time t can be given by an empirical formula in the form:

$$x = at^b + c \tag{5}$$

Here x is the distance in metres;
t is the time in seconds;
a, b, c are quantities dependent on the concentration of the mixture and the structural features of the chamber.

Differentiating the relation (5) with respect to t, it is easy to discover the velocity and acceleration of the flame at any moment of time. Figs. 5 (a) and (b) show curves giving the variation of the flame acceleration in time during combustion of hydrogen-oxygen mixtures in chambers of round and rectangular section.

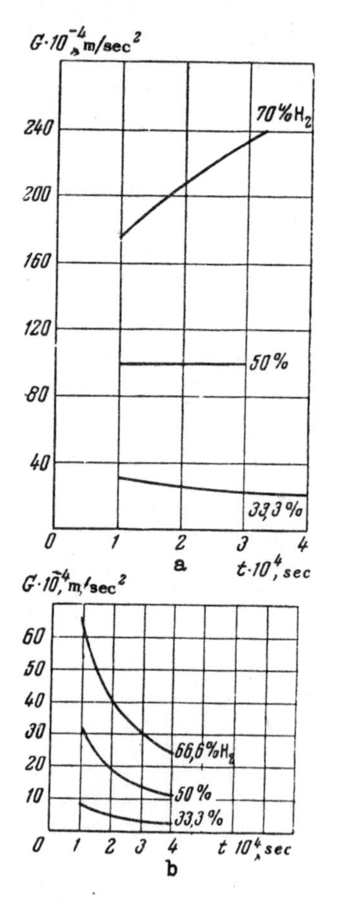

Fig. 5 a and b

It is easy to see that the acceleration of the flame depends on the structural features of the chamber, and for a given chamber on the concentration of the mixture. If, in the chamber of rectangular section, the combustion process takes place in such a way that, for all the hydrogen-oxygen mixtures considered by us, the flame acceleration decreases with the passage of time, then in the chamber of circular section having the same cross-sectional area as the chamber of rectangular section the dependence of flame acceleration on concentration stands out particularly clearly. In fact, in the mixture containing 70% H_2 the flame acceleration grows with time, in the mixture containing 50% H_2 the flame is propagated with uniform acceleration, and in mixtures with an even greater oxygen content the acceleration decreases slowly as the flame moves along the chamber. Since the rule which the flame acceleration follows must greatly influence the distance from the ignition to the point of "origin" of the shock discontinuity, one can say without carrying out calculations that in the chamber of circular section more favourable conditions are present for the development of a shock discontinuity than in the chamber of rectangular section. As an example, we will calculate at what distance from the ignition the disturbances emitted by a flame front will meet at a moment of time $t = 10^{-4}$ sec, for the case of combustion of a mixture containing 70% H_2 in a chamber of circular section.

Substituting the corresponding values of v and γ in the formula for determining X, and taking into consideration that the speed of sound in the fresh mixture is 567 m/sec, we find $X = 22.5$ cm. Taking into account that at the moment $t = 10^{-4}$ sec the front of the flame is at a distance of 2.4 cm from the end of the chamber, the distance from the ignition to the point of "origin" of the shock discontinuity is 24.9 cm. The value found by us is in good agreement with experiment, which indicates the accuracy of the adopted idealization of the process. The solution to the problem acquires particular clarity when use is made of the graphical method of characteristics.

b) Use of the graphical characteristic method to solve the problem of the non-steady-state one-dimensional flow of a gas before a flame front. Without dwelling on the derivation of the equation of characteristics, which is given in detail in [2], [3], we will proceed to the resolution of the problem in which we are interested.

Through a hydrogen-oxygen mixture in a tube at a constant pressure and temperature, the front of a flame is propagated. The law of propagation of the flame is given by the curve OA in the plane xt. The state of the gas before the flame front has to be found. We will plot the appropriate graph. The velocities of sound disturbances at moments of time 1, 2, 3, 4, 5, 6, 7, 8 are defined in the plane (v, a) by the characteristic shown in Fig. 6(c) as a straight line at an angle of 45° to the axes v and a. This angle of inclination is determined by the choice of ordinate scale.

The velocities of sound disturbances proceeding from the points 1, 2, 3, ... 8 [Fig. 6 (a)] are determined as the ordinates of the points the abscissae of which are the corresponding values of the velocity of the flame front.

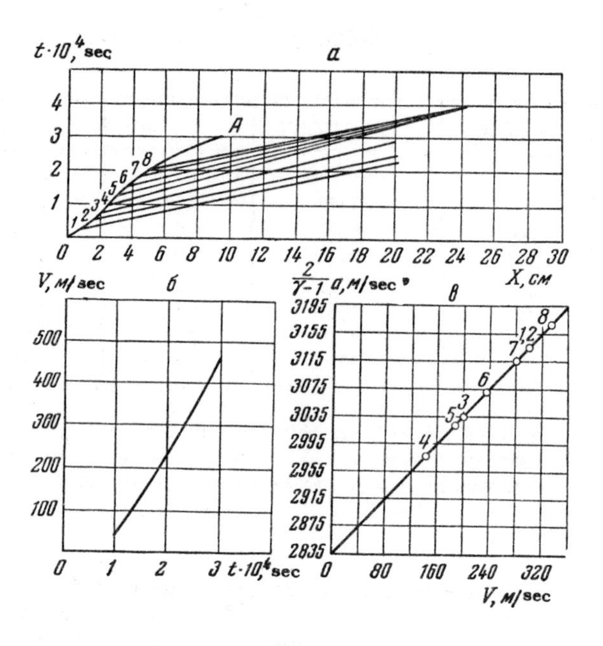

Figs. 6 (a), (b), (c)

Let us turn our attention to one feature of the problem we have set. Usually in the solution of the problem of the movement of a gas in front of a piston moving along a tube, the important role in the graph is played by the first disturbance produced by the piston at the initial moment and propagated at the speed of sound in the fresh gas. When the mixture is ignited even by a very weak spark, a disturbance also develops in the fresh gas, which is propagated at the speed of sound, but here the similarity ends. As is shown by experiment, the first disturbance produced in the gas by the ignition spark usually does not take part in the formation of the fairly intensive shock wave. In solving the problem by the characteristic method, therefore, this disturbance does not have to be taken into account. Results of the calculation of the sound disturbances emitted by the front of the flame at later moments are given in Table 1.

As is clear from the diagram, the characteristics appearing at the moments of time 1 and 2 are parallel, since the flame velocity on this section remains constant. Then the flame velocity drops, which produces a divergent bundle of characteristics. Beginning at the moment $t = 10^{-4}$ sec, the flame velocity increases. The characteristics appearing at the moments of time 4, 5, 6, 7, 8 intersect at a distance of $\simeq 24.5$ cm. The calculation is in good agreement with experiment. Calculations were carried out in a similar way for the case of combustion of a mixture containing 50% H_2 and 33.3% H_2.

TABLE 1

Point	v, m/sec	$\frac{2}{\gamma-1}a$, m/sec	a, m/sec	$v+a$, m/sec
1	300	3135	627	927
2	300	3135	627	927
3	200	3035	607	807
4	141	2976	595	736
5	187	3022	604	791
6	235	3070	614	849
7	282	3117	623	905
8	334	3169	634	968

As calculations carried out by the same method show, in the propagation of a flame in a chamber of rectangular section the shock discontinuity develops at a much greater distance from the ignition point than during combustion of the same mixture in a chamber of circular section.

The results of the plots made by us are presented in Table 2. It is easy to see from the table that the distance from the ignition to the point of development of the shock discontinuity depends to a great extent on the structural features of the chamber.

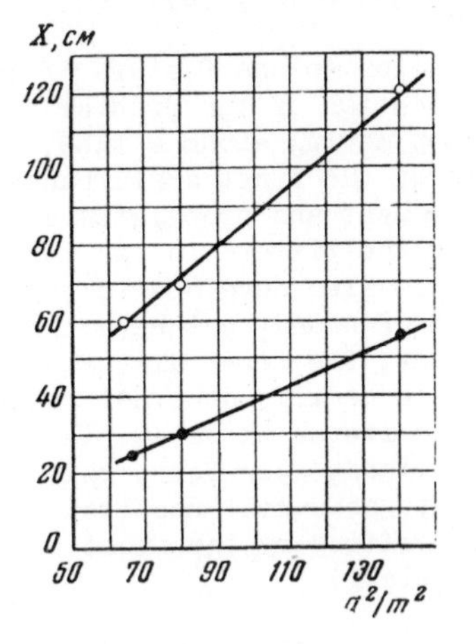

Fig. 7
The quantity X as a function of the square of the ratio of the speed of sound to the percentage content of hydrogen

With equal cross-sectional areas, in the chamber of circular section the shock discontinuity develops at half the distance from the ignition at which it develops during combustion of the same mixture in the chamber of rectangular section.

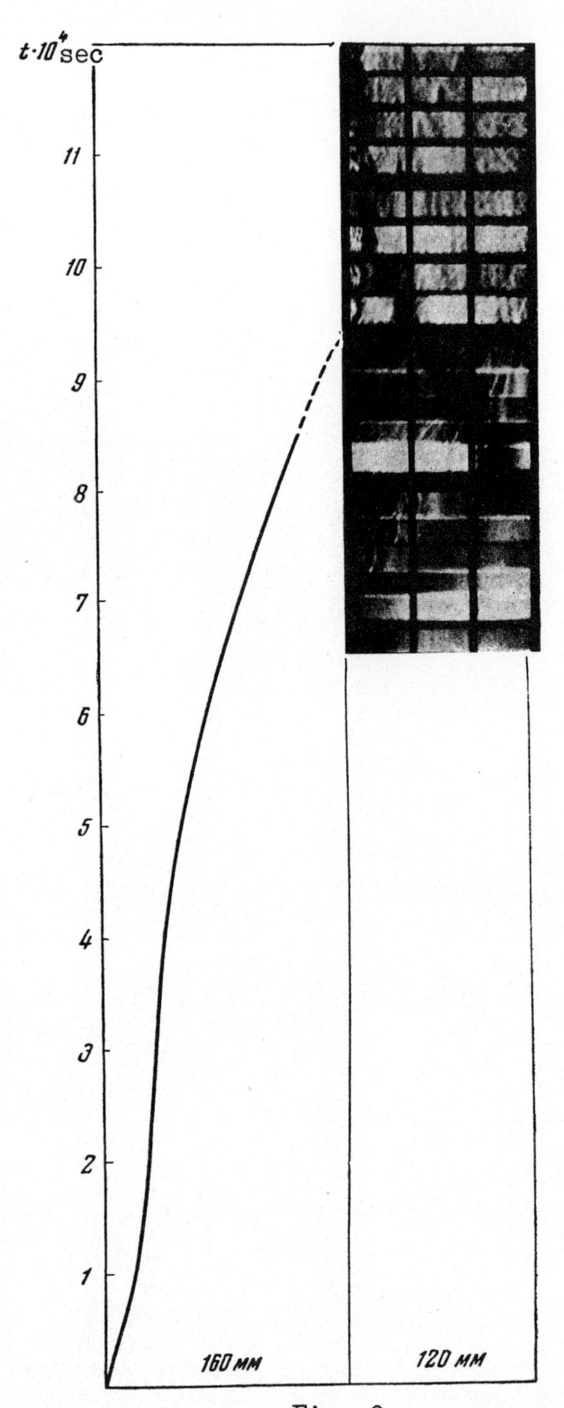

Fig. 8
Formation of a shock discontinuity in a short chamber

TABLE 2

% H_2 in mixture	Chamber of circular section		Chamber of rectangular section
	Distance from ignition to point of development of shock wave, cm (calcul.)	Distance from ignition to point of development of shock wave, cm (experiment)	Distance from ignition to point of development of shock wave, cm (calcul.)
70	24.5	25-26	
66.6			60
50	28.5	29-30	69
33.3	56	58	121

To link the distance from the ignition to the point of origin of the shock discontinuity, and the time of its development with the fuel characteristics of the mixture, we use formulae found by Hugoniot for calculating the quantities X and T. According to Hugoniot,

$$X \sim \frac{a^2}{\frac{dv}{dt}}; \qquad T \sim a \frac{dv}{dt}.$$

It has already been shown above that the acceleration of the flame, appearing in the denominators of both expressions, is a function of the design of the chamber, and for a given chamber is determined by the concentration of the burning mixture.

As is shown by calculation, during the time when the front of the flame is producing disturbances in the fresh gas which accumulate into a shock wave, the flame acceleration for mixtures in the range of concentrations in which we are interested is proportional to the square of the percentage content of hydrogen in the mixture, and consequently

$$X \sim \frac{a^2}{m^2}; \qquad T \sim \frac{a}{m}.$$

Fig. 7 shows the quantity X as a function of $\frac{a^2}{m^2}$. The abscissa shows the square of the ratio of the speed of sound to the percentage H_2 content, and the ordinate the distance from the ignition point to the point of origin of the shock discontinuity. The white points denote the values of X corresponding to the course of the process in the circular chamber, and the black points show the values of the quantity X during combustion of the mixture in the chamber of rectangular section.

Up to now we have considered the process of formation of the shock wave in chambers of fairly great length. In short chambers the elementary disturbances generated by a rapidly-moving flame do not succeed in accumulating into a shock discontinuity before they reach the ends of the chamber. In a short chamber, therefore, the process of formation of a shock discontinuity is complicated by the fact that disturbances reflected from the end of the chamber are involved in it.

c) <u>Formation of a shock wave in a short chamber</u>. The formation of a shock wave takes place in a given chamber length. If the disturbances produced by the flame in the fresh gas are not able to combine into a shock wave before meeting the end of the chamber, the shock discontinuity may develop as a result of the adding together of disturbances reflected from the end of the chamber or disturbances reflected from the flame front. Elementary disturbances, as a rule, do not pass through the front of the flame but are reflected from it as from a solid wall. Fig. 8 shows the process of formation of a shock discontinuity during combustion of a misture containing 33.3% H_2 in a chamber 280 mm long. The left side of the illustration shows the track of the flame front in the first section of the chamber. Before the flame front, appearing in the field of vision in the twelfth frame, the developing shock wave is clearly visible. In the first frames it takes the

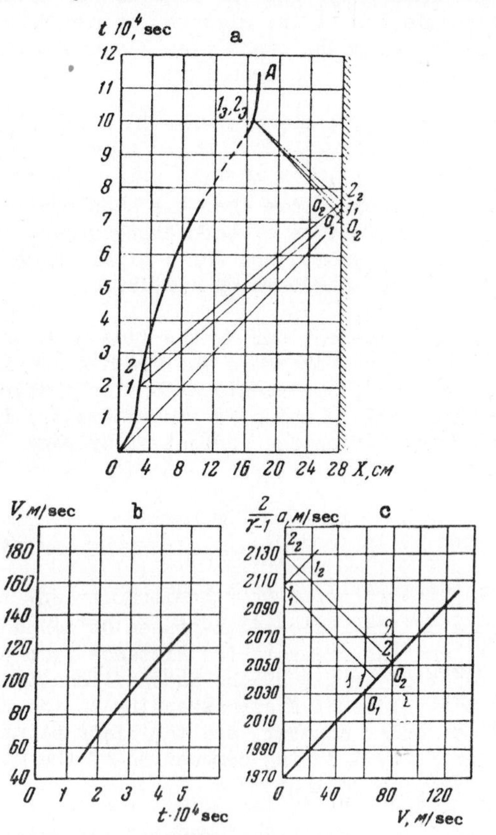

Fig. 9
Location of the point of development of the shock discontinuity by the characteristic method

form of a fairly wide light band. After reflection from the end of the chamber the disturbance being propagated in the opposite direction is recorded on the photograph in the form of a gradually contracting dark band. Apart from the developing shock wave, the photograph also shows clearly the disturbances produced by the flame front in the fresh gas. Propagated between the flame front and the end of the chamber, they form a dense network of non-interacting disturbances.

Since the front of the flame behaves towards the elementary disturbances as a solid wall, it is admissible in calculating the state of the gas between flame front and wall to compare the flame to a piston and solve the problem by the graphical method of characteristics. Fig. 9 shows the corresponding graphs for the case in the photograph. The law of propagation of the flame is given by the curve OA. The position of the wall is indicated by a vertical line with the co-ordinate $X = 28$ mm. Comparison of Fig. 8 and 9 (a) shows that the calculation of the point of development of the shock wave in a short chamber is in good agreement with experiment.

Conclusions

1. A flame accelerating along a tube produces disturbances in the unburnt gas. From a series of these disturbances, accumulating in one section of the tube or over some stretch of it, there forms a shock wave, clearly visible in photographs in the form of a gradually contracting light band, becoming finally a thin line.

2. The formation of the shock discontinuity takes place over a definite length of the chamber. If the disturbances caused by the flame in the unburnt gas are unable to combine into a shock wave before meeting the end of the chamber, a shock discontinuity may develop as the result of combination of the disturbances reflected from the end of the chamber and from the front of the flame: elementary disturbances, as a rule, do not pass through the front of the flame but are reflected from it as from a solid wall.

3. In calculating the process of formation of a shock wave before a flame front it is possible, by reducing the problem of the movement of the gas before the flame front to the problem of the movement of a gas before a piston, accelerating in accordance with the same law as the flame actually does, either to use Hugoniot's formulae for determining the distance from the ignition to the point of development of the shock discontinuity or to solve the problem by the graphical method of characteristics. The calculation carried out by us is in good agreement with experiment, which indicates the accuracy of the adopted idealization of the process.

4. The dependence of the distance from the ignition point to the point of development of the shock discontinuity X on the concentration of the mixture, in the range of concentrations studied by us, can be described by the relation: $X \sim \frac{a^2}{m^2}$ where a is the speed of sound in the mixture, m is the percentage content of hydrogen

in the mixture.

5. The distance from the ignition to the point of development of the shock discontinuity depends on the shape of the cross-section of the chamber. In a chamber of circular section, the acceleration of the flame front is much greater than in a chamber of rectangular section (with equal cross-sectional areas). In view of this, the quantity X in the first case is almost 60 per cent smaller than in the second.

REFERENCES

1. J. HUGONIOT, J. Ecole Polytechn., 57 (1887), 58 (1889).
2. N.E. KOCHIN, I.A. KIBEL', N.V. ROZE, Theoretical Hydromechanics (Teoreticheskaya gidromekhanika), Part II (1948).
3. V.A. POPOV, Izv. Akad. Nauk SSSR, otdel. tekh. nauk, No. 10, 1953.

G.D. Salamandra

Interaction of a Flame with a Shock Discontinuity

The process of propagation of a flame in a closed chamber is accompanied by a wave process. Acoustic waves are the cause of one of the distinctive propagations of a flame - vibrational combustion. The fluctuations of a flame are bound up with phenomena of a hydrodynamic nature which occur during combustion and differ from purely acoustic phenomena in their greater intensity. The first attempt to explain the development of fluctuations in a flame as the purely mechanical interaction of the disturbances occurring in the gas with the flame front was made by Dixon, who explained the fluctuations in the flame as the interaction of the reflected sound wave with the flame front. Plotting the path of the sound wave according to Dixon, Sokolik did not find coincidence of the reflected wave with the point of fluctuation of the flame, which is completely understandable, since the sound wave - a wave of infinitely small amplitude - cannot cause finite fluctuations in a flame. The fluctuations of the flame are caused by the action of shock waves on the flame front. Despite the fact that combustion with fluctuations has attracted the attention of investigators for a long time, the matter of an investigation of the interaction of the flame front with a shock wave has been paid little attention up to the present. The majority of studies devoted to this question relate to one individual case, which admittedly is of great practical and theoretical interest - the case when a detonation wave develops as the result of the interaction between the shock wave and the flame front. In direct opposition to this is the question of the interaction between shock wave and flame front which does not lead to detonation propagation of the flame. Without going into details about the mechanism of the formation of shock waves before a flame front, which is considered in [1], we note that, since the formation of the shock discontinuity takes place over a definite length of the chamber, the flame front may interact both with developing and with already developed shock waves. The process of interaction in the first and second cases will have its own characteristic features. To follow the details of this process we need to make visible the processes taking place in the fresh mixture which are not accompanied by their own illumination. In the process of interaction, changes are undergone both by the flame front and by the shock wave, and therefore to record the process it is desirable to use high-speed cinematography, which makes it possible to examine all its phases.

A detailed description of the optical part of the apparatus, allowing us to make visible even the weak disturbances caused by a flame in the fresh mixture, is given in [1]. This also describes the high-speed spark apparatus which makes it possible to obtain up to 200 different exposures of the process under study at a frequency of 50,000 frames per second.

This apparatus was used by us for studying the interaction of a flame front, propagated in closed chambers, with the shock wave forming before the front of the flame as the result of the accumulation of disturbances caused by the flame in the fresh gas. We used hydrogen-oxygen mixtures containing 25% H_2, 33.3% H_2, 50% H_2, 66.6% H_2 and 70% H_2. The length of the combustion chambers was varied from 280 to 480 mm. The photographs were made through windows cut in the side walls of the chamber of rectangular section 19×37 mm. The windows in the chamber were covered with optical glass. Metal strips clamping the glass to the body of the chamber were used as scale marks, recorded on the photographs in the form of dark bands parallel to the time axis. Photographing of the process was carried out by two methods: the scanning method and high-speed cinematography.

These preliminary remarks made, we will proceed to the examination of the problem of the interaction between a flame front and shock discontinuity.

1. Interaction of a Flame Front with a Shock Discontinuity

Fig. 1 shows photographs of the process of combustion of a hydrogen-oxygen mixture containing 50% H_2 in a chamber 280 mm long, obtained by the scanning method. On the left is recorded the development of the process in the first section of the two-section chamber, and on the right its development close to the second end surface. The flame accelerating along the tube excites in the fresh gas disturbances which, after reflecting from the end of the chamber, combine into a shock wave which passes freely through the flame front, almost stopping it. The flame is, as it were, "atomized". A second shock wave, forming as a result of the accumulation of disturbances emitted by the flame at later moments, is reflected from the end of the chamber and meets the already "atomized" flame, through which it also passes freely, pushing back its front slightly. From the photographs obtained by the scan method, it is impossible to say anything about the changes undergone by the front of the flame during this interaction. Fig. 2 shows series of photographs of the same process, obtained with spark photography at a frequency of 50,000 frames per second. Before the front of the flame, which has a clearly marked meniscus shape, the disturbances developing into the shock wave are clearly visible.

The meeting of the shock wave with the flame front is accompanied not only by a reduction in the rate of propagation of the flame, but also by deformation of the latter. In the formerly meniscus-shaped flame front there appears a small hollow, giving it a characteristic tulip-like shape. After passage of the shock wave through the flame front, there extends behind the flame front a long comet-like tail, in which the mixture burns out. The peculiar shape of the "tail" indicates a definite distribution of the rate-of-flow field accompanying the shock wave. The flame front acquires a honeycomb structure. The total surface of the front increases, which, in its turn, increases the rate of propagation of the flame. Gradually the flame front again acquires a meniscus-like shape. The second shock wave, meeting the flame front and accompanied by a comet-like "tail", is itself somewhat deformed through the region in which the mixture is burned out. On frames 35-37 of Fig. 2 (b) the twisting of the front of the shock wave along the comet-like "tail" is well marked. At the end of this zone the front of the shock wave again becomes flat. Since the shock waves running before the flame front meet the flame several times before it reaches the end of the chamber, the process of variation of the shape of the flame front during combustion with fluctuations has a periodic nature.

In the foregoing we examined the case of interaction of a flame front and a shock wave causing so-called combustion with fluctuations. In a fairly long combustion chamber the flame front can overtake the shock wave before the latter reaches the end of the chamber. In certain definite conditions governing the intensity of the shock wave and the rate of the reaction in the flame front, such an interaction of the wave and flame front causes the development of a detonation wave. The transition to a detonation is also observed in the combustion of a mixture in a chamber the length of which is less than the pre-detonation path. For this transition it is necessary that there should be an intensive shock wave and that the rate of reaction should be capable of maintaining the propagation of the detonation front.

The presence of an intensive shock wave, although a necessary, is not a sufficient condition for the transition from slow combustion into detonation, a fact which is evidenced by the series of photographs in Fig. 3 (a), (b), which record the combustion of a mixture containing 50% H_2 near the end surface of a chamber 480 mm long. Despite the fact that in both cases a shock wave of the same intensity is running towards the flame front, in the first case the process takes place in such a way that the meeting of shock wave and flame front does not lead to the formation of a detonation wave, while in the second case the transition from slow combustion to detonation takes place. Unfortunately the photographs do not record the interaction between wave and flame front, since it occurred in the section of the chamber not observed by us.

2. Interaction of Developing Shock Wave with Flame Front

If a shock wave passes freely through the flame front, the flame front behaves towards the developing shock wave as a distorting wall. The process of interaction between a developing shock wave and the flame front can be followed in the series of photographs (Fig. 4), which record the combustion of a mixture containing 33.3% H_2 in a chamber 280 mm long. The developing shock wave, running towards the flame front, is visible in the form of a gradually contracting dark band. Meeting with the flame front, it distorts it but cannot pass through the front. On the photographs it is very clear how the meniscus-shaped flame front assumes a tulip-like shape under the action of the shock wave. The deformation of the flame front with the reflection of the wave from it is probably the reason for the change in the angle of inclination of the front of the developing shock wave to the axis of the chamber after its being reflected.

The interaction of a developing shock wave with the flame front may lead to the formation of a new centre of combustion before the flame front. This process is clearly shown in the series of photographs [Fig. 5 (a)] on which is recorded the combustion of a mixture containing 25% H_2 in the second section of a chamber 280 mm long. The new centre of combustion, the appearance of which is very clear in the fourth and subsequent frames, takes the form of a gradually expanding dark region. Behind it the light band is a compression region enclosed between the two centres of combustion. The development of the new centre is caused, apparently, not by the igniting of the mixture through the compression in the wave, but by the ejection of reaction products into the fresh mixture; proof of this is given by the thin crosspiece linking the new centre of combustion with the flame front.

As can be seen from the photographs, the development of the new centre of combustion did not substantially change the nature of the combustion. The interaction between the second developing shock wave and the flame front leads, as can be seen from the last frames in Fig. 5, to a new change in the shape of the flame front and to a sudden increase in its surfaces, caused by the appearance of the honeycomb structure. The honeycomb structure is particularly clearly marked on the photographs [Fig. 5 (b)] which record the combustion of the same mixture in the second section of a three-section chamber 480 mm long.

Examination of the above experimental material allows us to make the following conclusions:

1. A developing shock discontinuity running towards the flame does not as a rule pass through the flame front but is reflected from it. The meeting of the developing shock wave with the flame front is accompanied by deformation of the latter. In certain cases there develops before the flame front a new centre of combustion, caused by ejection of reaction products into the fresh gas. The shock wave itself undergoes a change.

2. The developed shock wave easily passes through the flame front, pushing it back. The fluctuation in the flame is accompanied by deformation of its front. In the flame front, which is

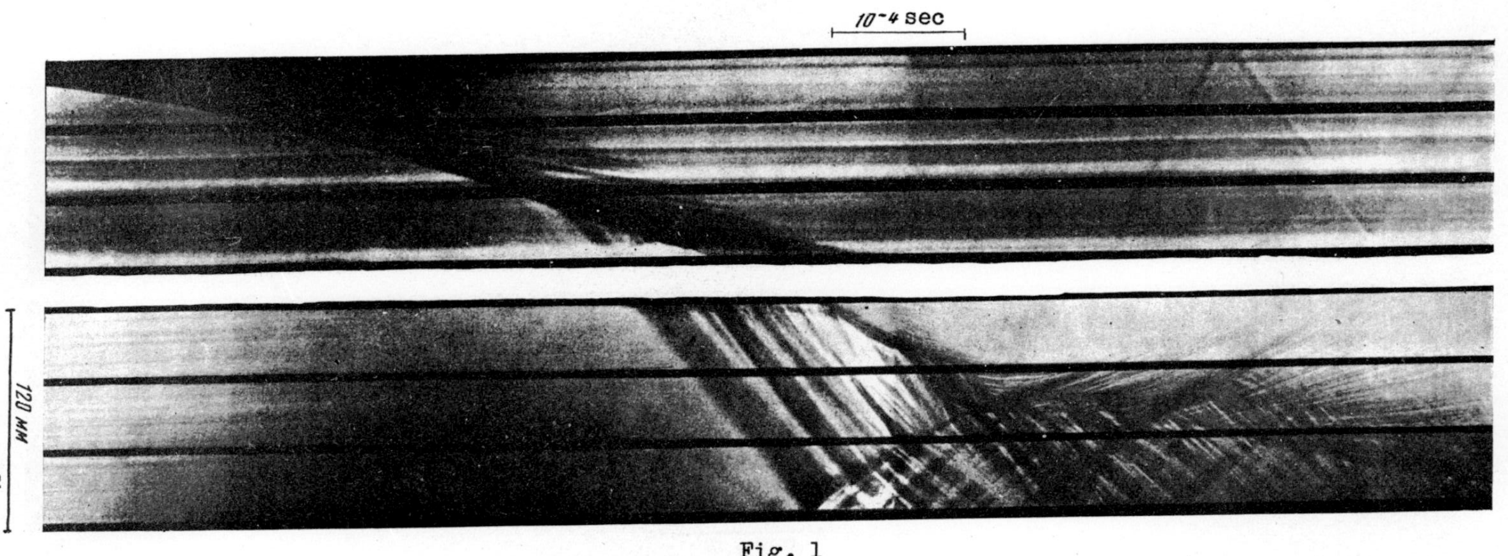

Fig. 1
Scan of the process of combustion of a hydrogen-oxygen mixture.

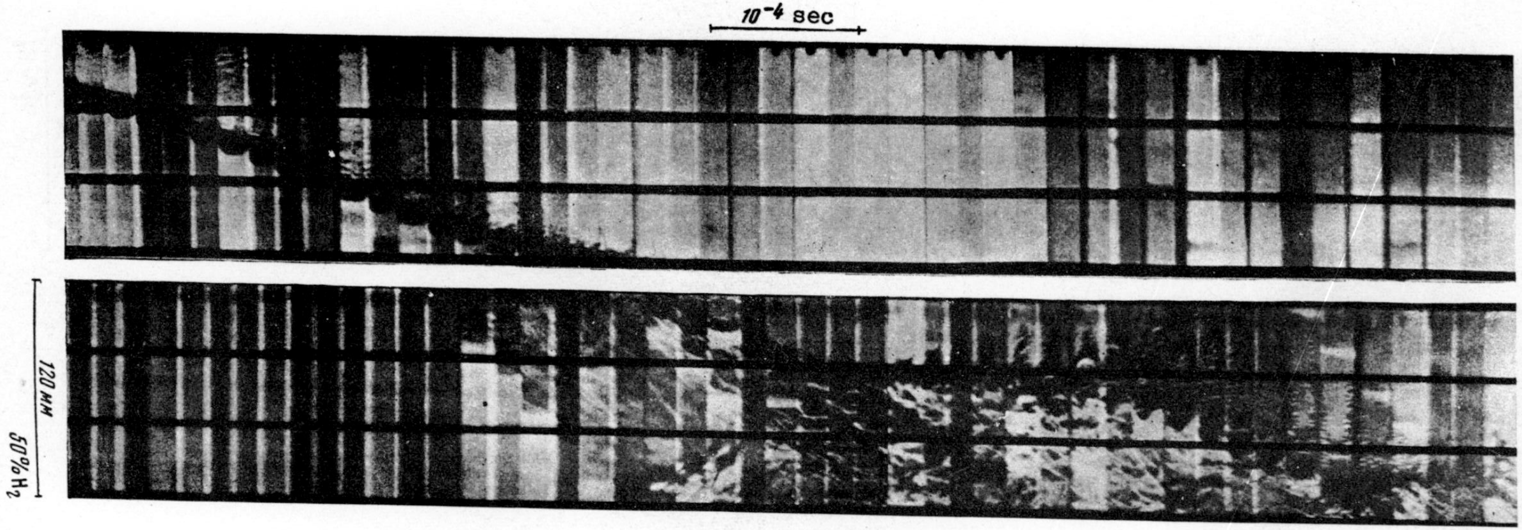

10^{-4} sec

120 мм

50% H_2

Fig. 2, a, b
Series of spark photographs of the same process

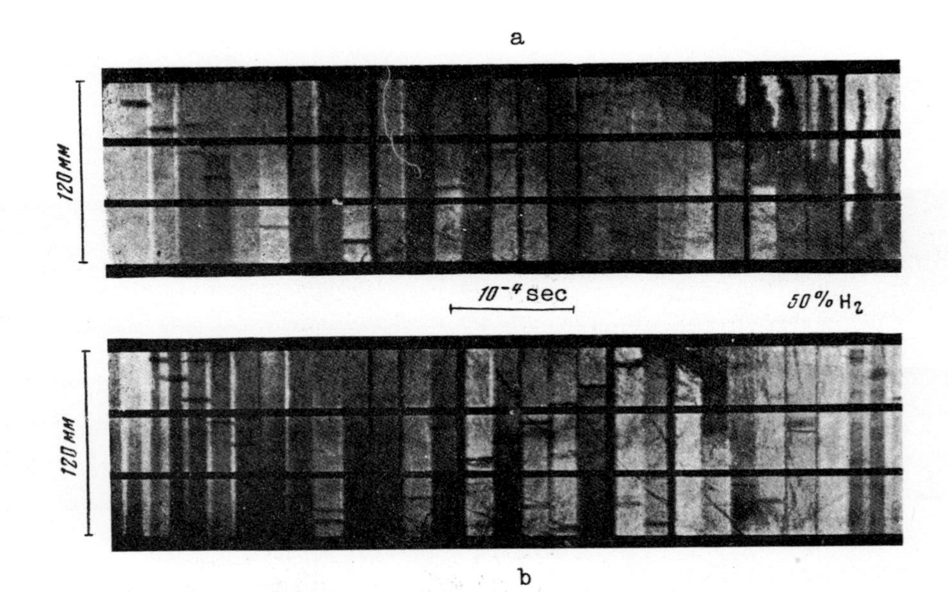

Fig. 3, a, b
Interaction between flame front and shock wave

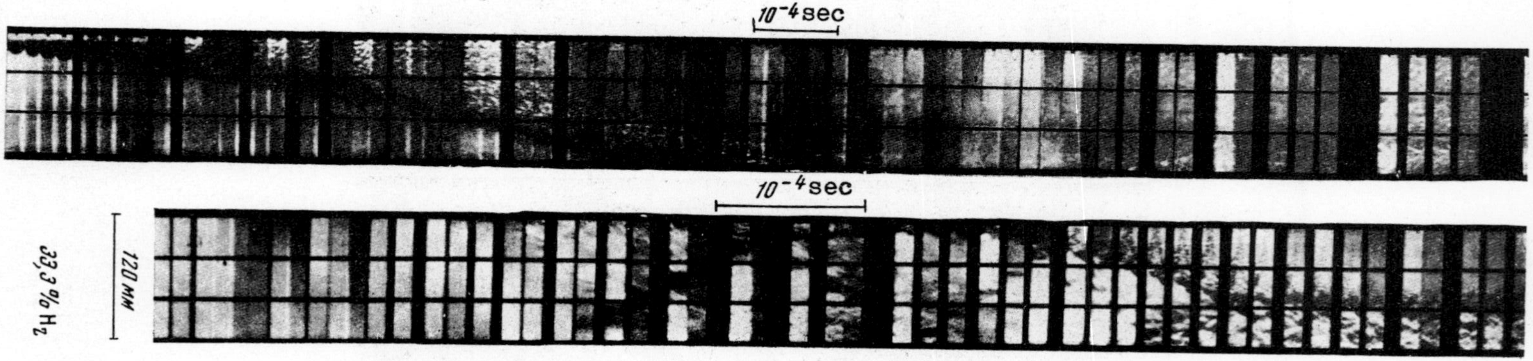

10^{-4} sec

10^{-4} sec

120 мм

33,3 % H_2

Fig. 4
Interaction between flame front and developing shock wave.

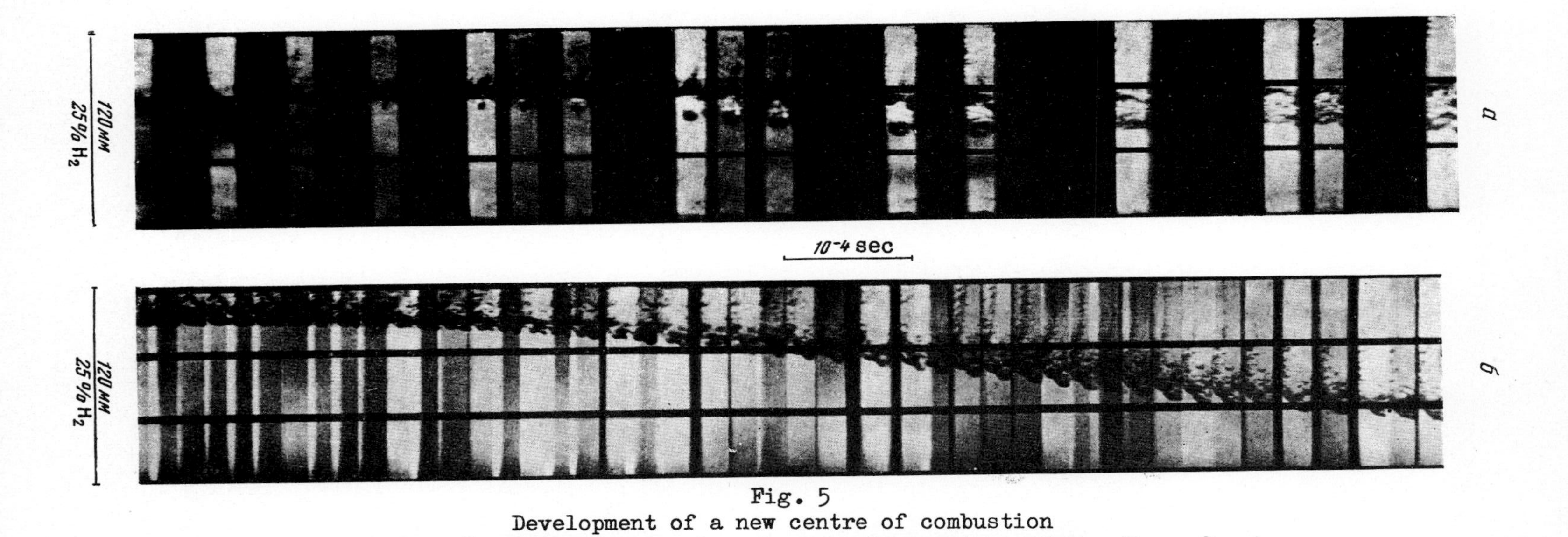

Fig. 5
Development of a new centre of combustion
a - before the flame front; b - honeycomb structure of the flame front

meniscus-shaped before it meets the shock wave, there appears a hollow, giving it a characteristic tulip-like shape. The structure of the flame front also changes, becoming covered by hollows which greatly increase the burning surface.

Behind the flame front there extends a long comet-like "tail", in which the mixture burns out. The increase in the flame surface leads to an increase in its rate of propagation. A new meeting of shock wave and flame causes a new distortion of the flame front, etc., which allows us to speak of a periodic change in the shape of the flame front during combustion with fluctuations. Passing through the flame front and the comet-like "tail" behind it, the front of the shock wave is distorted, assuming its initial form when leaving the region of the "tail".

REFERENCE

1. G.D. SALAMANDRA, O.A. TSUKHANOVA, Formation of a shock discontinuity before a flame front, page 164 supra.